D0966369

THE ADVENTURES OF
THE SECRET
7 7 7 **7** 7 7 7

Pam

George

Peter

Jack

Janet

Scamper

Barbara

Colin

THE ADVENTURES OF
THE SECRET
7 7 7 **7** 7 7 7

Five exciting stories in one volume

by

Enid Blyton

CHANCELLOR
PRESS

The stories in this volume were first published in Great Britain by Brockhampton Press Ltd (now Hodder and Stoughton Children's Books).

The Secret Seven first appeared in 1949.
Copyright © Darrell Waters Ltd
Illustrations copyright © 1968 Hodder and Stoughton Ltd

Secret Seven Adventure first appeared in 1950.
Copyright © Darrell Waters Ltd
Illustrations copyright © 1967 Hodder and Stoughton Ltd

Secret Seven Mystery first appeared in 1957.
Copyright © Darrell Waters Ltd
Illustrations copyright © 1971 Hodder and Stoughton Ltd

Secret Seven on the Trail first appeared in 1952.
Copyright © Darrell Waters Ltd
Illustrations copyright © 1968 Hodder and Stoughton Ltd

Fun for the Secret Seven first appeared in 1963.
Copyright © 1963 Enid Blyton
Illustrations copyright © 1974 Hodder and Stoughton Ltd

This collected edition published in 1986 by
Chancellor Press
59 Grosvenor Street
London W1

Arrangement and Design © 1986 Octopus Books Ltd

ISBN 1 85152 022 8

Printed in Czechoslovakia
50615

CONTENTS

THE
SECRET SEVEN

CONTENTS

One

Plans for an S.S. meeting

'WE'D better have a meeting of the Secret Seven,' said Peter to Janet. 'We haven't had one for ages.'

Oh, yes, let's!' said Janet, shutting her book with a bang. 'It isn't that we've forgotten about the Society, Peter – it's just that we've had such a lot of exciting things to do in the Christmas holidays we simply haven't had time to call a meeting.'

'But we must,' said Peter. 'It's no good having a Secret Society unless we use it. We'd better send out messages to the others.'

'Five notes to write,' groaned Janet. 'You're quicker at writing than I am, Peter – you write three and I'll write two.'

'Woof!' said Scamper, the golden spaniel.

'Yes, I know you'd love to write one, too, if you could,' said Janet, patting the silky golden head. 'You can carry one in your mouth to deliver. That can be *your* job, Scamper.'

'What shall we say?' said Peter, pulling a piece of paper towards him and chewing the end of his pen as he tried to think of words.

'Well – we'd better tell them to come here, I think,' said Janet. 'We could use the old shed at the bottom of the garden for a meeting-place, couldn't we? Mummy let us play there in the winter because it's next to the boiler that heats the greenhouse, and it's quite warm.'

'Right,' said Peter, and he began to write. 'I'll do this message first, Janet, and you can copy it. Let's see – we want one for Pam, one for Colin, one for Jack, one for Barbara – who's the seventh of us? I've forgotten.'

'George, of course,' said Janet. 'Pam, Colin, Jack, Barbara, George, you and me – that's the seven – the Secret Seven. It sounds nice, doesn't it?'

The Seven Society was one that Peter and Janet had invented. They thought it was great fun to have a little band of boys and girls who knew the password, and who wore the badge – a button with S.S. on.

'There you are,' said Peter, passing his sheet of paper to Janet. 'You can copy that.'

'It doesn't need to be my *best* writing, does it?' said Janet. 'I'm so slow if I have to do my best writing.'

'Well – so long as it's readable,' said Peter. 'It hasn't got to go by post.'

Janet read what Peter had written: 'IMPORTANT. A meeting of the Secret Seven will be held tomorrow morning in the shed at the bottom of our garden at 10 o'clock. Please give PASSWORD.'

'Oh, I say – what *was* the last password we had?' said Janet in alarm. 'It's so long since we had a meeting that I've forgotten.'

'Well, it's a good thing for you that you've got me to remind you,' said Peter. 'Our latest password is Wen-

ceslas, because we wanted a Christmassy one. Fancy you forgetting that!'

'Oh, yes, of course. Good King Wenceslas,' said Janet. 'Oh, dear – now I've gone and made a mistake in this note already. I really mustn't talk while I'm doing it.'

There was a silence as the two of them wrote their notes. Janet always wrote with her tongue out, which made her look very funny. But she said she couldn't write properly unless her tongue *was* out, so out it had to come.

Peter finished first. He let Scamper lick the envelopes. He was good at that; he had such a nice big wet tongue.

'You're a very licky dog,' said Peter, 'so you must be pleased when you have things like this to lick. It's a pity we're not putting stamps on the letters, then you could lick those, too.'

'Now shall we go and deliver the secret messages?' said Janet. 'Mummy said we could go out; it's a nice sunny morning – but won't it be cold!'

'Woof! woof!' said Scamper, running to the door when he heard the word 'out'. He pawed at the door impatiently.

Soon the three of them were out in the frost and snow. It was lovely. They went to Colin's first. He was out, so they left the note with his mother.

Then to George's. He was in, and was very excited when he heard about the meeting to be held in the shed.

Then to Pam's. Jack was there too, so Peter left two notes. Then there was only Barbara left. She was away!

'Bother!' said Peter. But when he heard she was coming back that night he was pleased. 'Will she be able to come and see us tomorrow morning?' he asked Barbara's mother, and she said yes, she thought so.

'Well, that's all five,' said Janet as they turned to go home. 'Come on, Scamper. We'll go, for a slide on the pond. The ice is as thick as anything!'

They had a lovely time on the pond, and how they laughed at poor Scamper! His legs kept sliding out from under him in all directions as he tried to run on the ice. In the end he slid along on his back, and the children, weak with laughing, had to haul him off the pond.

Scamper was cross. He turned and growled at the pond. He didn't understand it at all. He could drink it in the summer, and paddle in it – now look at it! Something queer had happened, and he didn't like it.

That afternoon the two children and Scamper went down to the old shed. It was warm, because the boiler was going well nearby to heat the big greenhouse. Peter looked round.

'It feels quite cosy. Let's arrange boxes for seats – and get the old garden cushions out. And we'll ask Mummy if we can have some lemonade or something, and biscuits. We'll have a really proper meeting!'

They pulled out some boxes and fetched the old cushions. They laid sacks on the ground for a carpet, and Janet cleaned a little shelf to put the lemonade and biscuits on, if their mother let them have them.

'There are only five boxes that are sittable on,' said Peter. 'Someone will have to sit on the floor.'

'Oh, no – there are two enormous flower-pots in the corner over there,' said Janet. 'Let's drag them out and turn them upside down. They'll be fine to sit on then.'

So, with the five boxes and the two flower-pots, there were seats for everyone.

The bell rang for tea. 'Well, we've just finished

nicely,' said Peter. 'I know what I'm going to do tonight, Janet.'

'What?' asked Janet.

'I'm going to draw two big letter S's,' said Peter, 'and colour them green – cut them out, mount them on cardboard, and then stick them to the door of the shed.'

'Oh, yes – S.S. – Secret Seven,' said Janet. 'That would be *grand*!'

Two

The Secret Seven Society

THE next morning five children made their way to Old Mill House, where Peter and Janet lived. It took its name from the ruined mill that stood up on the hill, some distance away, which had not been used for many years.

George came first. He walked down the garden and came to the shed. The first thing he saw was the sign on the door, S.S. There it was, bold and clear in bright green.

He knocked on the door. There was a silence. He knocked again. Still no reply, though he felt sure that Peter and Janet were there because he was certain he had seen Janet's face at the little window of the shed.

He heard a snuffling under the door. That must be Scamper! He knocked again, impatiently.

'Give the password, silly!' said Peter's voice.

'Oh, I forgot,' said George. 'Wenceslas!'

The door opened at once. George grinned and went in. He looked round. 'I say – this is jolly cosy. Is it to be our meeting-place these hols?'

'Yes. It's nice and warm here,' said Peter. 'Where's your badge? Your button with S.S. on?'

'Blow – I forgot it,' said George. 'I hope I haven't lost it.'

'You're not a very good member,' said Janet sternly. 'Forgetting to say the password, and forgetting your badge as well.'

'Sorry,' said George. 'To tell you the truth I'd almost forgotten about the Secret Society too!'

'Well, you don't deserve to belong then,' said Peter. 'Just because we haven't met for some time! I do think —'

There was another knock at the door. It was Pam and Barbara. There was silence in the shed. Everyone was listening for the password.

'Wenceslas,' hissed Barbara, in such a peculiar voice that everyone jumped.

'Wenceslas,' whispered Pam. The door opened, and in they went.

'Good – you're both wearing your badges,' said Peter, pleased. 'Now where are Colin and Jack? They're late.'

Jack was waiting for Colin at the gate. He had forgotten the password! Oh dear, whatever could it be? He thought of all sorts of things – Nowell – Wise Men – what *could* it be? He felt sure it was something to do with Christmas carols.

He didn't like to go to the meeting-place without knowing the password. Peter could be very strict. Jack didn't like being ticked off in front of people, and he racked his brains to try to think of the word. He saw Colin away in the distance and decided to wait for him. Colin would be sure to know the word!

'Hallo!' said Colin, as he came up. 'Seen the others yet?'

'I saw Pam and Barbara going in,' said Jack. 'Do you know the password, Colin?'

'Of course I do,' said Colin.

'I bet you don't!' said Jack.

'Well, I do – it's Wenceslas!' said Colin. 'Aha – sucks to you, Jack – you thought I didn't know it!'

'Thanks for telling me,' grinned Jack. 'I'd forgotten it. Don't tell Peter. Come on down the path. I *say* – look at the S.S. for Secret Seven on the door.'

They knocked. 'WENCESLAS,' said Colin in a very loud voice.

The door opened quickly and Peter's indignant face looked out. 'Whatever are you shouting for? Do you want everyone in the village to know our password, you donkey?'

'Sorry,' said Colin, going in. 'Anyway, there's nobody but us to hear.'

'Wenceslas,' said Jack, seeing that Peter was not going to let him in without the password. The door shut and the seven settled down. Peter and Janet took the flower-pots for themselves. Everyone else sat on the boxes.

'This is a jolly nice meeting-place,' said George. 'Warm and cosy, and right away from the house.'

'Yes. I must say you and Janet have got it very comfortable,' said Barbara. 'Even a little curtain at the window.'

Peter looked round at the little company. 'We'll have

our meeting first, and then we'll have the eats and drinks,' he said.

Everyone's eyes went to the neat little shelf behind Colin. On it were arranged seven mugs, a plate of oatmeal biscuits, and a bottle of some dark-looking liquid. Whatever could it be?

'First of all,' went on Peter, 'we must arrange a new password, because Wenceslas doesn't seem right for after Christmas – besides, Colin yelled it out at the top of his voice, so everyone probably knows it now.'

'Don't be so —' began Colin, but Peter frowned at him sternly.

'Don't interrupt. I'm the head of this society, and I say we will choose a new password. Also I see that two of you are not wearing your badges. George and Colin.'

'I told you I forgot about mine,' said George. 'I'll find it when I get home.'

'And I think I must have *lost* mine,' said Colin. 'I didn't forget it. I hunted all over the place. My mother says she'll make me another tonight.'

'Right,' said Peter. 'Now what about a new password?'

'Hey-diddle-diddle,' said Pam, with a giggle.

'Be sensible,' said Peter. 'This society is a serious one, not a silly one.'

'I thought of one last night,' said Jack. 'Would "Weekdays" do?'

'What's the sense of that?' asked Peter.

'Well – there are seven days in a week, aren't there –

and we're the Seven Society,' said Jack. 'I thought it was rather good.'

'Oh, I see. Yes – it *is* rather good,' said Peter. 'Though actually, there are only six *week*days! Hands up those who think it's good.'

Everybody's hand went up. Yes, 'Weekdays' was a good idea for a password for the Seven! Jack looked pleased.

'Actually I forgot our password today,' he confessed. 'I got it out of Colin. So I'm glad I've thought of a new one for us.'

'Well, nobody must forget this one,' said Peter. 'It might be very important. Now what about some grub?'

'Delumptious,' said Barbara, and everyone laughed.

'Do you mean "delicious" or "scrumptious"?' asked Janet.

'Both, of course,' said Barbara. 'What's that peculiar-looking stuff in the bottle, Janet?'

Janet was shaking it vigorously. I was a dark purple and had little black things bobbing about in it.

'Mummy hadn't any lemonade to give us, and we didn't particularly want milk because we'd had lots for breakfast,' she said. 'So we suddenly thought of a pot of blackcurrant jam we had! This is blackcurrant tea!'

'We mixed it with boiling water and put some more sugar into it,' explained Peter. 'It's awfully good – in fact, it's scrumplicious!'

'Oh – *that's* a mixture of scrumptious and delicious, too!' said Barbara with a squeal of laugher. 'Delumptious and scrumplicious – that just describes everything nicely.'

The blackcurrant tea really was good, and went very well with the oatmeal biscuits. 'It's good for colds, too,' said Janet, crunching up the skinny blackcurrants from her mug. 'So if anyone's getting a cold they probably won't.'

Everyone understood this peculiar statement and nodded. They set down their mugs and smacked their lips.

'It's a pity there's no more,' said Janet. 'But there wasn't an awful lot of jam left in the pot, or else we could have made heaps to drink.'

'Now, we have a little more business to discuss,' said Peter, giving Scamper a few crumbs to lick. 'It's no good having a Society unless we have some plan to follow – something to *do*.'

'Like we did in the summer,' said Pam. 'You know – when we collected money to send Lame Luke away to the sea.'

'Yes. Well, has anyone any ideas?' said Peter.

Nobody had. 'It's not really a good time to try and help people after Christmas,' said Pam. 'I mean – everyone's had presents and been looked after, even the very poorest, oldest people in the village.'

'Can't we solve a mystery, or something like that?' suggested George. 'If we can't find something wrong to put right, we might be able to find a mystery to clear up.'

'What kind of a mystery do you mean?' asked Barbara, puzzled.

'I don't really know,' said George. 'We'd have to be on the lookout for one – you know, watch for something strange or peculiar or queer – and solve it.'

'It sounds exciting,' said Colin. 'But I don't believe we'd find anything like that – and if we did the police would have found it first!'

'Oh, well,' said Peter, 'well just have to keep our eyes open and wait and see. If anyone hears of any good deed we can do, or of any mystery that wants solving, they must at once call a meeting of the Secret Seven. Is that understood?'

Everyone said yes. 'And if we have anything to report we can come here to this Secret Seven shed and leave a note, can't we?' said George.

'That would be the best thing to do,' agreed Peter. 'Janet and I will be here each morning, and we'll look and see if any of you have left a note. I hope somebody does!'

'So do I. It's not much fun having a Secret Society that doesn't *do* anything,' said Colin. 'I'll keep a jolly good lookout. You never know when something might turn up.'

'Let's go and build snowmen in the field opposite the old house down by the stream,' said George, getting up. 'The snow's thick there. It would be fun. We could build quite an army of snowmen. They'd look funny standing in the field by themselves.'

'Oh, yes. Let's do that,' said Janet, who was tired of sitting still. 'I'll take this old shabby cap to put on one of the snowmen! It's been hanging in this shed for ages.'

'And I'll take this coat!' said Peter, dragging down a dirty, ragged coat from a nail. 'Goodness knows who it ever belonged to!'

And off they all went to the field by the stream to build an army of snowmen!

Three

The cross old man

THEY didn't build an army, of course! They only had time to build four snowmen. The snow was thick and soft in the field, and it was easy to roll it into big balls and use them for the snowmen. Scamper had a lovely time helping them all.

Janet put the cap on one of the snowmen, and Peter put the old coat round his snowy shoulders. They found stones for his eyes and nose, and a piece of wood for his mouth. They gave him a stick under his arm. He looked the best of the lot.

'I suppose it's time to go home now,' said Colin at last. 'My dinner's at half-past twelve, worse luck.'

'We'd better all go home,' said Pam. 'We'll all have to wash and change our things and put our gloves to dry. Mine are soaking and oooh, my hands are cold!'

'So are mine. I know they'll hurt awfully as soon as they begin to get a bit warm,' said Barbara, shaking her wet hands up and down. 'They're beginning now.'

They left the snowmen in the field and went out of the nearby gate. Opposite was an old house. It was empty except for one room at the bottom, where dirty curtains hung across the window.

'Who lives there?' asked Pam.

'Only a caretaker,' said Janet. 'He's very old and very deaf – and awfully bad-tempered.'

They hung over the gate and looked at the desolate old house.

'It's quite big,' said Colin. 'I wonder who it belongs to, and why they don't live in it.'

'Isn't the path up to the house lovely and smooth with snow?' said Janet. 'Not even the caretaker has trodden

on it. I suppose he uses the back gate. Oh, Scamper –
you naughty dog come back!'

Scamper had squeezed under the gate and gone
bounding up the smooth, snowy path. The marks of his
feet were clearly to be seen. He barked joyfully.

The curtains at the ground-floor window moved and
a cross, wrinkled old face looked out. Then the window
was thrown up.

'You get out of here! Take your dog away! I won't
have children or dogs here, pestering little varmints!'

Scamper stood and barked boldly at the old caretaker.
He disappeared. Then a door opened at the side of the
house and the old man appeared, with a big stick. He
shook it at the alarmed children.

'I'll whack your dog till he's black and blue!' shouted
the man.

'Scamper, Scamper, come here!' shouted Peter. But
Scamper seemed to have gone completely deaf. The
caretaker advanced on him grimly, holding the stick up
to hit the spaniel.

Peter pushed open the gate and tore up the path to
Scamper, afraid he would be hurt.

'I'll take him, I'll take him!' he shouted to the old
man.

'What's that you say?' said the cross old fellow, lowering his stick. 'What do you want to go and send your dog
in here for?'

'I didn't. He came in himself!' called Peter, slipping
his fingers into Scamper's collar.

'Speak up, I can't hear you,' bellowed the old man, as if it was Peter who was deaf and not himself. Peter bellowed back:

'I DIDN'T SEND MY DOG IN!'

'All right, all right, don't shout,' grumbled the caretaker. 'Don't you come back here again, that's all, or I'll send the policeman after you.'

He disappeared into the side door again. Peter marched Scamper down the drive and out of the gate.

'What a bad-tempered fellow,' he said to the others. 'He might have hurt Scamper awfully if he'd hit him with that great stick.'

Janet shut the gate. 'Now you and Scamper have spoilt the lovely smooth path,' she said. 'Goodness, there's the church clock striking a quarter to one. We'll really have to hurry!'

'We'll let you all know when the next meeting is!' shouted Peter, as they parted at the corner. 'And don't forget the password and your badges.'

They all went home. Jack was the first in because he lived very close. He rushed into the bathroom to wash his hands. Then he went to brush his hair.

'I'd better put my badge away,' he thought, and put up his hand to feel for it. But it wasn't there. He frowned and went into the bathroom. He must have dropped it.

He couldn't find it anywhere. He must have dropped it in the field when he was making the snowmen with the others. Bother! Blow!

'Mother's away, so she can't make me a new one,' he thought. 'And I'm sure Miss Ely wouldn't.'

Miss Ely was his sister's governess. She liked Susie, Jack's sister, but she thought Jack was dirty, noisy and bad-mannered. He wasn't really, but somehow he never did behave very well with Miss Ely.

'I'll ask her if she *will* make one,' he decided. 'After all, I've been jolly good the last two days.'

Miss Ely might perhaps have said she would make

him his badge if things hadn't suddenly gone wrong at dinner-time.

'*I* know where you've been this morning,' said Susie, slyly, when the three of them were at table. 'Ha, ha. You've been to your silly Secret Society. You think I don't know anything about it. Well, I do!'

Jack glared at her. 'Shut up! You ought to know better than to talk about other people's secrets in public. You just hold that horrid, interfering tongue of yours.'

'Don't talk like that, Jack,' said Miss Ely at once.

'What's the password?' went on the annoying Susie. 'I know what the last one was because you wrote it down in your notebook so as not to forget and I saw it! It was –'

Jack kicked out hard under the table, meaning to get Susie on the shin. But most unfortunately Miss Ely's long legs were in the way. Jack's boot hit her hard on the ankle.

She gave a loud cry of pain. 'Oh! My ankle! How dare you, Jack! Leave the table and go without your dinner. I shall not speak another word to you all day long, if that is how you behave.'

'I'm awfully sorry, Miss Ely,' muttered Jack, scarlet with shame. 'I didn't mean to kick *you*.'

'It's the kicking that matters, not the person,' said Miss Ely, coldly. 'It doesn't make it any better knowing that you meant to kick Susie, not me. Leave the room, please.'

Jack went out. He didn't dare to slam the door, though he felt like it. He wasn't cross with Susie any more. He had caught sight of her face as he went out of the room, and had seen that she was alarmed and upset. She had meant to tease him, but she hadn't meant him to lose his nice dinner.

He kicked his toes against each step as he went upstairs. It was a pity he'd been sent out before the jamtarts were served. He liked those so much. Blow Miss Ely! Now she certainly wouldn't make a new badge for him, and probably he would be turned out of the Society for losing it. Peter had threatened to do that to anyone who turned up more than once without a badge.

'I seem to remember something falling off me when I was making that last snowman,' thought Jack. 'I think I'll go out and look this afternoon. I'd better go before it snows again, or I'll never find it.'

But Miss Ely caught him as he was going out and stopped him. 'No, Jack. You are to stay in today, after that extraordinary behaviour of yours at the dinner-table,' she said sternly. 'You will not go out to play any more today.'

'But I want to go and find something I lost, Miss Ely,' argued Jack, trying to edge out.

'Did you hear what I said?' said Miss Ely, raising her voice, and poor Jack slid indoors again.

All right! He would jolly well go out that night then, and look with his torch. Miss Ely should *not* stop him from doing what he wanted to do!

Four

What happened to Jack

JACK was as good as his word. He went up to bed at his usual time, after saying a polite good night to Miss Ely, but he didn't get undressed. He put on his coat and cap instead! He wondered whether he dared go downstairs and out of the garden door yet.

'Perhaps I'd better wait and see if Miss Ely goes to bed early,' he thought. 'She sometimes goes up to read in bed. I don't want to be caught. She'd only go and split on me when Mother comes home.'

So he took a book and sat down. Miss Ely waited for the nine o'clock news on the wireless and then she locked up the house and came upstairs. Jack heard her shut the door of her room.

Good! Now he could go. He slipped his torch into his pocket, because it really was a very dark night. The moon was not yet up.

He crept downstairs quietly and went to the garden door. He undid it gently. The bolt gave a little squeak but that was all. He stepped into the garden. His feet sank quietly into the snow.

He made his way to the lane and went down it to the field, flashing his little torch as he went. The snow glimmered up, and there was a dim whitish light all round from it. He soon came to the field where they had built the snowmen, and he climbed over the gate.

The snowmen stood silently in a group together, almost as if they were watching and waiting for him. Jack didn't altogether like it. He thought one moved, and he drew his breath in sharply. But, of course, it hadn't. It was just his imagination.

'Don't be silly,' he told himself, sternly. 'You know they're only made of snow! Be sensible and look for your dropped button!'

He switched on his torch and the snowmen gleamed whiter than ever. The one with eyes and nose and mouth, with the cap and the coat on, seemed to look at him gravely as he hunted here and there. Jack turned his back on him.

'You may only have stone eyes, but you seem to be able to *look* with them, all the same,' he said to the silent snowman. 'Now don't go tapping me on the shoulder and make me jump!'

Then he suddenly gave an exclamation. He had found his badge! There lay the button in the snow, with S.S. embroidered on it, for Secret Seven. Hurrah! He must have dropped it here after all then.

He picked it up. It was wet with snow. He pinned it carefully on his coat. That really *was* a bit of luck to find it so easily. Now he could go home and get into bed. He was cold and sleepy.

His torch suddenly flickered, and then went out. 'Blow!' said Jack. 'The battery's gone. It *might* have

lasted till I got home, really it might! Well, it's a good thing I know my way.'

He suddenly heard a noise down the lane, and saw the headlights of a car. It was coming very slowly. Jack was surprised. The lane led nowhere at all. Was the car lost? He'd better go and put the driver on the right road, if so. People often got lost when the roads were snowbound.

He went to the gate. The car came slowly by and then Jack saw that it was towing something – something rather big. What could it possibly be?

The boy strained his eyes to see. It wasn't big enough for a removal van, and yet it looked rather like the shape of one. It wasn't a caravan either, because there were no wide windows at the side. *Were* there any windows at all? Jack couldn't see any. Well, whatever *was* this curious van?

And where was it going? The driver simply *must* have made a mistake! The boy began to climb over the gate. Then he suddenly sat still.

The car's headlights had gone out. The car itself had stopped, and so had the thing it was towing. Jack could make out the dark shapes of the car and the van behind, standing quite still. What was it all about?

Somebody spoke to somebody else in a low voice. Jack could see that one or two men had got out of the car, but he could not hear their footsteps because of the snow.

How he wished the moon was up, then he could hide behind the hedge and see what was happening! He heard a man's voice speaking more loudly.

'Nobody about, is there?'

'Only that deaf fellow,' said another voice.

'Have a look-see, will you?' said the first voice. 'Just in case.'

Jack slipped quickly down from the gate, as he saw a powerful torch flash out. He crouched behind the snowy hedge, scraping snow over himself. There came the soft crunch of footsteps walking over frosty snow by the hedge. The flashlight shone over the gate and the man gave an exclamation.

'Who's there? Who are you?'

Jack's heart beat so hard against him that it hurt. He was just about to get up and show himself, and say who he was, when the man at the gate began to laugh.

'My word – look here, Nibs – a whole lot of snowmen standing out here! I thought they were alive at first, watching for us! I got a scare all right.'

Another man came softly to the first and he laughed too. 'Kids' work, I suppose,' he said. 'Yes, they look real all right, in this light. There's nobody about here at this time of night, Mac. Come on – let's get down to business.'

They went back towards the car. Jack sat up, trembling. What in the world could the men be doing down here in the snowy darkness, outside an old empty house? Should he try to see what they were up to? He didn't want to in the least. He wanted to go home as quickly as ever he could!

He crept to the gate again. He heard queer sounds from where the men were – as if they were unbolting something – opening the van perhaps.

And then there came a sound that sent Jack helter-skelter over the gate and up the lane as fast as his legs would take him! An angry, snorting sound, and then a curious high squeal – and then a noise of a terrific struggle, with the two men panting and grunting ferociously.

Jack couldn't think for the life of him what the noise was, and he didn't care, either. All he wanted was to get home before anything happened to *him*. Something was happening to somebody, that was certain, out there in the snowy lane. It would need a very, very brave person to go and interfere – and Jack wasn't brave at all, that night!

He came to his house, panting painfully. He crept in at the garden door and locked and bolted it. He went upstairs, not even caring if the stairs creaked under his feet! He switched on the light in his bedroom. Ah – that was better. He didn't feel so scared once he had the light on.

He looked at himself in the glass. He was very pale, and his coat was covered with snow. That was through lying in the snowy ditch below the hedge. He caught sight of his badge, still pinned on to his coat. Well, anyhow, he had *that*.

'I went out to find my badge – and goodness knows what else I've found,' thought the boy. 'Golly – I must tell the others. We must have a meeting tomorrow. This is something for the Secret Seven! I *say* – what a thrill for them!'

He couldn't wait to tell them the next day. He must slip out again – and go to the shed at the bottom of Peter's garden. He must leave a note there, demanding a meeting at once!

'It's important. Very, very important,' said Jack to himself, as he scribbled a note on a bit of paper. 'It really is something for the Society to solve.'

He slipped down the stairs again, and out of the garden door. He wasn't frightened any more. He ran all the way up the lane and round to Peter's house. The farmhouse stood dark and silent. Everyone was in bed; they did not stay up late at the farm.

Jack went down to the old shed. He fumbled at the door. It was locked. His hands felt the big letters, S.S., on the door itself. He bent down and slid his note under the crack at the bottom. Peter would find it the next day.

Then home he went again to bed – but not to sleep. Who had made that noise? What was that strange high van? Who were the men? It really was enough to keep anybody awake for hours!

Five

Exciting plans

NEXT morning Janet went down to the shed by herself. Peter was brushing Scamper. He was well and truly brushed every single morning, so it was no wonder his coat shone so beautifully.

'Just open the shed and give it an airing,' ordered Peter. 'We shan't be using it today. There won't be any meeting yet.'

Janet skipped down the path, humming. She took the key from its hiding-place – a little ledge beneath the roof of the shed – and slipped it into the lock. She opened the door.

The shed smelt rather stuffy. She left the door open and went to open the little window too. When she turned round she saw Jack's note on the floor.

At first she thought it was an odd piece of waste paper, and she picked it up and crumpled it, meaning to throw it away. Then she caught sight of a word on the outside of the folded paper.

'URGENT. VERY IMPORTANT INDEED.'

She was astonished. She opened the paper out and glanced down it. Her mouth fell open in amazement. She raced out of the shed at top speed, yelling for Peter.

'Peter! PETER! Where are you? Something's happened, quick!'

Her mother heard her and called to her. 'Janet, Janet, what's the matter, dear? What's happened?'

'Oh – nothing, Mummy,' called back Janet, suddenly remembering that this was Secret Society business.

'Well, why are you screeching for Peter like that?' said her mother. 'You made me jump.'

Janet flew up the stairs to where Peter was still brushing Scamper. 'Peter! Didn't you hear me calling? I tell you, something's happened!'

'What is it?' asked Peter, surprised.

'Look – I found this paper when I went to the shed this morning,' said Janet, and she gave him Jack's note. 'It's marked "Urgent, Very Important Indeed". Look what it says inside.'

Peter read out loud what Jack had written:

Peter, call a meeting of the Secret Seven at once. Very important Mystery to solve. It happened to me last night about half-past nine. Get the others together at ten if you can. I'll be there.

Jack

'What on *earth* does he mean?' said Peter, in wonder. 'Something happened to *him* last night? Well, why is it such a mystery then? I expect he's exaggerating.'

'He's not, he's not. I'm sure he's not,' cried Janet, dancing from one foot to another in her excitement. 'Jack doesn't exaggerate, you know he doesn't. Shall I go and tell the others to come at ten if they can? Peter, it's exciting. It's a mystery!'

'You wait and see what the mysery is before you get all worked up,' said Peter, who, however, was beginning to feel rather thrilled himself. 'I'll go and tell Colin and George – you can tell the girls.'

Janet sped off in one direction and Peter in another. How lovely to have to call a meeting already – and about something so exciting too.

It was about half-past nine when the two came back.

Everyone had promised to come. They were all very anxious to know what Jack had got to say.

'Remember your badges,' Janet said to the two girls. 'You won't be admitted to an important meeting like this unless you know the password and have your badge.'

Everyone turned up early, eager to hear the news. Everyone remembered the password, too.

'Weekdays!' and the door was opened and shut.

'Weekdays,' and once more the door was opened and shut. Member after member passed in, wearing the badge and murmuring the password. Both Colin and George had their badges this morning. George had found his and Colin's mother had already made him one.

Jack was the last of all to arrive, which was most annoying because everyone was dying to hear what he had to say. But he came at last.

'Weekdays,' said his voice softly, outside the shed door. It opened and he went in. Everybody looked at him expectantly.

'We got your note, and warned all the members to attend this meeting,' said Peter. 'What's up, Jack? Is it really important?'

'Well, you listen and see,' said Jack, and he sat down on the box left empty for him. 'It happened last night.'

He began to tell his story – how he had missed his badge and felt certain he had dropped it in the field where the snowmen were – how he had slipped out with his torch to find it, and what he had heard and seen from the field.

'That frightful noise – the snorting and the horrid squeal!' he said. 'It nearly made my hair stand on end. Why did those men come down that lane late at night? It doesn't lead anywhere. It stops a little further on just by a great holly hedge. And what could that thing be that they were towing behind?'

'Was it a cage, or something – or was it a closed van where somebody was being kept prisoner?' said Barbara, in a half-whisper.

'It wasn't a cage as far as I could see,' said Jack. 'I couldn't even see any windows to it. It was more like a small removal van than anything – but whatever was inside wasn't furniture. I tell you it snorted and squealed and struggled.'

'Was it a man inside, do you think?' asked Pam, her eyes wide with interest and excitement.

'No. I don't think so. It might have been, of course,' said Jack. 'But a man doesn't snort like that. Unless he had a gag over his mouth, perhaps.'

This was a new thought and rather an alarming one. Nobody spoke for a minute.

'Well,' said Jack, at last, 'it certainly is something for the Secret Seven to look into. There's no doubt about that. It's all very mysterious – very mysterious indeed.'

'How are we going to tackle it?' said George.

They all sat and thought. 'We had better find out if

we can tell anything by the tracks in the snow,' said Peter. 'We'll find out too if there are car-tracks up the drive to that old house.'

'Yes. And we could ask the old caretaker if he heard anything last night,' said Colin.

'Bags I don't do that,' said Pam at once. 'I'd just hate to go and ask him questions.'

'Well, somebody's got to,' said George. 'It might be important.'

'And we might try and find out who owns the old empty house,' said Colin.

'Yes,' said Peter. 'Well, let's split up the inquiries. Pam, you go with George and see if you can find out who owns the house.'

'How do we find out?' asked Pam.

'You will have to use your common sense,' said Peter. I can't decide *every*thing. Janet, you and Barbara can go down the lane and examine it for car-tracks and any-thing else you can think of.'

'Right,' said Janet, glad that she hadn't got to ques-tion the caretaker.

'And I and Colin and Jack will go into the drive of the old house and see if we can get the caretaker to tell us anything,' said Peter, feeling rather important as he made all these arrangements.

'What's Scamper to do?' asked Janet.

He's going to come with *us*,' said Peter. 'In case the caretaker turns nasty! Old Scamper can turn nasty too, if he has to!'

'Oh, yes – that's a good idea, to take Scamper,' agreed Jack, relieved at the thought of having the dog with him. 'Well – shall we set off?'

'Yes. Meet and report here this afternoon,' said Peter. 'You've discovered a most exciting mystery, Jack, and it's up to the Secret Seven to solve it as soon as they can!'

Six

Finding out a few things

ALL the Secret Seven set off at once, feeling extremely important. Scamper went with Peter, Colin and Jack, his tail well up, and he also felt very important. He was mixed up in a Mystery with the Society! No wonder he turned up his nose at every dog he met.

They left Pam and George at the corner, looking rather worried. The two looked at one another. '*How* are we going to find out who owns the house?' said Pam.

'Ask at the post office!' said George, feeling that he really had got a very bright idea. 'Surely if the house is owned by someone who has put in a caretaker, there must be letters going there.'

'Good idea!' said Pam, and they went off to the post office. They were lucky enough to see a postman emptying the letters from the pillar-box outside. George nudged Pam.

'Come on. We must start somewhere. We'll ask him!'

They went up to the man. 'Excuse me,' said George. 'Could you tell us who lives at the old house down by the stream – you know, the empty house there?'

'How can anyone live in an empty house?' said the postman. 'Don't ask silly questions and waste my time!

You children – you think you're so funny, don't you?'

'We didn't mean to be funny, or cheeky either,' said Pam in a hurry. 'What George means is – who owns the house? There's a caretaker there, we know. We just wondered who the house belongs to.'

'Why? Thinking of buying it?' said the postman, and laughed at his own joke. The children laughed too, wishing the man would answer their question.

'How would I know who owns the place?' he said, emptying the last of the letters into his sack. 'I never take letters there except to old Dan the caretaker, and he only gets one once in a month – his wages, maybe. Better ask at the estate office over there. They deal with houses, and they might know the owner – seeing as you're so anxious to find him!'

'Oh, *thank* you,' said Pam, joyfully, and the two of them hurried across to the estate office. 'We might have thought of this ourselves,' said Pam. 'But I say – what shall we say if the man here asks why we want to know? You only go to a house agent's if you want to buy or sell a house, don't you?'

They peeped in at the door. A boy of about sixteen sat at a table there, addressing some envelopes. He didn't look very frightening. Perhaps *he* would know – and wouldn't ask them why they wanted the name of the owner.

They went boldly in. The boy looked up.

'What do you want?' he said.

'We've been told to ask who owns the old house down

by the stream,' said George, hoping the boy might think that some grown-up had sent him to find out. Actually it was only Peter, of course, but he didn't see why he should say so.

'I don't think the house is on the market,' said the boy, turning over the pages of a big book. 'Do your parents want to buy it, or something? I didn't know it was to be sold.'

The two children said nothing, because they didn't really know what to say. The boy went on turning over the pages.

'Ah – here we are,' he said. 'No – it's not for sale – it was sold to a Mr. J. Holikoff some time ago. Don't know why he doesn't live in it, I'm sure!'

'Does Mr. Holikoff live anywhere here?' asked Pam.

'No – his address is 64, Heycom Street, Covelty,' said the boy, reading it out. ' 'Course, I don't know if he lives there now. Do your people want to get in touch with him? I can find out if this is his address now, if you like – he's on the telephone at this address.'

'Oh, no, thank you,' said George hastily. 'We don't want to know anything more, as the house is – er – not for sale. Thank you very much. Good morning.'

They went out, rather red in the face, but very pleased with themselves. 'Mr. Holikoff,' said Pam to George. 'It's a peculiar name, isn't it? Do you remember his address, George?'

'Yes,' said George. He took out his notebook and

wrote in it: 'Mr. J. Holikoff, 64, Heycom Street, Col-
velty. Well, we've done our part of the job! I wonder
how the others are getting on.'

They were getting on quite well. Janet and Barbara
were busy examining the tracks down the lane that led to
the stream. They felt quite like detectives.

'See – the car with the van behind, or whatever it was,
turned into the lane from the direction of Templeton; it
didn't come from our village,' said Janet. 'You can see
quite clearly where the wheels almost went into the
ditch.'

'Yes,' said Barbara, staring at them. 'The tracks of the
van wheels are narrower than the wheels of the car that
towed it, Janet. And look – just here in the snow you can
see *exactly* what the pattern was on the wheels of the
van. Not of the car, though – they're all blurred.'

'Don't you think it would be a good idea to take a note
of the pattern of the tyre?' said Janet. 'I mean – it just
might come in useful. And we could measure the width
of the tyre print too.'

'I don't see how those things can possibly matter,' said
Barbara, who wanted to go down the lane and join the
three boys.

'Well, I'm going to try and copy the pattern,' said
Janet firmly. 'I'd like to have *some*thing to show the
boys!'

So, very carefully, she drew the pattern in her notebook. It was a funny pattern, with lines and circles and
V-shaped marks. It didn't really look very good when

she had done it. She had measured the print as best she could. She had no tape-measure with her, so she had placed a sheet from her notebook over the track, and had marked on it the exact size. She felt rather pleased with herself, but she did wish she had drawn the pattern better. Barbara laughed when she saw it. 'Gracious! What a mess!' she said.

Janet looked cross and shut her notebook up. 'Let's follow the tracks down the lane now,' she said. 'We'll see exactly where they go. Not many vans come down here – we ought to be able to follow the tracks easily.'

She was quite right. It was very easy to follow them. They went on and on down the lane – and then stopped outside the old house. There were such a lot of all kinds of marks there that it was difficult to see exactly what they were – footprints, tyre-marks, places where the snow had been kicked and ruffled up – it was hard to tell anything except that this was where people had got out and perhaps had had some kind of struggle.

'Look – the tyre-marks leave all this mess and go on down the lane,' said Janet. She looked over the gate longingly. Were the boys in the old house with the caretaker?

'Let's go and see if we can find the boys,' said Barbara.

'No. We haven't quite finished our job yet,' said Janet. 'We ought to follow the tracks as far as they go. Come on – we'll see if they go as far as the stream. There are *two* lots of tracks all down the lane, as we saw – so it's clear that the car and trailer went down, and then up again. We'll find out where they turned.'

That was easy. The tracks went down to a field-gate, almost to the stream. Someone had opened the gate, and the car had gone in with the trailer, and had made a circle there, come out of the gate again, and returned up the lane. It was all written clearly in the tyre-tracks.

'Well, that's the story of last night,' said Janet, pleased at their discoveries. 'The car and the thing it was pulling came from the direction of Templeton, turned down into this lane, stopped outside the old house, where people got out and messed around – and then went down to the field, someone opened the gate, the car and trailer went in and turned, and came out again and went up the lane – and disappeared into the night. Who or what it brought in the trailer-van goodness knows!'

'Funny thing to do at that time of night,' said Barbara.

'Very queer,' agreed Janet. 'Now let's go back to the old house and wait for the boys.'

'It's almost one o'clock,' said Barbara. 'Do you think they're still there?

They hung over the gate and watched and listened. To their horror the old caretaker came rushing out as soon as he saw them, his big stick in his hand.

'More of you!' he cried. 'You wait till I get you. You'll feel my stick all right. Pestering, interfering children! You just wait!'

But Barbara and Janet didn't wait! They fled up the lane in fright, as fast as they could possibly go in the soft thick snow.

Seven

A talk with the caretaker

THE three boys and Scamper had had an exciting time. They had gone down the lane, noting the car-tracks as they passed. They came to the old house. They saw that the gate was shut. They leaned over the top and saw tracks going up the drive.

'There's my footprints that I made yesterday morning,' said Peter, pointing to them. 'And look, you can see Scamper's paw-marks here and there too – but our tracks are all overlaid with others – bigger footmarks – and other marks too, look – rather queer.'

'A bit like prints that would be made by someone wearing great flat, roundish slippers,' said Jack, puzzled. 'Who would wear slippers like that? Look, you can see them again and again, all over the place. Whoever wore them was prancing about a bit! Probably being dragged in.'

The boys leaned over the gate and considered all the marks carefully. They traced them with their eyes as far as they could see. 'Can any of you make out if the tracks go up the front door steps?' said Colin. 'I can't from here – but it rather looks to me as if the snow is smooth up the steps – not trampled at all.'

'I can't make out from here,' said Peter. 'Let's go up

the drive. After all, we've got to interview the caretaker and find out if he heard anything last night. So we've got to go in.'

'What shall we say if he asks us why we want to know?' said Colin. 'I mean – if he's in this mystery, whatever it is, he may be frightfully angry if he thinks we know anything about it.'

'Yes, he might,' said Peter. 'We'll have to be jolly clever over this. Let's think.'

They thought. 'I can't think of anything except to sort of lead him on a bit – ask him if he isn't afraid of burglars and things like that,' said Peter at last. 'See if we can make him talk.'

'All right,' said Colin. 'But it seems a bit feeble. Let's go in.'

Scamper ran ahead down the drive. He disappeared round a corner. The boys followed the footprints carefully, noting how the slipper-like ones appeared everywhere, as if the owner had gone from side to side and hopped about like mad!

'They *don't* go up the front door steps,' said Colin. 'I thought they didn't! They go round the side of the house – look here – right past the side door where the caretaker came out yesterday – and down this path – and round to the kitchen door!'

'Well – how queer!' said Peter, puzzled. 'Why did everyone go prancing round to the kitchen door when there's a front door and a side door? Yes – all three tracks are here – two sets of shoe-prints – and those funny round slipper-prints too. It beats me!'

They tried the kitchen door, but it was locked. They peered in at the window. The kitchen was completely bare and empty. But they saw a gas-stove, a sink piled with plates, and a pail nearby when they looked through the scullery window.

'I suppose the caretaker has the use of the scullery and that front room in the house,' said Jack.

'Look out – here he is!' said Peter suddenly.

The old fellow was shuffling into the empty kitchen.

He saw the three boys through the window and went to
fling it open in a rage.

'If you want that there dog of yours, he's round in the
front garden!' he shouted. 'You clear out. I won't have
kids round here. You'll be breaking windows before I
know where I am!'

'No, we shan't,' shouted Jack, determined to make the
deaf old man hear. 'We'll just collect our dog and go.
Sorry he came in here.'

'Aren't you rather lonely here?' shouted Colin.
'Aren't you afraid of burglars?'

'No. I'm not afraid,' said the old fellow, scornfully. 'I've got my big stick – and there's nothing to steal here.'

'Somebody's been round to the back door, all the same,' shouted Peter, seeing a chance to discuss this bit of mystery with the caretaker and see if he knew anything about it. He pointed to all the tracks leading to the back door. The old man leaned out of the window and looked at them.

'They're no more than the tracks you've made yourself, tramping about where you've no business to be!' he said angrily.

'They're not. I bet it was burglars or something last night,' said Peter, and all three boys looked closely at the caretaker to see if his face changed in any way.

'Pah!' he said. 'Trying to frighten me, are you, with your silly boys' nonsense!'

'No. I'm not,' said Peter. 'Didn't you hear anything at all last night? If burglars *were* trying to get in, wouldn't you hear them?'

'I'm deaf,' said the old man. 'I wouldn't hear nothing at all – but wait now – yes, I did think I heard something last night. I'd forgotten it. Ah – that's queer, that is.'

The boys almost forgot to breathe in their excitement. 'What did you hear?' said Jack, forgetting to shout. The old man took no notice. He frowned, and his wrinkled face became even more wrinkled.

'Seems like I heard some squealing or some such noise,' he said slowly. 'I thought it was maybe some noise in my ears – I get noises often, you know – and I didn't go to see if anything was up. But, there now, nobody took nothing nor did any damage – so what's the use of bothering? If people want to squeal, let 'em, I say!'

'Was the squealing in the house?' shouted Peter.

'Well, I guess I wouldn't hear any squealing *outside*,' said the old man. 'I'm deaf as a post, usually. Ah, you're just making fun of me, you are – trying to frighten an old man. You ought to be ashamed of yourselves!'

'Can we come in and look round?' shouted Colin, and the others looked eagerly at the caretaker. If only he would say yes! But he didn't, of course.

'What are you thinking of, asking to come in!' he cried. 'I know you kids – pestering creatures – wasting my time like this. You clear out and don't you come here again with your tale of burglars and such. You keep away. Kids like you are always up to mischief.'

Just at that moment Scamper came bounding up. He saw the old caretaker at the window and leapt up at him, in a friendly manner. The man jumped in alarm. He thought Scamper was trying to snap at him. He leaned forward and aimed a blow at him through the window with his stick. Scamper dodged and barked.

'I'm going to teach that dog a lesson!' cried the old fellow, in a fury. 'Yes, and you too – standing out there cheeking me! I'll teach you to make fun of me, you and your dog!'

He disappeared. 'He's going to dart out of the side door,' said Peter. 'Come on – we've learnt all we want to know. We'll go!'

Eight

Another meeting

THE meeting that afternoon was very interesting and full of excitement. Everyone had something to report. They came punctually to the old shed, giving the password without a pause.

'Weekdays!'

'Weekdays!'

'Weekdays!' One after another the Seven passed in, and soon they were sitting round the shed. They all looked very important. Scamper sat by Peter and Janet, his long ears drooping down like a judge's wig, making him look very wise.

'Pam and George – you report first,' said Peter.

So they reported, telling how they had found out that the old house had been sold to a Mr. J. Holikoff some time back, although he had never lived in it.

'Did you get his address?' asked Peter. 'It might be important.'

'Yes,' said George, and produced his note-book. He read the address.

'Good. We might have to get in touch with him if we find that he ought to know something queer is going on in his empty house,' said Peter.

Pam and George felt very proud of themselves. Then

the two girls reported. They told how they had discovered that the tracks came from the direction of the
town of Templeton, and had gone down to the gates of
the old house, where it was plain that they had stopped,
as Jack had noticed the night before, when he heard the
car. Then they told how the tracks had gone into the
field, circled round and come out again – and had
clearly gone up the lane and back the way they came.

'Good work,' said Peter. Janet took out her notebook
and went rather red in the face.

'I've just got this to report, too,' she said, showing the
page of the notebook on which she had tried to draw the
tyre pattern. 'I don't expect it's a bit of use, really – it's

the pattern on the tyres of the van or trailer or lorry, or whatever it was that was pulled behind the car. And I measured the width, too.'

Everyone looked at the scribbled pattern. It didn't look anything much, but Peter seemed pleased.

'Even if it's no use, it was a good idea to do it,' he said. 'Just suppose it *was* some use – and the snow melted – your drawing would be the only pattern we had to track down the tyres.'

'Yes,' said Colin, warmly. 'I think that was good, Janet.'

Janet glowed with pride. She put away her notebook. 'Now you three boys report,' she said, though she herself had already heard part of it from Peter while they were waiting for the others to come that afternoon.

Peter made the report for the three of them. Everyone listened in silence, looking very thrilled.

'So, you see,' finished Peter, '*some*body went to the old house last night, got in through the kitchen door, because the footsteps went right to there – and *I* think they left a prisoner behind!'

Pam gasped. 'A prisoner! What do you mean?'

'Well, isn't it clear that there was a prisoner in that big window-less van – a prisoner who was not to be seen or heard – someone who was dragged round to the kitchen and forced inside – and hidden somewhere in that house? Somebody who was hurt and who squealed loudly enough for even the old deaf caretaker to hear?' said Peter.

Everyone looked upset and uncomfortable.

'I don't like it,' said Colin. Nobody liked it. It was horrid to think of a poor, squealing prisoner locked up somewhere in that old, empty house.

'What about his food?' said Colin, at last.

'Yes – and water to drink,' said Janet. 'And *why* is he locked up there?'

'Kidnapped, perhaps,' said Jack. 'You know – this is really very serious, if we're right.'

There was a silence. 'Ought we to tell our parents?' asked Pam.

'Or the police?' said Jack.

'Well – not till we know a little bit more,' said Peter. 'There might be some quite simple explanation of all this – a car losing its way or something.'

'I've just thought of something!' said Jack. 'That van – could it have been some sort of ambulance, do you think! You know, the van that ill people are taken to hospitals in? Maybe it was, and the car took the wrong turning, and stopped when it found it had gone wrong. And the ill person cried out with pain, or something.'

'But the caretaker said he heard squealing too, inside the house,' said Peter. 'Still, that might have been some noises in his head, of course, like those he says he sometimes has. Well – it's an idea, Jack – it *might* have been an ambulance, pulled by a car, though I can't say I've ever seen one like the one you describe.'

'Anyway, we'd better not tell anyone till we've *proved* there's something queer going on,' said Colin. 'We

should feel most frightfully silly if we reported all this to the police and then they found it was just something perfectly ordinary!'

'Right. We'll keep the whole thing secret,' said Peter. 'But, of course, we've got to do something about it ourselves. We can't leave it.'

'Of *course* we've got to do something,' said George. 'But what?'

'We'll think,' said Peter. So they all thought again. What would be the best move to make next?

'I've thought of something,' said Jack at last. 'It's a bit frightening, though. We couldn't let the girls into it.'

'Whatever is it?' said all three girls at once.

'Well – it seems to me that if there *is* a prisoner locked up in one of the rooms of the old house, he will have to be fed and given water,' said Jack. 'And whoever does that would have to visit him at night. See? So what about us taking it in turn at night to go and watch outside the old house to see who goes in – then we might even follow them and see where they go, and who they've got there!'

'It seems a very good idea,' said Peter. 'But we'd have to watch two at a time. I wouldn't want to go and hide somewhere there all by myself!'

'*I* think that probably someone will be along tonight,' said George. 'Why shouldn't all four of us boys go and wait in hiding?'

'It would be difficult for four of us to hide and not be seen,' said Colin.

'Well – let's drape ourselves in white sheets or something and go and join the snowmen in the field!' said Peter, jokingly. To his surprise the other three boys pounced on his idea eagerly.

'Oh, *yes*, Peter – that's fine! Nobody would ever guess we weren't snowmen if we had something white round us!' said Colin.

'We get a good view of the lane, and could see and hear anyone coming along,' said George.

'Two could follow anyone into the house and two remain on guard outside, as snowmen, to give warning in case the other two got into trouble,' said Jack. 'I'd love to stand there with the snowmen! We'd have to wrap up jolly warmly, though.'

'Can't we girls come too?' asked Pam.

'I don't want to!' said Barbara.

'Well, you *can't* come, anyhow,' said Peter. 'That's absolutely certain. Boys only are in the performance to-night!'

'It will be super!' said Jack, his eyes gleaming with excitement. 'What about Scamper? Shall we take him?'

'We'd better, I think,' said Peter. 'He'll be absolutely quiet if I tell him.'

'I'll make him a little white coat,' said Janet. 'Then he won't be seen either. He'll look like a big lump of snow or something!'

They all began to feel very excited. 'What time shall we go?' said Colin.

'Well, it was about half-past nine, wasn't it, when the men arrived last night,' said Jack. 'We'll make it the same time then. Meet here at about nine tonight. My goodness – this *is* a bit of excitement, isn't it?'

Nine

Out into the night

JANET spent the whole of the afternoon making Scamper a white coat. Peter borrowed a ragged old sheet, and found an old white macintosh. He thought he could cut up the sheet and make it do for the other three, it was so big.

Janet helped him to cut it up and make arm-holes and neck-holes. She giggled when he put one on to see if it was all right.

'You do look peculiar,' she said. 'What about your head – how are you going to hide your dark hair? It will be moonlight tonight, you know.'

'You'll have to try and make white caps or something for us,' said Peter. 'And we'll paint our faces white!'

'There's some whitewash in the shed,' said Janet, with another giggle. 'Oh, dear – you *will* all look queer. Can I come to the shed at nine, Peter, and just see you all before you go?'

'All right – if you can creep down without anyone seeing you,' said Peter. 'I think Mummy's going out tonight, so it should be all right. If she's not, you mustn't come in case you make a noise and spoil the whole thing.'

Mummy *was* going out that night. Good! Now it

would be easy to slip down to the shed. Peter told Janet she must wrap up very warmly indeed – and if she had fallen asleep she was not to wake up!

'I *shan't* fall asleep,' said Janet, indignantly. 'You know I couldn't possibly. Mind *you* don't.'

'Don't be silly,' said Peter. 'As if the head one in an important plan like this could fall asleep! My word, Janet – the Secret Seven are in for an adventure this time!'

At half-past eight the children's lights were out, and didn't go on again. But torches lighted up their rooms, and Janet was very, very busy dressing up Scamper in his new white coat. He didn't like it at all, and kept biting at it.

'Oh, Scamper – you won't be allowed to go unless you look like a snow-dog!' said Janet, almost in despair. And whether or not Scamper understood what she said she didn't know – but from that moment he let her dress him up without any more trouble. He looked peculiar and very mournful.

'Come on, if you're coming – it's almost nine,' said a whispering voice. It was Peter's. Together the two children and Scamper crept down the stairs. They were very warmly wrapped up indeed – but as soon as they got out into the air they found that it was not nearly as cold as they expected.

'The snow's melting! There's no frost tonight,' whispered Janet.

'Golly, I hope those snowmen won't have melted,' said Peter, in alarm.

'Oh, they won't *yet*,' said Janet. 'Come on – I can see one of the others.'

The passwords were whispered softly at the door of the shed, and soon there were five of the Secret Seven there. Peter lighted a candle, and they all looked at one another in excitement.

'We've got to paint our faces white and put on our white things,' said Peter. 'Then we're ready.'

Jack giggled. 'Look at Scamper! He's in white too! Scamper, you look ridiculous.'

'Woof,' said Scamper, miserably. He *felt* ridiculous, too! Poor Scamper.

With squeals and gurgles of laughter the four boys painted their faces white. They had carefully put on their white things first so as not to mess their overcoats. Janet fitted the little white skull caps she had roughly made, over each boy's head.

'Well! I shouldn't like to meet you walking down the lane tonight!' she said. 'You look terrifying!'

'Time we went,' said Peter. 'Goodbye, Janet. Go to bed now and sleep tight. I'll tell you our adventures in the morning! I shan't wake you when I come in.'

'I shall stay awake till you come!' said Janet.

She watched them go off down the moonlit path, a row of queer white figures with horrid white faces. They really did look like walking snowmen, as they trod softly over the soft, melting snow.

They made their way quietly out of the gate and walked in the direction of the lane that led to the old house, keeping a sharp lookout for any passers-by.

They met no one except a big boy who came so quietly round a corner in the snow that not one of the four heard him. They stopped at once when they saw him.

He stopped too. He gazed at the four white snowmen in horror.

'Ooooh!' he said. 'Ow! What's this? Who are you?'

Peter gave a dreadful groan, and the boy yelled in alarm. 'Help! Four live snowmen! Help!'

He tore off down the road, shouting. The four boys collapsed in helpless giggles against the fence behind.

'Oh, dear!' said Jack. 'I nearly burst with laughter when you did that groan, Peter.'

'Come on – we'd better get away quickly before the boy brings somebody back here,' and they went chuckling on their way. They came to the lane where the old house stood and went down it. They soon came to the old house. It stood silent and dark, with its roof white in the moonlight.

'Nobody's here yet,' said Peter. 'There's no light anywhere in the house, and not a sound to be heard.'

'Let's go and join the merry gang of snowmen then,' said Jack. 'And I wish you'd tell Scamper not to get between my feet so much, Peter. He'll trip me up in this sheet thing I'm wearing.'

They climbed over the gate and went into the field. The snowmen still stood there, but alas! they were melting, and were already smaller than they had been in the morning. Scamper went and sniffed at each one solemnly. Peter called him.

'Come here! You've got to stand as still as we do – and remember, not a bark, not a growl, not a whine!'

Scamper understood. He stood as still as a statue beside Peter. The boys looked for all the world like neat snowmen as they stood there in the snowy field.

They waited and they waited. Nobody came. They waited for half an hour and then they began to feel cold. 'The snow is melting round my feet,' complained Jack. 'How much longer do you think we've got to stand here?'

The others felt tired of it too. Gone were their ideas of staying half the night standing quietly with the snowmen! Half an hour was more than enough.

'Can't we go for a little walk, or something?' said Colin, impatiently. 'Just to get us warm.'

Peter was about to answer when he stopped and stiffened. He had heard something. What was it?

Colin began to speak again. 'Sh!' said Peter. Colin stopped at once. They all listened. A faraway sound came to their straining ears.

'It's that squealing noise,' said Jack, suddenly. 'I know it is! Only very faint and far away. It's coming from the old house. There *is* somebody there!'

Shivers went down their backs. They listened again, and once more the queer, far-away sound came on the night air.

'I don't like it,' said Peter. 'I'm going to the old house to see if I can hear it there. I think we ought to tell someone.'

'Let's all go,' said Colin. But Peter was quite firm about that.

'No. Two to go and two to remain on guard. That's what we said. Jack, you come with me. Colin and George, stay here and watch.'

Peter and Jack, two queer white figures with strange white faces, went to the field gate, climbed it, and went to the gate of the old house. They opened it and shut it behind them. There was no noise at all to be heard now.

They went quietly up the drive, keeping to the shadows in case the old caretaker might possibly be looking out. They went to the front door and looked through the letter-box. Nothing was to be seen through there at all. All was dark inside.

They went to the side door. It was fastened, of course. Then they went to the back door and tried that. That was locked, too. Then they heard a queer thudding, thundering noise from somewhere in the house. They clutched at one another. What *was* going on in this old empty house?

'I say – that old man has left this window a bit open – the one he spoke to us out of this morning,' whispered Jack, suddenly.

'Goodness – has he, really? Then what about getting in and seeing if we can find the prisoner?' whispered Peter, in excitement.

It only took a minute or two to climb up and get inside. They stood in the dark kitchen, listening. There was no noise to be heard at all. Where could the prisoner be?

'Dare we search the whole house from top to bottom?' said Peter. 'I've got my torch.'

'Yes, we dare, because we jolly well ought to,' answered Jack. So, as quietly as they could they tip-toed into first the scullery and then an outhouse. Nobody there at all.

'Now into the hall and we'll peep into the rooms there,' said Peter.

The front rooms were bright with moonlight but the
back rooms were dark. The boys pushed open each door
and flashed the torch round the room beyond. Each one
was silent and empty.

They came to a shut door. Sounds came from behind
it. Peter clutched Jack. 'Somebody's in here. I expect the
door's locked, but I'll try it. Stand ready to run if we're
chased!'

Ten

In the old empty house

THE door wasn't locked. It opened quietly. The sounds became loud at once. Somebody was in there, snoring!

The same thought came to both boys at once. It must be the caretaker! Quietly Peter looked in.

Moonlight filled the room. On a low, untidy bed lay the old caretaker, not even undressed! He looked dirty and shabby, and he was snoring as he slept. Peter turned to go – and his torch suddenly knocked against the door and fell with a crash to the floor.

He stood petrified, but the old man didn't stir. Then Peter remembered how deaf he was! Thank goodness – he hadn't even *heard* the noise! He shut the door quietly and the two boys stood out in the hall. Peter tried his torch to see if he had broken it. No, it was all right. Good.

'Now we'll go upstairs,' he whispered. 'You're not afraid, are you, Jack?'

'Not very,' said Jack. 'Just a *bit*. Come on.'

They went up the stairs that creaked and cracked in a very tiresome manner. Up to the first floor with five or six rooms to peep into – all as empty as one another. Then up to the top floor.

'We'll have to be careful now,' said Jack. He spoke in such a whisper that Peter could hardly hear him. 'These are the only rooms we haven't been into. The prisoner must be here somewhere.'

All the doors were ajar! Well, then, how could there be a prisoner – unless he was tied up? The two boys looked into each room, half-scared in case they saw something horrid.

But there was absolutely nothing there at all. The rooms were either dark and empty, or full of moonlight and nothing else.

'It's queer, isn't it?' whispered Jack. 'Honestly I don't understand it. Surely those noises *did* come from the house somewhere? Yet there's nothing and no one here except the old caretaker!'

They stood there, wondered what to do next – and once more that far-away, muffled squealing came on the night air, a kind of whinnying noise, followed by a series of curious thuds and crashes.

'There *is* a prisoner here somewhere – and he's knocking for help – and squealing too,' said Peter, forgetting to whisper. 'Someone downstairs. But we've looked everywhere.'

Jack was making for the stairs. 'Come on – we must have missed a cupboard or something!' he called.

Down they went, not caring now about the noise they made. They came to the kitchen. The noises had stopped again. Then the thudding began once more. Jack clutched Peter.

'I know where it's coming from – under our feet! There's a cellar there. *That's* where the prisoner is!'

'Look for the cellar door then,' said Peter. They found it at last, in a dark corner of the passage between kitchen and scullery. They turned the handle – and what a surprise – the door opened!

'It's not locked!' whispered Jack. 'Why doesn't the prisoner escape then?'

Stone steps led downwards into the darkness. Peter flashed his torch down them. He called, in rather a shaky voice:

'Who's there? Who is it down there?'

There was no answer at all. The boys listened with straining ears. They could distinctly hear the sound of very heavy breathing, loud and harsh.

'We can hear you breathing!' called Jack. 'Do tell us who you are. We've come to rescue you.'

Still no reply. This was dreadful. Both boys were really scared. They didn't dare to go down the steps. Their legs simply refused to move downwards. Yet it seemed very cowardly to go back into the passage again.

And then another sound came to them – the sound of low voices somewhere! Then came the sound of a key being turned in a lock – and a door being opened!

Jack clutched Peter in a panic. 'It's those men I heard last night. 'They're back again. Quick – we must hide before they find us here.'

The two boys, strange little figures in white, stood for

a moment, not knowing where to go. Then Peter stripped off his white sheet and cap. 'Take yours off, too,' he whispered to Jack. 'We shan't be so easily seen in our dark overcoats, if we slip into the shadows somewhere.'

They threw their things into a corner and then slipped into the hall. They crouched there in a corner, hoping that the men would go straight down into the cellar.

But they didn't. 'Better see if that old caretaker is asleep,' said a voice, and two men came into the hall to open the caretaker's door.

And then one of them caught sight of Peter's whitewashed face, which gleamed queerly out of the middle of the dark shadows. Peter had forgotten his face was white!

'Good gracious – look there – in that corner! Whatever is it?' cried one of the men. 'Look – over there, Mac.'

The men looked towards the corner where the two boys were crouching. 'Faces! White faces!' said the other man. 'I don't like it. Here, switch on your torch. It's just a trick of the moonlight or something.'

A powerful torch was switched on, and the two boys were discovered at once! With a few strides the man called Mac went over to them. He picked up both boys at once, gave them a rough shake and set them on their feet.

'Now then – what's the meaning of this – hiding here with your faces all painted up like that! What are you doing?'

'Let go my arm. You're hurting,' said Jack, angrily. 'The thing is – what are *you* up to?'

'What do you mean?' said the man roughly.

The thudding noise began again, and the two boys looked at the men.

'That's what I mean,' said Jack. 'Who's down there? Who are you keeping prisoner?'

Jack got a clout on the head that made him see stars. Then he and Peter were dragged to a nearby cupboard and locked in. The men seemed furiously angry for some reason or other.

Peter put his ear to the crack and tried to hear what they were saying.

'What are we going to do now? If those kids get anyone here, we're done.'

'Right. Keep the kids here too, then. Put them down with Kerry Blue! We'll fetch him tomorrow night and clear off, and nobody will know anything. The job will be done by then.'

'What about the kids?'

'We'll leave them locked up here – and send a card to the old caretaker to tell him to look down in his cellar the day after tomorrow. He'll get a shock when he finds the kids prisoners there! Serve them right, little pests.'

Peter listened. Who was Kerry Blue? What a

peculiar name! He trembled when he heard the men coming to the door. But they didn't unlock it. One of them called through the crack.

'You can stay there for a while. Teach you to come poking your noses into what's no business of yours!'

Then began various curious noises. Something seemed to be brought into the scullery. The boys heard the crackling of wood as if a fire was being lighted. Then a nasty smell came drifting through the cracks of the door.

'Oooh! They're boiling something. Whatever is it?' said Peter. 'Horrible smell!'

They couldn't think what it was. They heard a lot of squealing again, and some snorting, and a thundering noise like muffled hooves thudding on stone. It was all very, very extraordinary.

The cupboard, made to take a few coats, was small and cold and airless. The two boys were very uncomfortable. They were glad when one of the men unlocked the door and told them to come out.

'Now, you let us go,' began Peter, and got a rough blow on his shoulder at once.

'No cheek from you,' said one of the men and hustled the boys to the cellar door. He thrust both of them through it, and they half-fell down the top steps. The door shut behind them. They could hear it being locked. Blow, blow! blow! Now *they* were prisoners too!

A noise came from below them. Oh dear – was Kerry Blue down there, whoever he was? 'Switch your torch on,' whispered Jack. 'For goodness sake let's have a look at the prisoner and see what he's like!'

Eleven

The prisoner

PETER switched on his torch, his hand trembling as he did so. What were they going to see?

What they saw was so surprising that both boys gave a gasp of amazement. They were looking down on a beautiful horse, whose pricked ears and rolling eyes showed that he was as scared as they were!

'A *horse*!' said Jack, feebly. 'It's a *horse*!'

'Yes – that squealing was its frightened whinny – and thudding was its hooves on the stone floor when it rushed about in panic,' said Peter. 'Oh, Jack – poor, poor thing! How *wicked* to keep a horse down here like this! Why do they do it!'

'It's such a beauty. It looks like a racehorse,' said Jack. 'Do you suppose they've stolen it? Do you think they're hiding it here till they can change it to another colour, or something – horse thieves do do that, you know – and then sell it somewhere under a different name.'

'I don't know. You may be right,' said Peter. 'I'm going down to him.'

'Aren't you afraid?' said Jack. 'Look at his rolling eyes!'

'No, I'm not afraid,' said Peter, who was quite used

to the horses on his father's farm, and had been
brought up with them since he was a baby. 'Poor
thing – it wants talking to and calming.'

Peter went down the steps, talking as he went. 'So
you're Kerry Blue, are you? And a beautiful name it is,
too, for a beautiful horse! Don't be frightened, beauty.
I'm your friend. Just let me stroke that velvety nose of
yours and you'll be all right!'

The horse squealed and shied away. Peter took no
notice. He went right up to the frightened creature and
rubbed his hand fearlessly down its soft nose. The horse

stood absolutely still. Then it suddenly nuzzled against the boy and made queer little snorting sounds.

'Jack, come on. The horse is friendly now,' called Peter. 'He's such a beauty. What brutes those men are to keep a horse down in a dark cellar like this. It's enough to make it go mad!'

Jack came down the steps. He stroked the horse's back and then gave an exclamation. 'Ugh! He feels sticky and wet!'

Peter shone his torch on to the horse's coat. It gleamed wetly. 'Jack! You were right! Those men *have* been dyeing him!' cried Peter. 'His coat's still wet with the dye.'

'And that's the horrid smell we smelt – the dye being boiled up ready to use,' said Jack. 'Poor old Kerry Blue! What have they been doing to you?'

The horse had a mass of straw in one corner and a rough manger of hay in another. Oats were in a heavy pail. Water was in another pail.

'Well, if *we* want a bed, we'll have to use the straw,' said Peter. 'And have oats for a feed!'

'We shan't need to,' said Jack. 'I bet old Colin and George will come and look for us soon. We'll shout the place down as soon as we hear them!'

They settled down on the straw to wait. Kerry Blue decided to lie down on the straw too. The boys leaned against his warm body, wishing he didn't smell so strongly of dye.

Up in the field, where the snow was now rapidly

melting, Colin and George had been waiting impatiently for a long time. They had seen Jack and Peter disappear over the gate, and had had a difficult time holding Scamper back, because he wanted to follow them. They had stood there quietly for about half an hour, wondering whenever Peter and Jack were coming back, when Scamper began to growl.

'He can hear something,' said Colin. 'Yes – a car – coming down the lane. I do hope it's not those men again. Jack and Peter will be caught, if so!'

The car had no trailer-van behind it this time. It stopped at the gate of the old house and two men got out. Scamper suddenly barked loud, and was at once cuffed by Colin. 'Idiot!' hissed Colin. 'Now you've given us away!'

One of the men came to the field gate at once. He gazed at the six snowmen. 'Come and look here!' he called to the other man, who went to stand beside him. How Colin and George trembled and quaked!

'What? Oh, we saw the snowmen there last night. Don't you remember?' he said. 'Some kids have been messing about again today and built a few more. Come on. That dog we heard barking must be a stray one about somewhere.'

The men left the gate and went up the drive to the house. Colin and George breathed freely again. That was a narrow escape! Thank goodness for their white faces, caps and sheets! Thank goodness Scamper was in white, too.

For a long time there was no sound at all. Colin and George got colder and colder and more and more impatient. WHAT was happening? They wished they knew. Were Jack and Peter caught?

At last, just as they thought they really must give up and go and scout round the house themselves to see what was happening, they heard sounds again. Voices! Ah, the men were back again. There was the sound of a car door being shut quietly. The engine started up. The car moved down the lane to turn in at the field gate again, go round in a circle and come out facing up the lane. It went by quickly, squelching in the soft, melting snow.

'They're gone,' said Colin. 'And we were *awful* mutts not to have stolen up to the gate and taken the car's number! Now it's too late.'

'Yes. We *could* have done that,' said George. 'What shall we do now? Wait to see if Peter and Jack come out?'

'Yes, but not for too long,' said Colin. 'My feet are really frozen.'

They waited for about five minutes, and still no Peter or Jack came. So, sloshing through the fast-melting snow, the two boys went to the gate. They climbed over. Soon they were in the drive of the old house, hurrying up to the front door, with Scamper at their heels.

'But, of course, they couldn't get in there, nor in the other doors either. And then, like Jack and Peter, they discovered the open window! In they went. They stood on the kitchen floor and listened. They could hear nothing at all.

They called softly. 'Jack! Peter! Are you here?'

Nobody answered. Not a sound was to be heard in the house. Then Scamper gave a loud bark and ran into the passage between the scullery and the kitchen. He scraped madly at a door there.

The boys followed at once, and no sooner had they got there than they heard Peter's voice.

'Who's there? That you, Colin and George? Say the password if it's you!'

'Weekdays! Where are you?' called George.

'Down here, in the cellar. We'll come up,' said Peter's voice. 'We're all right. Can you unlock the door – or has the key been taken?'

'No, it's here,' said Colin. 'Left in the door.'

He turned the key and unlocked the door. He pushed it open just as Jack and Peter came up to the top of the cellar steps!

And behind them came somebody else – somebody whose feet made a thudding sound on the stone steps – Kerry Blue! He wasn't going to be left behind in the dark cellar, all alone! He was going to keep beside these nice kind boys.

Colin and George gaped in astonishment. They stared at Kerry Blue as if they had never seen a horse in their lives before. A horse – down in the cellar – locked up with Peter and Jack. How extraordinary!

'Have the men gone?' asked Peter, and Colin
nodded.

'Yes. Away in their car. That's why we came to look
for you. They saw us in the field because Scamper
barked – but they thought we were just snowmen! I
say – what happened here?'

'Let's get out of the house,' said Peter. 'I just can't
bear being here any longer.'

He led Kerry Blue behind him, and Colin was surprised that the horse made so little noise on the wooden

floor of the kitchen. He looked down at the horse's hooves and gave an exclamation.

'Look! What's he's got on his feet?'

'Felt slippers, made to fit his great hooves,' said Peter, with a grin. 'That explains the curious prints we saw in the snow. I guess he had those on so that he wouldn't make too much noise down in the cellar! My word, he *was* scared when we found him. Come on – I'm going home!'

Twelve

The end of the adventure

SIX figures went up the snowy lane – two boys in dark anoraks, two in curious white garments and caps, a dog in a draggled white coat, and a proud and beautiful horse. All the boys had gleaming white faces and looked extremely queer, but as they didn't meet anyone it didn't matter.

Peter talked hard as he went, telling of all that had happened to him and Jack. Colin and George listened in astonishment, half-jealous that they, too, had not shared in the whole of the night's adventure.

'I'm going to put Kerry Blue into one of the stables at our farmhouse,' said Peter. 'He'll be all right now. What sucks for the men to find him gone! And tomorrow we'll tell the police. Meet at half-past nine – and collect Pam and Barbara on the way, will you? This really has been a wonderful mystery, and I do think the Secret Seven have done well! Goodness, I'm tired. I shall be asleep in two shakes of a duck's tail!'

They were all in bed and asleep in under half an hour. Janet was fast asleep when Peter got in. He had carefully stabled Kerry Blue who was now quite docile and friendly.

In the morning, what an excitement! Peter told his

father and mother what had happened and his father, in amazement, went to examine Kerry Blue.

'He's a very fine racehorse,' he said. 'And he's been dyed with some kind of brown stuff, as you can see. I expect those fellows meant to sell him and race him under another name. Well, you've stopped that, you and your Society, Peter!'

'What about getting on to the police now?' said the children's mother, anxiously. 'It does seem to me they ought to be after these men at once.'

'There's a meeting of the Secret Seven down in the shed at half-past nine,' said Peter. 'Perhaps the police could come to it.'

'Oh, no – I hardly think the police would want to sit on your flower-pots and boxes,' said Mummy. 'You must all meet in Daddy's study. That's the proper place.'

So, at half-past nine, when the Seven were all waiting in great excitement, and Scamper was going quite mad, biting a corner of the rug, the bell rang, and in walked two big policemen. They looked most astonished to see so many children sitting round in a ring.

'Good morning,' said the Inspector. 'Er – what is all this about? You didn't say much on the phone, sir.'

'No. I wanted you to hear the story from the children,' said Peter's father. He unfolded the morning paper and laid it out flat on the table. The children crowded round.

On the front page was a big photograph of a lovely

horse. Underneath it were a few sentences in big black letters.

KERRY BLUE STOLEN.
FAMOUS RACEHORSE DISAPPEARS.
NO SIGN OF HIS HIDING-PLACE.

'I expect you saw that this morning,' said Peter's father. 'Peter, tell him where Kerry Blue is.'

'In our stables!' said Peter, and thoroughly enjoyed the look of utter amazement that came over the faces of the two policemen.

They got out notebooks. 'This is important, sir,' said the Inspector to Peter's father. 'Can you vouch for the fact that you've got the horse?'

'Oh, yes – there's no doubt about it,' said Peter's father. 'You can see him whenever you like. Peter, tell your story.'

'We're going to take it in turns to tell bits,' said Peter. He began. He told about how they had made snowmen in the field. Then Jack went on to tell how he had gone to look for his Secret Seven badge in the field, and how he had seen the car and its trailer-van.

'Of course I know now it was a horse-box,' he said. 'But I didn't know then. I couldn't think what it was – it looked like a small removal van, or something. I couldn't see any proper windows either.'

So the story went on – how they had interviewed the caretaker and what he had said – how they had tracked

the car down to the field gate and up the lane again. Then how four boys had dressed up as snowmen with Scamper and gone to watch.

Then came the exciting bit about Peter and Jack creeping into the house to find the prisoner – and being caught themselves. And then Colin and George took up the tale and told how they in their turn went into the old house to find Jack and Peter.

'Adventurous kids, aren't they?' said the Inspector, with a twinkle in his eye, turning to Peter's mother.

'Very,' she said. 'But I don't at all approve of this night-wandering business, Inspector. They should all have been in bed and asleep.'

'Quite,' said the Inspector, 'I agree with you. They should have told the police, no doubt about that, and left *them* to solve the mystery. Wandering about at night dressed up as snowmen – I never heard anything like it!'

He spoke in such a severe voice that the three girls felt quite alarmed. Then he smiled and they saw that actually he was very pleased with them.

'I'll have to find out the name of the owner of the old house,' he said, 'and see if he knows anything about these goings-on.'

'It's a Mr. Holikoff, 64, Heycom Street, Covelty,' said George at once. 'We – Pam and I – found that out.'

'Good work!' said the Inspector, and the other police-man wrote the address down at once. 'Very good work indeed.'

'I suppose they don't know the number of the car, do they?' asked the second policeman. 'That would be a help.'

'No,' said Colin, regretfully. 'But the other two girls here know something about the horse-box, sir. They took the measurements of the tyres and even drew a copy of the pattern on them – it showed in the snow, you see.'

'Janet did that,' said Barbara, honestly, wishing she hadn't laughed at Janet for doing it. Janet produced the paper on which she had drawn the pattern and taken the measurements. The Inspector took it at once, looking very pleased.

'Splendid. Couldn't be better! It's no good looking for tracks today, of course, because the snow's all melted. This is a very, very valuable bit of evidence. Dear me, what bright ideas you children have!'

Janet was scarlet with pleasure. Peter looked at her and smiled proudly. She was a fine sister to have – a really good member of the Secret Seven!

'Well, these children seem to have done most of the work for us,' said the Inspector, shutting his notebook. 'They've got the address of the owner – and if he happens to have a horse-box in his possession, whose tyres match these measurements and this pattern, then he'll have to answer some very awkward questions.'

The police went to see Kerry Blue. The children crowded into the stable too, and Kerry Blue put his ears back in alarm. But Peter soon soothed him.

'Yes. He's been partly dyed already,' said the Inspector, feeling his coat. 'If he'd had one more coat of colour he'd be completely disguised! I suppose those fellows meant to come along and do that tonight – and then take him off to some other stable. But, of course, they had to hide him somewhere safe while they changed the colour of his coat – and so they chose the cellars of the old empty house – belonging to Mr. J. Holikoff. Well, well, well – I wonder what *he* knows about it!'

The children could hardly wait to hear the end of the adventure. They heard about it at the very next meeting of the Secret Seven – which was called, not by the members themselves, but by Peter's father and mother.

It was held in the shed, and the two grown-ups had the biggest boxes as seats. Janet and Peter sat on the floor.

'Well,' said Peter's father. 'Mr. Holikoff *is* the owner of the horse-box – and of the car as well. The police waited in the old house for the two men last night – and they came! They are now safely under lock and key. They were so surprised when they found Kerry Blue gone that they hardly made a struggle at all!'

'Who does Kerry Blue belong to, Daddy?' said **Peter**. 'The papers said he was owned by Colonel James Healey. Is he sending someone to fetch him?'

'Yes,' said his father. 'He's sending off a horse-box for him today. And he has also sent something for the Secret Seven. Perhaps you'd like to see what it is, Peter.'

Peter took an envelope from his father and opened it. Out fell a shower of tickets. Janet grabbed one.

'Oooh – a circus ticket – and a pantomime ticket too! Are there seven of each?'

There were! Two lovely treats for everyone – except Scamper.

'But he can have a great big delumptious, scrumplicious bone, can't he, Mummy?' cried Janet, hugging him.

'Whatever are you talking about? Is that some foreign language?' asked her mother in astonishment, and everyone laughed.

On the envelope was written, 'For the Secret Seven Society, with my thanks and best wishes, J.H.'

'How awfully decent of him,' said Peter. 'We didn't want any reward at all. The adventure was enough reward – it was super!'

'Well, we'll leave you to talk about it,' said his mother, getting up. 'Or else we shall find that *we* belong to your Society too, and that it's the Secret Nine, instead of the Secret Seven!'

'No – it's the Secret *Seven*,' said Peter, firmly. 'The best Society in the world. Hurrah for the Secret Seven!'

SECRET SEVEN
ADVENTURE

CONTENTS

One

A Secret Seven meeting

THE Secret Seven Society was having its usual weekly meeting. Its meeting place was down in the old shed at the bottom of the garden belonging to Peter and Janet. On the door were the letters S.S. painted in green.

Peter and Janet were in the shed, waiting. Janet was squeezing lemons into a big jug, making lemonade for the meeting. On a plate lay seven ginger biscuits and one big dog biscuit.

That was for Scamper, their golden spaniel. He sat with his eyes on the plate, as if he was afraid his biscuit might jump off and disappear!

'Here come the others,' said Peter, looking out of the window. 'Yes – Colin – George – Barbara – Pam and Jack. And you and I make the Seven.'

'Woof,' said Scamper, feeling left out.

'Sorry, Scamper,' said Peter. 'But you're not a member – just a hanger-on – but a very *nice* one!'

Bang! Somebody knocked at the door.

'Password, please,' called Peter. He never unlocked the door until the person outside said the password.

'Rabbits!' said Colin, and Peter unlocked the door. 'Rabbits!' said Jack, and 'Rabbits,' said the others in turn. That was the very latest password. The Secret

Seven altered the word every week, just in *case* anyone should get to hear of it.

Peter looked at everyone keenly as they came in and sat down. 'Where's your badge, Jack?' he asked.

Jack looked uncomfortable. 'I'm awfully sorry,' he said, 'but I think Susie's got it. I hid it in my drawer, and it was gone when I looked for it this morning. Susie's an awful pest when she likes.'

Susie was Jack's sister. She badly wanted to belong to the Society, but as Jack kept patiently pointing out, as long as there were Seven in the Secret Seven, there couldn't possibly be any more.

'Susie wants smacking,' said Peter. 'You'll have to get back the badge somehow, Jack, and then in future don't hide it in a drawer or anywhere, but pin it on to your pyjamas at night and wear it. Then Susie can't get it.'

'Right,' said Jack. He looked round to see if everyone else was wearing a badge. Yes – each member had a little round button with the letters S.S. neatly worked on it. He felt very annoyed with Susie.

'Has anyone anything exciting to report?' asked Peter, handing round the seven ginger biscuits. He tossed Scamper the big dog biscuit, and the spaniel caught it deftly in his mouth. Soon everyone was crunching and munching.

Nobody had anything to report at all. Barbara looked at Peter.

'This is the fourth week we've had nothing to

report, and nothing has happened,' she said. 'It's very dull. I don't see much point in having a Secret Society if it doesn't *do* something – solve some mystery or have an adventure.'

'Well, think one up, then,' said Peter, promptly. 'You seem to think mysteries and adventures grow on trees, Barbara.'

Janet poured out the lemonade. '*I* wish something exciting would happen, too,' she said. 'Can't we make up some kind of adventure, just to go on with?'

'What sort?' asked Colin. 'Oooh, this lemonade's sour!'

'I'll put some more honey in,' said Janet. 'Well, I mean, couldn't we dress up as Red Indians or something, and go somewhere and stalk people without their knowing it? We've got some lovely Red Indian clothes, Peter and I.'

They talked about it for a while. They discovered that between them they had six sets of Red Indian clothes.

'Well, I know what we'll do, then,' said George. 'We'll dress up, and go off to Little Thicket. We'll split into two parties, one at each end of the thicket – and we'll see which party can stalk and catch Colin – he's the only one without a Red Indian dress. That'll be fun.'

'I don't much want to be stalked by all six of you,' said Colin. 'I hate being jumped on all at once.'

'It's only a game!' said Janet. 'Don't be silly.'

'Listen – there's somebody coming!' said Peter.

Footsteps came up the path right to the shed. There was a tremendously loud bang at the door, which made everyone jump.

'Password!' said Peter, forgetting that all the Secret Seven were there.

'Rabbits!' was the answer.

'It's *Susie*!' said Jack in a rage. He flung open the

door, and there, sure enough, was his cheeky sister, wearing the S.S. button, too!

'I'm a member!' she cried. 'I know the password and I've got the badge!'

Everyone got up in anger, and Susie fled, giggling as she went. Jack was scarlet with rage.

'I'm going after her,' he said. 'And now we'll have to think of a new password, too!'

'The password can be Indians!' Peter called after him. 'Meet here at half-past two!'

Two

A Red Indian afternoon

AT half-past two the Seven Society arrived by ones and twos. Jack arrived first, wearing his badge again. He had chased and caught Susie, and taken it from her.

'I'll come and bang at the door again and shout the password,' threatened Susie.

'That won't be any good,' said Jack.

'We've got a new one!'

Everyone said the new password cautiously, just in *case* that tiresome Susie was anywhere about.

'Indians!'

'Indians!' The password was whispered time after time till all seven were gathered together. Everyone had brought Red Indian suits and head-dresses. Soon they were all dressing, except Colin, who hadn't one.

'Now off we go to Little Thicket,' said Peter, prancing about with a most terrifying-looking hatchet. Fortunately, it was only made of wood. 'I'll take Janet and Jack for my two men, and George can have Barbara and Pam. Colin's to be the one we both try to stalk and capture.'

'No tying me to trees and shooting off arrows at me,' said Colin, firmly. 'That's fun for you, but not for me. See?'

They had all painted their faces in weird patterns, except Colin. Jack had a rubber knife which he kept pretending to plunge into Scamper. They really did look a very fierce collection of Indians indeed.

They set off for Little Thicket, which was about half a mile away, across the fields. It lay beside a big mansion called Milton Manor, which had high walls all round it.

'Now, what we'll do is to start out at opposite ends of Little Thicket,' said Peter. 'My three can take this end, and you three can take the other end, George. Colin can go to the middle. We'll all shut our eyes and count one hundred – and then we'll begin to hunt for Colin and stalk him.'

'And if I spot any of you and call your name, you have to get up and show yourselves,' said Colin. 'You'll be out of the game then.'

'And if any one of us manages to get right up to you and pounce on you, then you're his prisoner,' said Peter. 'Little Thicket is just the right kind of place for this!'

It certainly was. It was a mixture of heather and bushes and trees. Big, heathery tufts grew there, and patches of wiry grass, small bushes, and big and little trees. There were plenty of places to hide, and anyone could stalk a person from one end of the thicket to the other without being seen, if he crawled carefully along on his tummy.

The two parties separated, and went to each end of Little Thicket. A fence bounded one side and on the other the walls of Milton Manor grounds rose strong and high. If Colin could manage to get out of either end of Little Thicket uncaptured, he would be clever!

He went to stand in the middle, waiting for the others to count their hundred with their eyes shut. As soon as Peter waved a handkerchief to show that the counting had begun, Colin ran to a tree. He climbed quickly up into the thick branches, and sat himself on a broad bough. He grinned.

'They can stalk me all they like, from one end of the thicket to the other, but they won't find me!' he thought. 'And when they're all tired of looking and give up, I'll shin down and stroll up to them!'

The counting was up. Six Red Indians began to spread out and worm their way silently through heather and thick undergrowth and long grass.

Colin could see where some of them were by the movement of the undergrowth. He kept peeping between the boughs of his tree, chuckling to himself. This was fun!

And then something very surprising caught his eye. He glanced over to the high wall that surrounded the grounds of Milton Manor, and saw that somebody was astride the top! Even as he looked the man jumped down and disappeared from view, and Colin heard the crackling of undergrowth. Then everything was still. Colin couldn't see him at all. He was most astonished. What had the man been doing, climbing over the wall?

Colin couldn't for the life of him think what was best to do. He couldn't start yelling to the others from the tree. Then he suddenly saw that Peter, or one of the others, was very near where the man had gone to ground!

It was Peter. He had thought he had heard somebody not far from him, and he had felt sure it was Colin, squirming his way along. So he squirmed in that direction too.

Ah! He was sure there was somebody hiding in the middle of that bush! It was a great gorse bush, in full bloom. It must be Colin hiding there.

Cautiously Peter wriggled on his tummy right up to the bush. He parted the brown stems, and gazed in amazement at the man there. It wasn't Colin, after all!

As for the man, he was horrified. He suddenly saw a dreadful, painted face looking at him through the bush, and saw what he thought was a real hatchet aimed at him. He had no idea it was only wood!

He got up at once and fled – and for a moment Peter was so amazed that he didn't even follow!

Three

A shock for Colin

By the time Peter had stood up to see where the horrified man had gone, he had completely disappeared. There wasn't a sign of him anywhere.

'Blow!' said Peter, vexed. 'Fat lot of good I am as a Red Indian. Can't even stalk somebody right under my nose. Where in the world has the fellow gone?'

He began to hunt here and there, and soon the others, seeing him standing up, knew that something had happened. They called to him.

'Peter – what is it? Why are you showing yourself?'

'There was a man hiding under one of the bushes,' said Peter. 'I just wondered why. But he got up and shot away. Anyone see where he went?'

No one had seen him at all. They clustered round Peter, puzzled. 'Fancy – seven of us crawling hidden in this field – and not one saw the man run off,' said Pam. 'We haven't even seen Colin!'

'The game's finished for this afternoon,' said Peter. He didn't want the girls to come suddenly on the man in hiding – it would give them such a fright. 'We'll call Colin.'

So they yelled for him. 'Colin! Come out, wherever you are! The game's finished.'

They waited for him suddenly to stand up and appear. But he didn't. There was no answer to their call, and no Colin suddenly appeared.

'Colin!' yelled everyone. 'Come on out.'

Still he didn't come. He didn't even shout back. It was queer.

'Don't be funny!' shouted George. 'The game's over! Where are you?'

Colin was where he had been all the time – hidden up in his tree. Why didn't he shout back? Why didn't he shin down the tree and race over to the others, pleased that he hadn't been caught?

He didn't show himself for a very good reason. He was much too frightened to!

He had had a shock when he saw the man drop down from the wall, and run to the thicket and hide – and he had an even greater shock when he saw him suddenly appear from a nearby bush, and run to the foot of the tree that he himself was hiding in.

Then he heard the sounds of someone clambering up at top speed – good gracious, the man was climbing the very tree that Colin himself had chosen for a hiding place!

Colin's heart beat fast. He didn't like this at all. What would the man say if he suddenly climbed up on top of him? He would certainly be very much annoyed.

The man came steadily up. But when he was almost up to the branch on which Colin sat, he stopped. The branch wasn't strong enough to hold a

man, though it was quite strong enough for a boy.

The man curled himself up in a fork of the tree just below Colin. He was panting hard, but trying to keep his breathing as quiet as possible. Peter was not so very far away and might hear it.

Colin sat as if he was turned to stone. Who was this man? Why had he come over the wall? Why had he hidden in Little Thicket? He would never have done that if he had known it was full of the Secret Seven playing at Red Indians!

And now here he was up Colin's tree, still in hiding – and at any moment he might look up and see Colin. It was very unpleasant indeed.

Then Colin heard the others shouting for him. 'Colin! Come out, wherever you are – the game's finished!'

But poor Colin didn't dare to come out, and certainly didn't dare to shout back. He hardly dared to breathe, and hoped desperately that he wouldn't have to sneeze or cough. He sat there as still as a mouse, waiting to see what would happen.

The man also sat there as still as a mouse, watching the six children below, peering at them through the leaves of the tree. Colin wished they had brought old Scamper with them. He would have sniffed the man's tracks and gone to the foot of the tree!

But Scamper had been left behind. He always got much too excited when they were playing Red Indians, and by his barking gave away where everyone was hiding!

After the others had hunted for Colin and called him, they began to walk off. 'He must have escaped us and gone home,' said Peter. 'Well, we'll go too. We can't find that man, and I don't know that I want to, either. He looked a nasty bit of work to me.'

In despair, Colin watched them leave Little Thicket and disappear down the field-path. The man saw them go too. He gave a little grunt and slid down the tree.

Colin had been able to see nothing of him except the top of his head and his ears. He could still see nothing of the man as he made his way cautiously out of the thicket. He was a far, far better Red Indian than any of the Secret Seven, that was certain!

And now – was it safe for Colin to get down? He certainly couldn't stay up in the tree all night!

Four

Is it an adventure?

COLIN slid down the tree. He stood at the foot, look-ing warily round. Nobody was in sight. The man had completely vanished.

'I'll run at top speed and hope for the best,' thought Colin, and off he went. Nobody stopped him! Nobody yelled at him. He felt rather ashamed of himself when he came to the field-path and saw the cows staring at him in surprise.

He went back to the farmhouse where Peter and Janet lived. Maybe the Secret Seven were still down in the shed, stripped of their Red Indian things and wiping the paint off their faces.

He ran down the path to the shed. The door was shut as usual. The S.S. showed up well with the two letters painted so boldly. There was the sound of voices from inside the shed.

Colin knocked. 'Let me in!' he cried. 'I'm back too.'

There was a silence. The door didn't open. Colin banged again impatiently. 'You know it's only me. Open the door!'

Still it didn't open. And then Colin remembered. He must give the password, of course! What in the world was it? Thankfully he remembered it, as he

caught a glimpse of brilliant Red Indian feathers
through the shed-window.

'Indians!' he shouted.

The door opened. 'And now *every*body in the district knows our latest password,' said Peter's voice in
disgust. 'We'll have to choose another. Come in.
Wherever have you been? We yelled and yelled for
you at Little Thicket.'

'I know. I heard you,' said Colin, stepping inside. 'I
say, I'm sorry I shouted out the password like that. I
wasn't thinking. But I've got some news – most
peculiar news!'

'What?' asked everyone, and stopped rubbing the
paint from their faces.

'You know when Peter stood up and shouted out that he'd found a man in hiding, don't you?' said Colin. 'Well, I was quite nearby – as a matter of fact, I was up a tree!'

'Cheat!' said George. 'That's not playing Red Indians!'

'Who said it wasn't?' demanded Colin. 'I bet Red Indians climbed trees as well as wriggling on their tummies. Anyway, I was up that tree – and, will you believe it, the man that Peter found came running up to my tree, and climbed it too!'

'Golly!' said George. 'What did you do?'

'Nothing,' said Colin. 'He didn't come up quite as far as I was – so I just sat tight, and didn't make a sound. I saw him before Peter did, actually. I saw him on the top of the wall that surrounds Milton Manor – then he dropped down, ran to the thicket and disappeared.'

'What happened in the end?' asked Janet, excited.

'After you'd all gone, he slid down the tree and went,' said Colin. 'I didn't see him any more. I slid down too, and ran for home. I felt a bit scared, actually.'

'Whatever was he doing, behaving like that?' wondered Jack. 'What was he like?'

'Well, I only saw the top of his head and his ears,' said Colin. 'Did *you* see him closely, Peter?'

'Yes, fairly,' said Peter. 'But he wasn't anything out of the ordinary really – clean-shaven, dark-haired – nothing much to remember him by.'

'Well, I suppose that's the last we'll hear of him,' said Barbara. 'The adventure that passed us by! We shall never know exactly what he was doing, and why.'

'He spoilt our afternoon, anyway,' said Pam. 'Not that we'd have caught Colin – hiding up a tree like that. We'll have to make a rule that trees are not to be climbed when we're playing at stalking.'

'When's our next meeting – and are we going to have a new password?' asked Janet.

'We'll meet on Wednesday evening,' said Peter. 'Keep your eyes and ears open for anything exciting or mysterious or adventurous, as usual. It *is* a pity we didn't capture that man – or find out more about him. I'm sure he was up to no good.'

'What about a password?' asked Janet again.

'Well – we'll have "Adventure", I think,' said Peter. 'Seeing we've just missed one!'

They all went their several ways home – and, except for Colin, nobody thought much more of the peculiar man at Little Thicket. But the radio that evening suddenly made all the Secret Seven think of him again!

'Lady Lucy Thomas's magnificent and unique pearl necklace was stolen from her bedroom at Milton Manor this afternoon,' said the announcer. 'Nobody saw the thief, or heard him, and he got away in safety.' Peter and Janet sprang up at once. 'That's the man we saw!' yelled Peter. 'Would you believe it! Call a meeting of the Secret Seven for tomorrow, Janet – this is an adventure again!'

Five

An important meeting

THAT night the Secret Seven were very excited. Janet and Peter had slipped notes into everyone's letterbox. 'Meeting at half-past nine. IMPORTANT! S.S.S.'

Colin and George had no idea at all what was up, because they hadn't listened to the wireless. But the others had all heard of the theft of Lady Lucy Thomas's necklace, and, knowing that she lived by Little Thicket, they guessed that the meeting was to be about finding the thief!

At half-past nine the Society met. Janet and Peter were ready for them in the shed. Raps at the door came steadily. 'Password!' called Peter, sternly, each time.

'Adventure!' said everyone in a low voice. 'Adventure!' 'Adventure!' One after another the members were admitted to the shed.

'Where's that awful sister of yours – Susie?' Peter asked Jack. 'I hope she's not about anywhere. This is a really important meeting today. Got your badge?'

'Yes,' said Jack. 'Susie's gone out for the day. Anyway, she doesn't know our latest password.'

'What's the meeting about?' asked Colin. 'I know

something's up by the look on Janet's face. She looks as if she's going to burst!'

'*You'll* feel like bursting when you know,' said Janet. 'Because you're going to be rather important, seeing that you and Peter are the only ones who saw the thief we're going after.'

Colin and George looked blank. They didn't know what Janet was talking about, of course. Peter soon explained.

'You know the fellow that Colin saw yesterday, climbing over the wall that runs round Milton Manor?' said Peter. 'The one *I* saw hiding in the bush – and then he went and climbed up into the very tree Colin was hiding in? Well, it said on the radio last night that a thief had got into Lady Lucy Thomas's bedroom and taken her magnificent pearl necklace.'

'Gracious!' said Pam with a squeal. 'And that was the man you and Colin saw!'

'Yes,' said Peter. 'It must have been. And now the thing is – what do we do about it? This is an adventure – if only we can find that man – and if *only* we could find the necklace too – that would be a fine feather in the cap of the Secret Seven.'

There was a short silence. Everyone was thinking hard. 'But how can we find him?' asked Barbara at last. 'I mean – only you and Colin saw him, Peter – and then just for a moment.'

'And don't forget that *I* only saw the top of his head and tips of his ears,' said Colin. 'I'd like to know how I could possibly know anyone from those things. Anyway, I can't go about looking at the tops of people's heads!'

Janet laughed. 'You'd have to carry a stepladder about with you!' she said, and that made everyone else laugh too.

'Oughtn't we to tell the police?' asked George.

'I think we ought,' said Peter, considering the matter carefully. 'Not that we can give them any help at all, really. Still – that's the first thing to be done. Then maybe we could help the police, and, anyway, we could snoop round and see if we can find out anything on our own.'

'Let's go down to the police station now,' said George. 'That would be an exciting thing to do! Won't the inspector be surprised when we march in, all seven of us!'

They left the shed and went down to the town. They trooped up the steps of the police station, much to the astonishment of the young policeman inside.

'Can we see the inspector?' asked Peter. 'We've got some news for him – about the thief that stole Lady Lucy's necklace.'

The inspector had heard the clatter of so many feet and he looked out of his room. 'Hallo, *hallo*!' he said, pleased. 'The Secret Seven again! And what's the password this time?'

Nobody told him, of course. Peter grinned.

'We just came to say we saw the thief climb over the wall of Milton Manor yesterday,' he said. 'He hid in a bush first and then in a tree where Colin was hiding. But that's about all we know!'

The inspector soon got every single detail from the Seven, and he looked very pleased. 'What beats me is how the thief climbed that enormous wall!' he said. 'He must be able to climb like a cat. There was no ladder used. Well, Secret Seven, there's nothing much you can do, I'm afraid, except keep your eyes open in case you see this man again.'

'The only thing is – Colin only saw the top of his head, and I only caught a quick glimpse of him, and he looked so very, *very* ordinary,' said Peter. 'Still you may be sure we'll do our best!'

Off they all went again down the steps into the street. 'And *now*,' said Peter, 'we'll go to the place where Colin saw the man getting over the wall. We just *might* find something there – you never know!'

Six

Some peculiar finds

THE Seven made their way to Little Thicket, where they had played their game of Red Indians the day before.

'Now, where exactly did you say that the man climbed over?' Peter asked Colin. Colin considered. Then he pointed to a holly tree.

'See that holly? Well – he came over the wall between that tree and the little oak. I'm pretty certain that was exactly the place.'

'Come on, then – we'll go and see,' said Peter. Feeling really rather important, the Seven walked across Little Thicket and came to the place between the holly tree and the little oak. They stood and gazed up at the wall.

It was at least ten or eleven feet high. How could anyone climb a sheer wall like that without even a ladder?

'Look – here's where he leapt down,' said Pam, suddenly, and she pointed to a deep mark in the ground near the holly tree. They all looked.

'Yes – that must have been where his feet landed,' said George. 'Pity we can't tell anything from the mark – I mean, if it had been footprints, for instance, it would have helped a lot. But it's only just a deep mark – probably made by his heels.'

'I wish we could go to the other side of the wall,' said Peter, suddenly. 'We might perhaps find a footprint or two there. Let's go and ask the gardener if we can go into the grounds. He's a friend of our cow-man and he knows me.'

'Good idea,' said George, so off they all went again. The gardener was working inside the front garden, beyond the great iron gates. The children called to him, and he looked up.

'Johns!' shouted Peter. 'Could we come in and snoop round? About that thief, you know. We saw him climb over the wall, and the inspector of police has asked us to keep our eyes open. So we're looking round.'

Johns grinned. He opened the gates. 'Well, if I come with you, I don't reckon you can do much harm,' he said. 'Beats me how that thief climbed those walls. I was working here in the front garden all yesterday afternoon, and if he'd come in at the gates I'd have seen him. But he didn't.'

The seven children went round the walls with Johns. Colin saw the top of the holly tree and the top of the little nearby oak jutting above the wall. He stopped.

'This is where he climbed up,' he said. 'Now let's look for footprints.'

There were certainly marks in the earth – but no footprints.

The Seven bent over the marks.

'Funny, aren't they?' said Peter, puzzled. 'Quite round and regular – and about three inches across – as if someone had been pounding about with a large-sized broom handle – hammering the end of it into the ground. What could have made these marks, Johns?'

'Beats me,' said Johns, also puzzled. 'Maybe the police will make something of them, now they know you saw the thief climb over the wall just here.'

Everyone studied the round, regular marks again. There seemed no rhyme or reason for them at all. They looked for all the world as if someone had been stabbing the ground with the tip of a broom handle or something – and why should anyone do that? And anyway, if they did, how would it help them to climb over a wall?

'There's been no ladder used, that I *can* say,' said Johns. 'All mine are locked up in a shed – and there they all are still – and the key's in my pocket. How that fellow climbed this steep wall, I can't think.'

'He must have been an acrobat, that's all,' said Janet, looking up to the top of the wall. Then she spotted something, and pointed to it in excitement.

'Look – what's that – caught on that sharp bit of brick there – half-way up?'

Everybody stared. 'It looks like a bit of wool,' said Pam at last. 'Perhaps, when the thief climbed up, that sharp bit caught his clothes, and a bit of wool was pulled out.'

'Help me up, George,' ordered Peter. 'I'll get it. It might be a very valuable clue.'

George hoisted him up, and Peter made a wild grab at the piece of wool. He got it, and George let him down to the ground again. They all gathered round to look at it.

It was really rather ordinary – just a bit of blue

wool thread with a tiny red strand in it. Everyone looked at it earnestly.

'Well – it *might* have been pulled out of the thief's jersey,' said Janet at last. 'We can all look out for somebody wearing a blue wool pullover with a tiny thread of red in it!'

And then they found something else – something *much* more exciting!

Seven

Scamper finds a clue

IT was really Scamper the spaniel who found the biggest clue of all. He was with them, of course, sniffing round eagerly, very interested in the curious round marks. Then he suddenly began to bark loudly.

Everyone looked at him. 'What's up, Scamper?' said Peter.

Scamper went on barking. The three girls felt a bit scared, and looked hastily round, half afraid that there might be somebody hidden in the bushes!

Scamper had his head up, and was barking quite madly. 'Stop it,' said Peter, exasperated. 'Tell us what you're barking at, Scamper! Stop it, I say.'

Scamper stopped. He gave Peter a reproachful look and then gazed up above the children's heads. He began to bark again.

Everyone looked up, to see what in the world the spaniel was barking at. And there, caught neatly on the twig of a tree, was a cap!

'Look at that!' said Peter, astonished. 'A cap! Could it belong to the thief?'

'Well, if it does, why in the world did he throw his cap up there?' said Janet. 'It's not a thing that thieves usually do – throw their caps up into trees and leave them!'

The cap was far too high to reach. It was almost as high up as the top of the wall! Johns the gardener went to get a stick to knock it down.

'It could only have got up there by being thrown,' said George. 'So it doesn't really seem as if it could have belonged to the thief. He really wouldn't go throwing his cap about like that, leaving such a very fine clue!'

'No. You're right, I'm afraid,' said Peter. 'It can't be his cap. It must be one that some tramp threw over the wall some time or other.'

Johns came back with a bamboo stick. He jerked the cap off the twig and Scamper pounced on it at once.

'Drop it, Scamper; drop it!' ordered Peter, and Scamper dropped it, looking hurt. Hadn't he spotted the cap himself? Then at least he might be allowed to throw it up into the air and catch it!

The Seven looked at the dirty old cap. It was made of tweed, and at one time must have showed a rather startling check pattern – but now it was so dirty that it was difficult even to see the pattern. Janet looked at it in disgust.

'Ugh! What a dirty cap! I'm sure that some tramp had finished with it and threw it over the wall – and it just stuck up there on that tree branch. I'm sure it isn't a clue at all.'

'I think you're right,' said Colin, turning the cap over and over in his hands. 'We might as well chuck it over into Little Thicket. It's no use to us. Bad luck, Scamper – you thought you'd found a thumping big clue!'

He made as if to throw the cap up over the wall, but Peter stopped him. 'No, don't! We'd better keep it. You simply never know. We'd kick ourselves if we threw away something that might prove to be a clue of some kind – though I do agree with you, it probably isn't.'

'Well, *you* can carry the smelly thing then,' said Colin, giving it to Peter. 'No wonder somebody threw it away. It smells like anything!'

Peter stuffed it into his pocket. Then he took the tiny piece of blue wool thread, and put that carefully into the pages of his notebook. He looked down at the ground where the curious marks were.

'I almost think we'd better make a note of these too,' he said. 'Got a measure, Janet?'

She hadn't, of course. But George had some string,

and he carefully measured across the round marks, and then snipped the string to the right size. 'That's the size of the marks,' he said, and gave his bit of string to Peter. It went carefully into his notebook too.

'I can't help thinking those funny marks all over the place are some kind of clue,' he said, putting his notebook away. 'But what, I simply can't imagine!'

They said good-bye to Johns, and made their way home across the fields. Nobody could make much of the clues. Peter did hope the adventure wasn't going to fizzle out, after all!

'I still say that only an acrobat could have scaled that high wall,' said Janet. 'I don't see how any ordinary person could have done it!'

Just as she said this, they came out into the lane. A big poster had been put up on a wall nearby. The children glanced at it idly. And then Colin gave a shout that made them all jump!

'Look at that – it's a poster advertising a circus! And see what it says – Lion-tamers, Daring Horse-riders, Performing Bears – Clowns – and Acrobats! Acrobats! Look at that! Supposing – just supposing ...'

They all stared at one another in excitement. Janet might be right. This must be looked into at once!

Eight

A visit to the circus

PETER looked at his watch. 'Blow!' he said in dismay. 'It's nearly dinner-time. We must all get back home as fast as we can. Meet at half-past two again, Secret Seven.'

'We can't!' said Pam and Barbara. 'We're going to a party.'

'*Don't* have a meeting without us,' begged Pam.

'I can't come either, said George. 'So we'd better make it tomorrow. Anyway, if the thief *is* one of the acrobats at the circus, he won't be leaving this afternoon! He'll stay there till the circus goes.'

'Well – it's only just a *chance* he might be an acrobat,' said Janet. 'I only just *said* it could only be an acrobat that scaled that high wall. I didn't really mean it!'

'It's worth looking into, anyhow,' said Peter. 'Well – meet tomorrow at half-past nine, then. And will everybody please think hard, and have some kind of plan to suggest? I'm sure we shall think of something good!'

Everyone thought hard that day – even Pam and Barbara whispered together in the middle of their party! 'I vote we go and see the circus,' whispered Pam. 'Don't you think it would be a good idea? Then we can see if Peter recognizes any of the acrobats as the thief he saw hiding under that bush!'

When the Secret Seven met the next day, muttering the password as they went through the door of the shed, everyone seemed to have exactly the same idea!

'We should visit the circus,' began George.

'That's just what Pam and I thought!' said Barbara.

'I thought so too,' said Colin. 'In fact, it's the only sensible thing to do. Don't you think so, Peter?'

'Yes. Janet and I looked in the local paper, and we found that the circus opens this afternoon,' said Peter. 'What about us all going to see it? I don't know if I would recognize any of the acrobats as the thief – I really only caught just a glimpse of him, you know – but it's worth trying.'

'You said he was dark and clean-shaven,' said Colin. 'And I saw that his hair was black, anyway. He had a little thin patch on the top. But it isn't much to go on, is it?'

'Has anyone got any money?' asked Pam. 'To buy circus tickets, I mean? I haven't any at all, because I had to buy a birthday present to take to the party yesterday.'

Everyone turned out their pockets. The money was put in a pile in the middle and counted.

'The tickets are thirty pence for children,' said Peter with a groan. 'Thirty pence! They must think that children are *made* of money. We've got one pound twenty here, that's all. Only four of us can go.'

'I've got sixty pence in my money-box,' said Janet.

'And I've got twenty-nine pence at home,' said Colin. 'Anyone got the odd penny?'

'Oh yes – I'll borrow it from Susie,' said Jack.

'Well, don't go and tell her the password in return for the penny!' said Colin, and got a kick from Jack and an angry snort.

'Right. That looks as if we can all go, after all,' said Peter, pleased. 'Meet at the circus field ten minutes before the circus begins. Don't be late, anyone! And keep your eyes skinned for anyone wearing a dark blue pullover with a tiny thread of red in it – because it's pretty certain the thief must have worn a jersey or pullover made of that wool.'

Everyone was very punctual. All but Pam had money with them, so Peter gave her enough for her ticket. They went to the ticket-box and bought seven tickets, feeling really rather excited. A circus was always fun – but to go to a circus and keep a look out for a thief was even more exciting than usual!

Soon they were all sitting in their seats, looking down intently on the sawdust-strewn ring in the middle of the great tent. The band struck up a gay tune and a drum boomed out. The children sat up, thrilled.

In came the horses, walking proudly, their feathery plumes nodding. In came the clowns, somersaulting

and yelling; in came the bears; in came all the performers, one after another, greeting the audience with smiles.

The children watched out for the acrobats, but they were all mixed up with the other performers — five clowns and conjurers, two clever stilt-walkers, and five men on ridiculous bicycles. It was impossible to tell which were the acrobats.

'They are third on the programme,' said Peter. 'First come the horses – then the clowns – and then the acrobats.'

So they waited, clapping the beautiful dancing horses, and laughing at the ridiculous clowns until their sides ached.

'Now for the acrobats!' said Peter, excitedly. 'Watch, Colin, watch!'

Nine

A good idea – and a disappointment

THE acrobats came in, turning cart-wheels and springing high into the air. One came in with his body bent so far over backwards that he was able to put his head between his legs. He looked very peculiar indeed.

Peter nudged Colin. 'Colin! See that fellow with his head between his legs – he's clean-shaven like the man I saw hidden in the bush – and he's got black hair!'

Colin nodded. 'Yes – he may be the one! All the others have moustaches. Let's watch him carefully and see if he could really leap up a high wall, and over the top.'

All the Secret Seven kept their eyes glued on this one acrobat. They had seen that the others had moustaches, so that ruled them out – but this one fitted the bill – he was dark-haired and had no moustache!

Could he leap high? Would he show them that he could easily leap up a steep wall to the top? They watched eagerly. The clean-shaven acrobat was easily the best of them all. He was as light as a feather.

When he sprang across the ring it almost seemed as if his feet did not even touch the ground.

He was a very clever tight-rope walker too. A long ladder was put up, and was fixed to a wire high up in the roof of the tent. The children watched the acrobat spring lightly up the ladder, and they turned to look at one another – yes – if he could leap up a ladder like that, hardly touching the rungs with feet or hands, he could most certainly leap up a twelve-foot wall to the top!

'I'm sure that one's the thief,' whispered Janet to Peter. He nodded. He was sure, too. He was so sure, that he settled down to enjoy the circus properly, not bothering to look out for a thief any longer, now that he had made up his mind this was the one.

It was quite a good circus. The performing bears came on, and really seemed to enjoy themselves boxing with each other and with their trainer. One little bear was so fond of its trainer that it kept hugging his leg, and wouldn't let him go!

Janet wished she had a little bear like that for a pet. 'He's just like a big teddy,' she said to Pam, and Pam nodded.

The clowns came in again – and then the two stilt-walkers, with three of the clowns. The stilt-walkers were ridiculous. They wore long skirts over their stilts, so that they looked like tremendously tall people, and they walked stiffly about with the little clowns teasing them and jeering at them.

Then a strong cage was put up, and the lions were

brought in, snarling. Janet shrank back. 'I don't like this,' she said. 'Lions aren't meant to act about. They only look silly. Oh dear – look at that one – he won't get up on his stool. I know he's going to pounce on his keeper.'

But he didn't, of course. He knew his performance and went through it very haughtily with the others. They ambled away afterwards, still snarling.

Then a big elephant came in and began to play cricket with his trainer. He really enjoyed that, and when he hit the ball into the audience six times running, everyone clapped like mad.

Altogether, the children enjoyed themselves enormously. They were sorry when they found themselves going out into the big field again.

'If we could only hunt for thieves in circuses every time, it would be very enjoyable,' said Janet. 'Peter – what do you think? Is that dark-haired, clean-shaven acrobat the thief? He's the only likely one of the acrobats, really.'

'Yes – all the others have moustaches,' said Peter. 'I wonder what we ought to do next? It would be a good thing, perhaps, to go and find him and talk to him. He might let something slip that would help us.'

'But what excuse can we give for going to find him?' said George.

'Oh – ask him for his autograph!' said Peter. 'He'll think that quite natural!'

The others stared at him in admiration. What a

brainwave! Nobody had thought of half such a good idea.

'Look,' whispered Barbara. 'Isn't that him over there, talking to the bear-trainer? Yes, it is. Does he look like the thief to you, Peter, now that you can see him close?'

Peter nodded. 'Yes, he does. Come on – we'll all go boldly up and ask him for an autograph. Keep your eyes and ears open.'

They marched up to the acrobat. He turned round in surprise. 'Well – what do you want?' he asked with

a grin. 'Want a lesson on how to walk the tight-rope?'

'No – your autograph, please,' said Peter. He stared at the man. He suddenly seemed much older than he had looked in the ring. The acrobat laughed. He mopped his forehead with a big red handkerchief.

'It was hot in the tent,' he said. 'Yes, you can have my autograph – but just let me take off my wig first. It makes my head so hot!'

And, to the children's enormous surprise, he loosened his black hair – and lifted it off completely! It was a wig – and under it, the acrobat was completely bald. Well – *what* a disappointment!

Ten

Trinculo the acrobat

THE Seven stared at him in dismay. Why – his head was completely bald except for a few grey hairs right on the very top. He couldn't possibly be the thief. Colin had distinctly seen the top of the thief's head when he had sat above him in the tree – and he had said that his hair was black, except for a little round bald patch in the centre.

Colin took the wig in his hand. He looked at it carefully, wondering if perhaps the thief had worn the wig when he had stolen the necklace. But there was no little round bald patch in the centre! It was a thick black wig with no bare patches at all.

'You seem to be very interested in my wig,' said the acrobat, and he laughed. 'No acrobat can afford to be bald, you know. We have to look as young and beautiful as possible. Now, I'll give you each my autograph, then you must be off.'

'Thank you,' said Peter, and handed the man a piece of paper and a pencil.

The little bear came ambling by, all by itself, snorting a little.

'Oh, *look*!' said Janet in delight, 'Oh, will it come to us, do you think? Come here, little bear.'

The bear sidled up and rubbed against Janet. She

put her arms round it and tried to lift it – but it was unexpectedly heavy. A queer, sulky-looking youth came after it, and caught it roughly by the fur at its neck.

'Ah, bad boy!' he said, and shook the little creature. The bear whimpered.

'Oh, don't!' said Janet in distress. 'He's so sweet. He only came over to see us.'

The youth was dressed rather peculiarly. He had on a woman's bodice, spangled with sequins, a bonnet with flowers in – and dirty flannel trousers!

Peter glanced at him curiously as he led the little bear away. 'Was he in the circus?' he asked. 'I don't remember him.'

'Yes – he was one of the stilt-walkers,' said the acrobat, still busily writing autographs. 'His name's Louis. He helps with all the animals. Do you want to come and see the bears in their cage some time? – they're very tame – and old Jumbo would love to have a bun or two if you like to bring him some. He's as gentle as a big dog.'

'Oh yes – we'd *love* to!' said Janet, at once thinking how much she would love to make friends with the dear little bear. 'Can we come tomorrow?'

'Yes – come tomorrow morning,' said the acrobat. 'Ask for Trinculo – that's me. I'll be about somewhere.'

The children thanked him and left the field. They said nothing till they were well out of hearing of any of the circus folk.

'I'm glad it wasn't that acrobat,' said Janet. 'He's nice. I like his funny face, too. I did get a shock when he took off his black hair!'

'So did I,' said Peter. 'I felt an idiot, too. I thought I had remembered how the thief had looked – when I saw Trinculo's face, I really did think he looked like the thief. But he doesn't, of course. For one thing, the man I saw was much younger.'

'We'd better not go by faces, it seems to me,' said Colin. 'Better try to find someone who wears a blue pullover with a red thread running through it!'

'We can't go all over the district looking for *that*,' said Pam. 'Honestly, that's silly.'

'Well, have you got a better idea?' asked Colin.

She hadn't, of course. Nor had anyone else. 'We're stuck,' said Peter, gloomily. 'This is a silly sort of mystery. We keep thinking we've got somewhere – and then we find we haven't.'

'Shall we go to the circus field tomorrow?' asked Pam. 'Not to try to find the thief, of course, because we know now that he isn't any of the acrobats. But should we go just to see the animals?'

'Yes. I did like that little bear,' said Janet. 'And I'd like to see old Jumbo close to, as well. I love elephants.'

'I don't think I'll come,' said Barbara. 'I'm a bit scared of elephants, they're so enormous.'

'I won't come, either,' said Jack. 'What about you, George? We said we'd swop stamps tomorrow, you know.'

'Yes – well, we won't go either,' said George. 'You don't mind, do you, Peter? I mean, it's nothing to do with the Society, going to make friends with bears and elephants.'

'Well, Janet and Pam and Colin and I will go,' said Peter. 'And mind – everyone is to watch out for a blue pullover with a little red line running through it. You simply *never* know what you'll see if you keep your eyes open!'

Peter was right – but he would have been surprised to know what he and Janet were going to spot the very next day!

Eleven

Pam's discovery

NEXT morning Janet, Peter, Colin and Pam met to go to the circus field. They didn't take Scamper, because they didn't think Jumbo the elephant would like him sniffing round his ankles.

He was very angry at being left, and they could hear his miserable howls all the way up the lane. 'Poor Scamper!' said Janet. 'I wish we could have taken him – but he might get into the lions' cage or something. He's so very inquisitive.'

They soon came to the field. They walked across it, eyeing the circus folk curiously. How different they looked in their ordinary clothes – not *nearly* so nice, thought Janet. But then, how exciting and magnificent they looked in the ring.

One or two of them had built little fires in the field and were cooking something in black pots over the flames. Whatever it was that was cooking smelt most delicious. It made Peter feel very hungry.

They found Trinculo, and he was as good as his word. He took them to make friends with Jumbo, who trumpeted gently at them, and then, with one swing of his strong trunk, he set Janet high up on his great head. She squealed with surprise and delight.

They went to find the little bear. He was delighted

to see them, and put his paws through the bars to reach their hands. Trinculo unlocked the cage and let him out. He lumbered over to them and clasped his arms round Trinculo's leg, peeping at the rest of them with a roguish look on his funny bear-face.

'If only he wasn't so *heavy*,' said Janet, who always loved to pick up any animal she liked and hug it. 'I wish I could buy him.'

'Goodness – whatever would Scamper say if we took him home?' said Peter.

Trinculo took them to see the great lions in their cages. The sulky youth called Louis was there with someone else, cleaning out the cages. The other man in the cage grinned at the staring children. One of the lions growled.

Janet backed away. 'It's all right,' said the trainer. 'They're all harmless so long as they are well fed, and don't get quarrelsome. But don't come too near, Missy, just in case. Here you, Louis. Fill the water-trough again – the water's filthy.'

Louis did as he was told. The children watched him tip up the big water-trough and empty out the dirty water. Then he filled it again. He didn't seem in the least afraid of the lions. Janet didn't like him, but she couldn't help thinking how brave he was!

They were all sorry when it was time to go. They said good-bye to Trinculo, went to pat the little bear once more, and then wandered across the field to Jumbo. They patted as far as they could reach up his pillar-like leg, and then went along by the row of gay caravans to the gate at the end of the field.

Some of the caravanners had been doing their washing. They had spread a good deal of it out on the grass to dry. Others had rigged up a rough clothes-line, and had pegged up all kinds of things to flap in the wind.

The children wandered by, idly looking at every-thing they passed. And then Pam suddenly stopped short. She gazed closely at something hanging on one of the lines. When she turned her face towards them, she looked so excited that the others hurried over to her.

'What is it?' asked Peter. 'You look quite red! What's up?'

'Is anybody looking at us?' asked Pam in a low voice. 'Well, Peter – hurry up and look at these socks hanging on this line. What do they remind you of?'

The others looked at the things on the line – torn handkerchiefs, little frocks belonging to children, stockings and socks. For a moment Peter felt sure that Pam had spotted a blue pullover!

But there was no pullover flapping in the wind. He wondered what had attracted Pam's attention. Then he saw what she was gazing at.

She was looking very hard indeed at a pair of blue wool socks – and down each side of them ran a pattern in red! Peter's mind at once flew to the scrap of wool he had in his pocket-book – did it match?

In a trice he had it out and was comparing it with

the sock. The blue was the same. The red was the same. The wool appeared to be exactly the same too.

'And see here,' whispered Pam, urgently. 'There's a little snag in this sock – just here – a tiny hole where a bit of the wool has gone. I'm pretty certain, Peter, that that's where your bit of blue wool came from – this sock!'

Peter was sure of it, too. An old woman came up and shooed them away. 'Don't you dare touch those clothes!' she said.

Peter didn't dare to ask who the socks belonged to. But if only, only he could find out, he would know who the thief was at once!

Twelve

One-leg William

THE old circus woman gave Pam a little push. 'Didn't you hear me say go away!' she scolded. They all decided to go at once. Pam thought the old woman looked really rather like a witch!

They walked quickly out of the field, silent but very excited. Once they were in the lane they all talked at once.

'We never *thought* of socks! We thought we had to look for a pullover!'

'But it's socks all right – that pair is made of exactly the same wool as this bit we found caught on to that wall!'

'Gracious! To think we didn't dare to ask whose socks they were!'

'If only we had, we'd know who the thief was.'

They raced back to the farmhouse, longing to discuss what to do next. And down in the shed, patiently waiting for them, were Jack, George and Barbara! They didn't give the others a chance to tell about the socks – they immediately began to relate something of their own.

'Peter! Janet! You know those queer round marks we saw on the inside of the wall! Well, we've found some more, exactly like them!' said Jack.

'Where?' asked Peter.

'In a muddy patch near old Chimney Cottage,' said Jack. 'George and I saw them and went to fetch Barbara. Then we came to tell you. And what's more, Barbara knows what made the marks!'

'You'll never guess!' said Barbara.

'Go on – tell us!' said Janet, forgetting all about the socks.

'Well, when I saw the marks – round and regular, just like the ones we saw – I couldn't think what they were at first,' said Barbara. 'But then, when I remembered who lived in the nearby cottage, I knew.'

'What were they?' asked Peter, eagerly.

'Do you know who lives at Chimney Cottage?' asked Barbara. 'You don't. Well, I'll tell you – it's One-leg William! He had a leg bitten off once by a shark, and he's got a wooden leg – and when he walks in the mud with it, it leaves round marks – *just* like the marks we saw on the other side of the wall. It must be One-leg William who was the thief.'

The others sat and thought about this for a few moments. Then Peter shook his head.

'No. One-leg William couldn't possibly be the thief. He couldn't have climbed over the wall with one leg – and besides – the thief wore a pair of socks – and that means *two* legs!'

'How do you know he wore socks?' asked Barbara, astonished.

They told her about the socks on the line away in the circus field. Barbara thought hard.

'Well – I expect the thief *was* a two-legged man with socks – but I don't see why One-leg William couldn't have been with him to help in some way – give him a leg-up, or something. The marks are *exactly* the same! What was One-leg William doing there, anyway?'

'That's what we must find out,' said Peter, getting up. 'Come on – we'll go and ask him a few questions – and see those marks. Fancy them being made by a one-legged man – I never, never thought of that!'

They made their way to Chimney Cottage. Just outside was a very muddy patch – and sure enough, it was studded with the same round, regular marks that the children had seen over Milton Manor wall. Peter bent down to study them.

He got out his notebook and took from it the bit of string that George had cut when he measured the width of the other round marks. He looked up in surprise.

'No – these marks *aren't* the same – they're nearly an inch smaller – you look!' He set the string over one of the marks, and the others saw at once that it was longer than the width of the marks.

'Well! Isn't that queer!' said George. 'It *couldn't* have been One-leg William, then. Is there another man with a wooden leg in the district? One whose leg might be a bit wider and fit the marks?'

Everyone thought hard – but nobody could think of a man with a wooden leg. It was really exasperating! 'We keep *on* thinking we're solving things, and we aren't,' said Peter. 'There's no doubt in my mind that a man with a wooden peg-leg was there with the thief, though goodness knows why – but it wasn't One-leg William. And we do know that the *thief* can't have only one leg because he definitely wears two socks!'

'We know his socks – but we don't know *him*!' said Janet. 'This mystery is getting more mysterious than ever. We keep finding out things that lead us no-where!'

'We shall have to go back to the circus field tomorrow and try to trace those socks,' said Peter. 'We can't ask straight out whose they are – but we could watch and see who's wearing them!'

'Right,' said Colin. 'Meet there again at ten – and we'll have a squint at every sock on every foot in that field!'

Thirteen

A coat to match the cap

At ten o'clock all the Secret Seven were in the circus field. They decided to go and see Trinculo the acrobat again, as an excuse for being there. But he was nowhere to be found.

'He's gone off to the town,' said one of the other acrobats. 'What do you want him for?'

'Oh – just to ask him if we can mess around a bit,' said Jack. 'You know – have a squint at the animals and so on.'

'Carry on,' said the acrobat, and went off to his caravan, turning cart-wheels all the way. The children watched him in admiration. 'How *do* they turn themselves over and over their hands and feet like that?' asked Pam. 'Just exactly like wheels turning round and round!'

'Have a shot at it,' said George, with a grin. But when Pam tried to fling herself over on her hands, she crumpled up at once, and lay stretched out on the ground, laughing.

A small circus-girl came by, her tangled hair hanging over her eyes. She laughed at Pam, and immediately cart-wheeled round the field, turning over and over on her hands and feet just as cleverly as the acrobat.

'Look at that,' said George, enviously. 'Even the kids can do it. We shall have to practise at home.'

They went to look at the little bear, who, however, was fast asleep. Then they wandered cautiously over to the clothes line. The socks were gone! Aha! Now perhaps someone was wearing them. Whoever it was would be the thief.

The children strolled round the field again, looking at the ankles of every man they saw. But to their great annoyance all they could see had bare ankles! Nobody seemed to wear any socks at all. How maddening!

Louis came up to the lions' cage and unlocked it. He went inside and began to do the usual cleaning. He took no notice of the lions at all, and they took no notice of him. Janet thought it must be marvellous to go and sweep all round the feet of lions and not mind at all!

He had his dirty flannel trousers rolled up to his knees. His legs, also dirty, were quite bare. On his feet were dirty old rubber shoes.

The children watched him for a little while, and then turned to go. Another man came up as they left, and they glanced casually down at his ankles, to see what kind of socks he wore, if any. He was bare-legged, too, of course!

But something caught Jack's eyes, and he stopped and stared at the man intently. The fellow frowned. 'Anything wrong with me?' he said, annoyed. 'Stare away!'

Jack turned to the others, his face red with excitement. He pushed them on a little, till he was out of the man's hearing.

'Did you see that coat he was wearing?' he asked. 'It's like that cap we found up in the tree – only not quite so filthy dirty! I'm sure it is!'

All seven turned to look round at the man, who was by now painting the outside of the lions' cage, making it look a little smarter than before. He had taken off his coat and hung it on the handle of the lions' cage. How the Seven longed to go and compare the cap with the coat!

'Have you got the cap with you?' asked Pam in a whisper. Peter nodded, and patted his coat pocket. He had all the 'clues' with him, of course!

Their chance suddenly came. The man was called away by someone yelling for him, and went off, leaving his paint-pot, brush and coat. Immediately the children went over to the coat.

'Pretend to be peering into the lions' cage while I compare the cap with the coat,' said Peter in a low voice. They all began to look into the cage and talk about the lions, while Peter pulled the cap out of his pocket and quickly put it against the coat.

He replaced the cap at once. There was no doubt about it – the cap and coat matched perfectly. Then was this fellow who was painting the lions' cage the thief? But how did it happen that he had thrown his cap high up in a tree? Why did he leave it behind? It just didn't make sense.

The man came back, whistling. He stooped down to pick up his paint-brush, and Colin got a splendid view of the top of his head. He gazed at it.

Then all the children moved off in a body longing to ask Peter about the cap. Once they were out of hearing, he nodded to them. 'Yes,' he said. 'They match. That fellow *may* be the thief, then. We'll have to watch him.'

'No good,' said Colin, unexpectedly. 'I just caught sight of the top of his head. He's got black hair – but no round bare patch at the crown, like the man had who sat below me in that tree. *He's* not the thief!'

Fourteen

The peculiar marks again

THE Seven went to sit on the rails of the fence that ran round the circus field.

They felt disheartened.

'To think we find somebody wearing a coat that *exactly* matches the cap we found – and yet he can't possibly be the thief because the top of his head is wrong!' groaned Peter. 'I must say this is a most aggravating adventure. We keep finding out exciting things – and each time they lead us nowhere at all!'

'And if we find anyone wearing those socks that we are sure belong to the thief, it won't be him at all either,' said Janet. 'It will probably be his aunt, or something!'

That made everyone laugh. 'Anyway,' said Peter, 'we're not absolutely *certain* that the cap has anything to do with the theft of the necklace. We only found it flung high up in a tree, you know, near where the thief climbed over the wall.'

'It has got something to do with the mystery,' said George. 'I'm sure of it – though I can't for the life of me think how.'

They all sat on the fence and gazed solemnly over the field. What an annoying adventure this was! And then Janet gave a little squeal.

'What is it? Have you thought of something?' asked Peter.

'No. But I'm seeing something,' said Janet, and she pointed over to the right. The others looked where she pointed, and how they stared!

The field was rather wet just there, and in the damp part were round, regular marks just like those they had seen by the wall – and very like the smaller marks made by the one-legged man near his cottage!

'I think *these* marks are the right size,' said Peter, jumping down in excitement. 'They look bigger than the marks made by the one-legged man's wooden leg. I'll measure them.'

He got out his bit of string and laid it carefully across one of the marks. Then across another and another. He looked up joyfully.

'See that. Exactly the same size! Every one of these round marks is the same as those we saw in the ground below the wall the thief climbed!'

'Then – there must be another one-legged man here, in the circus – a man with a wooden leg that measures the same as those round marks,' said Colin, excitedly. 'He's not the thief, because a one-legged man couldn't climb the wall, but he must have been *with* the thief!'

'We must find him,' said George. 'If we can find who his friend is, or who he shares a caravan with, we shall know his friend is the thief – and I expect we'll find that the thief is wearing those socks, too! We're getting warmer!'

Peter beckoned to the small circus girl who had turned cart-wheels some time before. 'Hey, you!' he called. 'We want to talk to the one-legged man here. Which is his his caravan?'

'Don't be daft,' said the small girl. 'There bain't no one-legged man here. What'd he be doing in a circus? All of us here have got our two legs – and need 'em! Your're daft!'

'Now look here,' said Peter, firmly. 'We know there *is* a one-legged man here and we mean to see him. Here's some chocolate if you'll tell us where he is.'

The little girl snatched the chocolate at once. Then she laughed rudely. 'Chocolate for nothing!' she said.

'You're nuts! I tell you, there bain't no one-legged fellow here!'

And before they could ask her anything else, she was gone, turning over on hands and feet as fast as any clown in the circus!

'You run after her and spank her,' called a woman from a nearby caravan. 'But she won't tell you no different. We ain't got no one-leggy man here!'

She went into her caravan and shut the door. The Seven felt quite taken aback. 'First we find marks outside Chimney Cottage and are certain they belong to the thief,' groaned Peter, 'but they belong to a one-legged man who is nothing to do with this adventure – and then we find the *right* marks, right size and all – and we're told there isn't a one-legged man here at all! It's really very puzzling!'

'Let's follow the marks,' said Janet. 'We shall find them difficult to see in the longer grass – but maybe we can spot enough to follow them up.'

They did manage to follow them. They followed them to a small caravan parked not far off the lions' cage, next to a caravan where Louis was sitting on the steps. He watched them in surprise.

They went up the steps of the small caravan and peered inside. It seemed to be full of odds and ends of circus properties. Nobody appeared to live there.

A stone skidded near to them and made them jump. 'You clear off, peeping and prying where you've no business to be!' shouted Louis, and picked up another stone. 'Do you hear me? Clear off!'

Fifteen

A shock for Peter and Colin

THE Seven went hurriedly out of the circus field and into the lane. George rubbed his ankle where one of Louis's stones had struck him.

'Beast!' he said. 'Why didn't he want us to peep in that little old caravan? It's only used for storing things, anyway.'

'Maybe the thief has hidden the pearls there!' said Janet with a laugh.

Peter stared at her and thought hard. 'Do you know – you might be right!' he said, slowly. 'We are certain the thief belongs to the circus – we're certain the pearls must be there – and why should Louis be so upset when we just peeped into that caravan?'

'I wish we could search it and see,' said Colin, longingly. 'But I don't see how we can.'

'Well, *I* do!' said Peter. 'You and I will go to *to-night's* performance of the circus, Colin – but we'll slip out at half-time, when all the performers are in the ring, or behind it – and we'll see if those pearls *are* hidden there!'

'But surely they won't be?' asked Pam. 'It seems such a silly place.'

'I've got a sort of a hunch about it,' said Peter, obstinately. 'I just can't explain it. Those queer round marks seemed to lead there, didn't they? Well, that's peculiar enough, to begin with.'

'It certainly is,' said Barbara. 'Marks made by a one-legged man who doesn't exist! This is a silly adventure, I think.'

'It isn't really,' said George. 'It's a bit like a jigsaw puzzle – the bits look quite odd and hopeless when they're all higgledy-piggledy – but as soon as you fit them together properly, they make a clear picture.'

'Yes – and what we've got so far is a lot of odd bits that really belong to one another – but we don't know how they fit,' said Pam. 'A bit of blue wool belonging to socks we saw on the line – a tweed cap that matches a coat worn by someone we know isn't the thief! Queer marks that turn up everywhere and don't tell us anything.'

'Come on – let's get home,' said Jack, looking at his watch. 'It's almost dinner-time. We've spent all the morning snooping about for nothing. Actually I'm beginning to feel quite muddled over this adventure. We keep following up trails that aren't any use at all.'

'No more meetings today,' said Peter, as they walked down the lane. 'Colin and I will meet tonight by ourselves and go to the circus. Bring a torch, Colin. Golly – suppose we found the pearls hidden in that old caravan!'

'We shan't,' said Colin. 'I can't think why you're so set on searching it. All right – meet you at the circus gate tonight!'

He was there first. Peter came running up a little later. They went in together, groaning at having to pay out sixty pence more. 'Just for half the show, too,' whispered Peter.

The two boys went into the big tent and found seats near the back, so that they could easily slip out unnoticed. They sat down and waited for the show to begin.

It really was very good, and the clowns, stiltwalkers and acrobats seemed better than ever. The boys were quite sorry to slip out before the show was over.

It was dark in the circus field now. They stopped to get their direction. 'Over there,' said Peter, taking Colin's arm. 'See – that's the caravan, I'm sure.'

They made their way cautiously towards the caravan. They didn't dare to put on their torches in case someone saw them and challenged them. Peter fell over the bottom step of the caravan, and then began to climb up carefully.

'Come on,' he whispered to Colin. 'It's all clear! The door isn't locked, either. We'll creep in, and begin our search immediately!'

The two boys crept into the caravan. They bumped into something in the darkness. 'Dare we put on our torches yet?' whispered Colin.

'Yes. I can't hear anyone near,' whispered back Peter. So, very cautiously, shading the beam with their hands, they switched on their torches.

They got a dreadful shock at once. They were in

the wrong caravan! This wasn't the little caravan in
which all kinds of things from the circus were stored –
this was a caravan people lived in. Good gracious!
Suppose they were caught, what a row they would get
into.

'Get out, quickly!' said Peter. But even as he spoke,
Colin clutched his arm. He had heard voices outside!
Then someone came up the step. Whatever *were* they
going to do now!

Sixteen

Prisoners

'QUICK! Hide under that bunk thing – and I'll hide under this,' whispered Peter in a panic. He and Colin crawled underneath, and pulled the hangings over them. They waited there, trembling.

Two men came into the caravan, and one of them lit a lamp. Each sat down on a bunk. Peter could see nothing of them but their feet and ankles.

He stiffened suddenly. The man on the bunk opposite had pulled up his trouser legs, and there, on his feet, were the blue socks with the faint red lines running down each side!

To think he was sitting opposite the man who must be the thief – and he couldn't even see his face to know who it was! Who could it be?

'I'm clearing out tonight,' said one man. 'I'm fed up with this show. Nothing but grousing and quarrelling all the time. And I'm scared the police'll come along sooner or later about that last job.'

'You're always scared,' said the man with the socks. 'Let me know when it's safe to bring you the pearls. They can stay put for months, if necessary.'

'Sure they'll be all right?' asked the other man. The man with the socks laughed, and said a most peculiar thing.

'The lions will see to that,' he said.

Peter and Colin listened, frightened and puzzled. It was plain that the thief was there – the man with the socks, whose face they couldn't see – and it was also quite plain that he had hidden the pearls away for the time being – and that the first man had got scared and was leaving.

'You can say I'm feeling too sick to go on again in the ring tonight,' said the first man, after a pause.

'I'll go now, I think, while everyone's in the ring. Get the horse, will you?'

The man with the socks uncrossed his ankles and went down the steps. Peter and Colin longed for the other fellow to go too. Then perhaps they could escape. But he didn't go. He sat there, drumming on something with his fingers. It was plain that he felt nervous and scared.

There were sounds outside of a horse being put between the shafts. Then the man with the socks called up the steps.

'All set! Come on out and drive. See you later.'

The man got up and went out of the caravan. To the boys' intense dismay he locked the door! Then he went quietly round to the front of the van, and climbed up to the driving seat. He clicked to the horse and it ambled off over the field.

'I say!' whispered Colin. 'This is awful! He locked that door! We're prisoners!'

'Yes. What a bit of bad luck,' said Peter, crawling out from his very uncomfortable hiding-place. 'And did you notice, Colin, that one of the men had those socks on! He's the thief. And he's the one we've left behind, worse luck.'

'We've learnt a lot,' said Colin, also crawling out. 'We know the pearls are somewhere in the circus. What did he mean about the lions?'

'Goodness knows,' said Peter. 'Unless he's put them into the lions' cage and hidden them somewhere there. Under one of the boards, I expect.'

'We'll have to escape somehow,' said Colin, desperately. 'Could we get out of a window, do you think?'

The boys peeped cautiously out of the window at the front, trying to see where they were. The caravan came to a bright street lamp at that moment – and Peter gave Colin a sharp nudge.

'Look!' he whispered, 'that fellow who's driving the caravan has got on the tweed coat that matches the old cap we found up in the tree. It must be the fellow we saw painting the outside of the lions' cage!'

'Yes. And probably the thief borrowed his cap to wear, seeing that they live in the same caravan,' said Colin. 'That makes *one* of the bits of jigsaw pieces fit into the picture, anyway.'

They tried the windows. They were tightly shut. Colin made a noise trying to open the window and the driver looked back sharply into the van. He must have caught sight of the face of one of the boys by the light of a street lamp, for he at once stopped the horse, jumped down, and ran round to the back of the van.

'Now we're for it!' said Peter in despair. 'He's heard us. Hide quickly, Colin! He's unlocking the door!'

Seventeen

Back at the circus field

THE key turned in the lock and the door of the caravan was pushed open. A powerful torch was switched on, and the beam flashed round the inside of the van.

The boys were under the bunks and could not be seen. But the man was so certain that somebody was inside the van that he pulled aside the draperies that hung over the side of the bunk where Peter was hiding. At once he saw the boy.

He shouted angrily and dragged poor Peter out. He shook him so hard that the boy yelled. Out came Colin at once to his rescue!

'Ah – so there are two of you!' said the man. 'What are you doing here? How long have you been in this van?'

'Not long,' said Peter. 'We came in by mistake. We wanted to get into another van – but in the dark we missed our way.'

'A pretty poor sort of story!' said the man, angrily. 'Now I'm going to give you each a good hiding – that will teach you to get into other people's caravans.'

He put down his torch on a shelf, so that its beam lighted the whole caravan. He pushed back his coat sleeves and looked very alarming indeed.

Colin suddenly kicked up at the torch. It jerked

into the air and fell to the floor with a crash. The bulb was broken and the light went out. The caravan was in darkness.

'Quick, Peter, go for his legs!' yelled Colin, and dived for the man's legs. But in the darkness he missed them, shot out of the door, and rolled down the steps, landing with a bump on the road below.

Peter got a slap on the side of his head and dodged in the darkness. He, too, dived to get hold of the man's legs and caught one of them. The man hit out again and then staggered and fell. Peter wriggled away, half fell down the steps and rolled into the hedge.

At the same moment the horse took fright and galloped off down the road with the caravan swinging from side to side behind it in a most alarming manner. The man inside must have been very, very surprised indeed!

'Colin! Where are you?' shouted Peter. 'Come on, quickly. The horse has bolted with the caravan and the man inside it. Now's our chance!'

Colin was hiding in the hedge, too. He stepped out to join Peter, and the two set off down the road as fast as they could, running at top speed, panting loudly.

'Every single thing in this adventure goes wrong,' said Colin at last, slowing down. 'We can't even get into the right caravan when we want to – we have to choose the wrong one.'

'Well, we learnt quite a bit,' said Peter. 'And we know the thief is wearing those socks now, even if we

still don't know who he is. Funny thing is – I seem to know his voice.'

'Have you any idea at all where we are?' asked Colin. 'I mean – do you suppose we're running *towards* home, or away from it? As this is a most contrary adventure, I wouldn't be surprised if we're running in the wrong direction as fast as ever we can!'

'Well, we're not,' said Peter. 'I know where we are all right. In fact, we'll soon be back at the circus field. I say – should we slip into the field again and just have a squint round for the man who's wearing the socks? I feel as if I simply *must* find out who he is!'

Colin didn't want to. He had had enough adventure for one night. But he said he would wait for Peter outside the gate if he badly wanted to go into the field again.

So Peter slipped over the fence and made his way to where he saw many lights. The show was over, and the people had gone home. But the circus folk were now having their supper, and the light from lanterns and fires looked very bright and gay.

Peter saw some children playing together. One of them appeared very tall indeed – and Peter saw that she was walking on stilts, just as the stilt-walkers did in the ring. It was the rude little girl who had told him there was no one-legged man in the circus. She came walking over to where he stood by a caravan, but she didn't see him. She was absorbed in keeping her balance on the stilts.

She came and went – and Peter stared at something showing on the ground. Where the child had walked, her stilts had left peculiar marks pitted in the ground – regular, round marks – just like the ones by the wall round Milton Manor! There they were, showing clearly in the damp ground, lit by the flickering light of a nearby lantern!

'Look at that!' said Peter to himself. 'We were *blind*! Those marks weren't made by a one-legged man – they were made by a stilt-walker! Why ever didn't we think of it before?'

Eighteen

Peter tells his story

PETER gazed down at the number of queer round marks. He looked over at the child who was stilt-walking – yes, everywhere she went, her stilts left those round marks on the ground. Now another bit of the jigsaw had fitted into place.

'The thief was a stilt-walker,' said Peter to himself. 'He took his stilts with him to help him get over the wall. I must find Colin and tell him!'

He ran over to where Colin was waiting for him. 'Colin, I've discovered something exciting!' he said. 'I know what makes those peculiar round marks – and they're nothing to do with a one-legged man!'

'What makes them then?' asked Colin, surprised.

'Stilts!' said Peter. 'The ends of stilts! The thief was on stilts – so that he could easily get over that high wall. What a very clever idea!'

'But how did he do it?' said Colin puzzled. 'Come on, let's go home, Peter. I shall get into an awful row, it's so late. I'm terrribly tired, too.'

'So am I,' said Peter. 'Well, we won't discuss this exciting evening any more now – we'll think about it and have a meeting tomorrow morning. I'll send Janet round for the others first thing. As a matter of fact, I haven *quite* worked out how the thief did climb over the wall with stilts.'

Colin yawned widely. He felt that he really could not try to think out anything. He was bruised from his fall out of the caravan, he had banged his head hard, and he felt rather dazed. All he wanted to do was to get into bed and go to sleep!

Janet was fast asleep when Peter got home, so he didn't wake her. He got into bed, meaning to think everything out carefully – but he didn't, because he fell sound asleep at once!

In the morning he wouldn't tell Janet a word about the night's adventures. He just sent her out to get the others to a meeting. They came, wondering what had happened. One by one they hissed the password – 'Adventure!' – and passed through the door. Colin was last of all. He said he had overslept!

'What happened last night? Did you find the pearls? Do you know who the thief is?' asked Pam, eagerly.

'We didn't find the pearls – but we know everything else!' said Peter, triumphantly.

'*Do* we!' said Colin, surprised. 'You may, Peter – but I don't. I still feel sleepy!'

'Peter, tell us,' said George. 'Don't keep us waiting. Tell us everything!'

'Come on up to Little Thicket and I'll show you exactly how the thief got over that wall,' said Peter, suddenly deciding that that would be a very interesting way of fitting all the bits of the jigsaw together.

'Oh – you *might* tell us now!' wailed Janet, bitterly disappointed.

'No. Come on up to Little Thicket,' said Peter. So they all went together to Little Thicket, and walked over to the big gates of Milton Manor. Johns the gardener was there again, working in the front beds of the drive.

'Johns! May we come in again?' shouted Peter. 'We won't do any harm.'

Johns opened the gates, grinning. 'Discovered anything yet?' he asked as the children crowded through.

'Yes, lots,' said Peter, and led the way to the place where the thief had climbed over the wall. 'Come along with us and I'll tell you what we've discovered, Johns!'

'Right – but I'll just let this car in at the gates first,' said Johns, as a big black car hooted outside.

The children soon came to the place where they had been before. 'Now look,' said Peter, 'this is what happened. The thief was a stilt-walker, so all he had to do was to come to the outside of this wall, get up on his stilts – walk to the wall, lean on the top, take his feet from the stilts and sit on the wall. He then draws his stilts over the wall and uses them on this soft ground. On the hard garden paths they don't mark, and he is safe to come to earth and hide his stilts along the box hedging of the border.'

'Go on!' said Janet in excitement.

'He gets into the house, takes the pearls, and comes back to the wall,' said Peter. 'Up he gets on his stilts again and walks to the wall – and he leaves more of these peculiar round stilt-marks behind in the earth, of course!'

'Goodness – *that's* what they were!' said Pam.

'Yes. And as he clambers on to the wall, his cap catches a high branch of a tree and is jerked off,' said Peter. 'He leaves it there because he doesn't want to waste time getting it back. He catches one of his socks on that little sharp piece of brick and leaves a bit of wool behind . . . then he's up on the top of the wall, and down he jumps on the other side !'

'Which I heard him do !' said Colin. 'But, Peter – he had no stilts when I saw him. *What did he do with his stilts?*'

Nineteen

Where are the pearls?

'You want to know what he did with the stilts he used when he climbed up on the wall after he had stolen the pearls?' said Peter. 'Well – I don't really know – but if all my reasoning is right, he must have flung them into a thick bush, somewhere, to hide them!'

'Yes – of course,' said Pam. 'But which bush?'

They all looked round at the bushes and trees near by. 'A holly bush!' said Colin, pointing over the wall. 'That's always so green and thick, and people don't go messing about with holly because it's too prickly!'

'Yes – that would certainly be the best,' said Peter. 'Come on, everyone.' He led the rest out of the Manor grounds and round to the other side of the wall at top speed.

They were soon finding out what a very scratchy, prickly job bending back the branches of the thick holly tree could be. But what a reward they had! There, pushed right into the very thickest part, were two long stilts! Colin pulled out one and Peter pulled out the other.

'You were right, Peter!' said Janet. 'You *are* clever! We've explained simply everything now – the old cap high up on a branch – the bit of wool – the

peculiar round marks – how the thief climbed an un-
climbable wall. Really, I think the Secret Seven have
been very, very clever!'

'And so do I!' shouted another voice. They all
turned, and there, flushed and breathless, was their
friend the inspector of police, with Johns the gardener
still a good ten yards off.

'Hallo!' said Peter, surprised. 'I say – did you hear
that?'

'Yes,' said the inspector, beaming but breathless.
'Johns here opened the gate to my car, and told me he
thought you had solved the mystery. We knew you
must be hot on the scent of something when you chased
out of the gate like that. Well, what's your explanation? You've certainly beaten the police this time!'

Peter laughed. 'Ah well, you see – we can go snooping about the circus without anyone suspecting us –
but if you sent seven policemen to snoop round the
circus field, you'd certainly be suspected of something!'

'No doubt we should,' agreed the inspector. He
picked up the stilts and examined them. 'A very ingenious way of scaling an enormously high wall. I
suppose you can't also tell me who the thief is, can
you?'

'Well – it's a stilt-walker, of course,' said Peter.
'And I *think* it's a fellow called Louis. If you go to the
circus you'll probably find him wearing blue socks
with a little red thread running down each side.'

'And he'll have black hair with a little round bare

place at the crown,' said Colin. 'At least – the thief *I* saw had a bare place there.'

'Astonishing what a lot you know!' said the inspector, admiringly; 'you'll be telling me the colour of his pyjamas next! What about coming along to find him now? I've got a couple of men out in the car. We can all go.'

'Oooh,' said Pam, imagining the Secret Seven appearing on the circus field with three big policemen. 'I say – won't the circus folk be afraid when they see us?'

'Only those who have reason to be afraid,' said the inspector. 'Come along. I do want to see if this thief of yours has a bare place on the crown of his head. Now, *how* do you know that, I wonder? Most remarkable!'

They all arrived at the circus field at last. The police got there first, of course, as they went in their car, but they waited for the children to come. Through the gate they all went, much to the amazement of the circus folk there.

'There's Louis,' said Peter, pointing out the sullen-looking young fellow over by the lions' cage. 'Blow – he's got no socks on again!'

'We'll look at the top of his head then,' said Colin.

Louis stood up as they came near. His eyes looked uneasily at the tall inspector.

'Got any socks on?' inquired the inspector, much to Louis's astonishment. 'Pull up your trousers.'

But, as Peter had already seen, Louis was bare-legged. 'Tell him to bend over,' said Colin, which astonished Louis even more.

'Bend over,' said the inspector, and Louis obediently bent himself over as if he were bowing to everyone.

Colin gave a shout. 'Yes – that's him all right! See the bare round patch at the crown of his head? Just like I saw when I was up in the tree!'

'Ah – good,' said the inspector. He turned to Louis again. 'And now, young fellow, I have one more thing to say to you. Where are the pearls?'

Twenty

The end of the adventure

Louis stared at them all sullenly. 'You're mad!' he said. 'Asking me to pull up my trouser legs, and bend over – and now you start talking about pearls. What pearls? I don't know nothing about pearls – never did.'

'Oh yes, you do,' said the inspector. 'We know all about you, Louis. You took your stilts to get over that high wall – didn't you? – the one that goes round Milton Manor. And you got the pearls, and came back to the wall. Up you got on to your stilts again, and there you were, nicely on top, ready to jump down the other side.'

'Don't know what you're talking about,' mumbled Louis sulkily, but he had gone very pale.

'I'll refresh your memory a little more then,' said the inspector. 'You left stilt marks behind you – and this cap on a high branch – and this bit of wool from one of your socks. You also left your stilts behind you, in the middle of a holly bush. Now, you didn't do all those things for nothing. Where are those pearls?'

'Find 'em yourself,' said Louis. 'Maybe my brother's gone off with them in the caravan. He's gone, anyway.'

'But he left the pearls here – he said so,' said Peter,

192

suddenly. 'I was in the caravan when you were talking together!'

Louis gave Peter a startled and furious glance. He said nothing.

'And *you* said the pearls would be safe with the lions!' said Peter. 'Didn't you?'

Louis didn't answer. 'Well, well!' said the inspector, 'we'll make a few inquiries from the lions themselves!'

So accompanied by all the children, and the two policemen, and also by about thirty interested circus folk, and by the little bear who had somehow got free and was wandering about in delight, the inspector went over to the big lions' cage. He called for the lion-keeper.

He came, astonished and rather alarmed.

'What's your name?' asked the inspector. 'Riccardo,' replied the man. 'Why?' 'Well, Mr. Riccardo, we have reason to believe that your lions are keeping a pearl necklace somewhere about their cage or their persons.'

Riccardo s eyes nearly fell out of his head. He stared at the inspector as if he couldn't believe his ears.

'Open the cage and go in and search,' said the inspector. 'Search for loose boards or anywhere that pearls could be hidden.'

Riccardo unlocked the cage, still looking too astonished for words. The lions watched him come in, and one of them suddenly purred like a cat, but much more loudly.

Riccardo sounded the boards. None was loose. He turned, puzzled, to the watching people. 'Sir,' he said, 'you can see that this cage is bare except for the lions – and they could not hide pearls, not even in their manes – they would scratch them out.'

Peter was watching Louis's face. Louis was looking at the big water-trough very anxiously indeed. Peter nudged the inspector.

'Tell him to examine the water-trough!' he said.

Riccardo went over to it. He picked it up and emptied out the water. 'Turn it upside down,' called the inspector. Riccardo did so – and then he gave an exclamation.

'It has a false bottom soldered to it!' he cried. 'See, sir – this should not be here!'

He showed everyone the underneath of the water-trough. Sure enough, someone had soldered on an extra piece, that made a most ingenious false bottom. Riccardo took a tool from his belt and levered off the extra bottom.

Something fell out to the floor of the cage. 'The pearls!' shouted all the children at once, and the lions looked up in alarm at the noise. Riccardo passed the pearls through the bars of the cage, and then turned to calm his lions. The little bear, who was now by Janet, grunted in fear when he heard the lions snarling. Janet tried to lift him up, but she couldn't.

'Very satisfactory,' said the inspector, putting the magnificent necklace into his pocket. The children heard a slight noise, and turned to see Louis being marched firmly away by the two policemen. He passed a clothes-line – and there again were the blue socks, that had helped to give him away, flapping in the wind!

'Come along,' said the inspector, shooing the seven children in front of him. 'We'll all go and see Lady Lucy Thomas – and *you* shall tell her the story of your latest adventure from beginning to end. She'll want to reward you – so I hope you'll have some good ideas! What do *you* want, Janet?'

'I suppose,' said Janet, looking down at the little bear still trotting beside her, 'I suppose she wouldn't give me a little bear, would she? One like this, but smaller so that I could lift him up? Pam would like one, too, I know.'

The inspector roared with laughter. 'Well, Secret Seven, ask for bears or anything you like – a whole circus if you want it. You deserve it. I really don't know what I should do without the help of the S.S.S! You'll help me again in the future, won't you?'

'Rather!' said the Seven at once. And you may be sure they will!

SECRET SEVEN MYSTERY

CONTENTS

One

Something interesting

PETER and Janet were having breakfast with their father and mother one lovely spring morning. Scamper, their golden spaniel, was lying as usual under the table.

'Dad,' began Peter, but his mother frowned at him.

'Your father is reading the paper,' she said. 'Don't bother him just now!'

His father put down the paper and smiled. 'Do the Secret Seven want to make themselves really useful?' he asked. 'Because I've just read something in my paper that may be right up their street!'

'Oh, Dad – what?' cried Peter, and Janet put down her egg-spoon and looked at him expectantly.

'It's about a girl who's run away from home,' said their father, looking at his paper. 'She stole some money from the desk of her form-mistress, but when the police went to see her aunt about it, she ran away.'

'But – what can the Secret Seven do about it?' asked Peter, surprised.

'Listen – I'll read you the piece,' said his father, and propped the paper up in front of him again. 'Elizabeth Mary Wilhemina Sonning, after being accused of stealing money from the desk of her form-mistress, was found to be missing from her aunt's home. She took nothing with her but the clothes she was wearing, and is in school uniform and school hat. It is stated that her parents are abroad, and that she has a brother who is at present away in France.'

Peter's father looked up from the paper. 'Now comes the bit that might interest *you*,' he said. 'Elizabeth was seen on the evening of that day in Belling Village, and it is thought that she might be going to her grandmother, who lives not far off.'

'Belling Village! Why that's the next village to ours,' said Janet. 'Oh – you think that the Secret Seven could keep a look-out for Elizabeth, Daddy! Yes – we could! What's she like?'

'There's a photograph here,' said her father, and passed the paper across. 'Not a very good one – but in her school uniform, which is a help.'

Peter and Janet stared at the picture in the paper. They saw the photograph of a merry, laughing girl a little older than themselves, with a mass of fluffy hair round her face. They thought she looked rather nice.

Though she can't be really, if she stole money and then ran away, thought Janet. She turned to her father. 'Whereabouts in Belling Village does her granny live?'

'It doesn't say, does it?' said her father, reaching for his paper again. 'You'll have to read this evening's paper and see if there are any more details. If the child goes to her granny's she'll be found at once, of course. But if she hides somewhere around the place, you might be able to spot her.'

'Yes. We might,' said Peter. 'The Secret Seven haven't had *anything* interesting to do lately. We'll call a meeting tomorrow. Good thing it's Saturday!'

That evening, Janet sat down to write notices to each of

the Secret Seven to call them to a meeting the next day. Each notice said the same things.

'Dear S. S. Member,

'A meeting will be held tomorrow morning, Saturday, at ten sharp, in the shed. Wear your badges and remember the password.'

Peter signed each one, and then he and Janet fetched their bicycles and rode off to deliver the notices, Scamper trotting beside them. They felt pleasantly excited. This new affair might not come to anything – but at least it was something to talk about and to make plans for.

'We'd better buy an evening paper on our way back

and see if there's anything else in it about Elizabeth Mary Wilhemina Sonning,' said Peter.

So they stopped at the little newsagent's shop and bought one. They stood outside the shop, eagerly looking through the pages for any mention of the runaway girl. At last they found a small paragraph, headed 'MISSING GIRL'.

'Here it is,' said Peter, thrilled. 'Look, Janet, it says, "Elizabeth Sonning is still missing, and her grandmother states that she has not seen her. Anyone seeing a child whose appearance tallies with the following description is asked to get in touch with the police." Then, see, Janet, there's a good description of her. That's fine – we can read it out to the Seven tomorrow.'

'Good!' said Janet. 'Come on, Scamper – we'll have to bike home pretty fast, so you'll have to run at top speed!'

Scamper puffed and panted after them, his long silky ears flopping up and down as he ran. He wasn't a member of the Secret Seven, but he certainly belonged! No meeting was complete without him.

'What's the password, Peter?' asked Janet, as they put their bicycles away. 'It's ages since we had a meeting.'

'It's a jolly good thing *I* never forget it,' said Peter. 'I shan't tell it to you – but I'll give you a hint. Think of *lamb* – that ought to remind you!'

'Lamb?' said Janet, puzzled. 'Well – it reminds me of sheep, Peter – or Mary had a little lamb – or lamb chops. Which is it?'

'None of them!' said Peter, grinning. 'Have another shot, Janet – and tell me at the meeting tomorrow!'

Two

Knock – Knock

'HAVE you remembered the password yet?' asked Peter next morning, when Janet and he were tidying their shed ready for the meeting.

'No, I haven't,' said Janet. 'And I think you might tell me, because you know jolly well I've got to come. I've been thinking of lamb – lamb – lamb for ages, but it doesn't remind me of anything except what I've already told you. Tell me the word, Peter, do!'

'No,' said Peter firmly. 'You're always forgetting. It's time you were taught a lesson. I shan't let you into the meeting unless you remember it. Look – go and ask mummy if we can have some of those biscuits she made last week.'

'Go yourself,' said Janet, crossly.

'I'm the head of the Secret Seven,' said Peter. 'Obey orders, Janet!'

Janet went off, not feeling at all pleased. She was quite afraid that Peter *wouldn't* let her into the meeting! He was very strict about rules.

She went into the kitchen, but mummy wasn't there. Some lamb chops lay on the table, and Janet looked at them frowning. 'Lamb! Oh dear – whatever ought you to remind me of? I simply can't think! Oh – here's mummy. Mummy, *may* we have some of your ginger biscuits, please? Oh, what's that you've got? Mint – let me smell it. I love the smell. I wouldn't mind mint scent on my hanky!'

'It's for mint sauce with the chops,' said mummy. 'Now I'll just—'

'Mint sauce! Of *course*! That's the password, Mint sauce! What a fathead I am!' said Janet. Then she grew serious and looked solemnly at her mother.

'I shouldn't have said the password out loud! We're not supposed to tell a soul. Mummy, don't remember it, will you?'

'What are you gabbling about?' said her mother, and went to get her tin of ginger biscuits. 'Here you are – you can have all of these. I'm making some more for tomorrow.'

'Oh, *thank* you!' said Janet, delighted, and skipped off down the garden with the tin. As she came near the shed she shouted out to Peter.

'Mint sauce, mint sauce, mint sauce!'

'Have you gone mad?' said a cross voice, and Peter looked out of the shed, frowning. 'Shouting out the password for everyone to know! I'm glad you've remembered it at last.'

'Well, mummy came in with mint to make mint sauce. Wasn't it lucky?' said Janet. 'Oh, Scamper, you know I've got some ginger biscuits, don't you? I expect there'll be one for you. Peter it's almost ten o'clock.'

'I know,' said Peter. 'I'm just ready. Are there enough things to sit on? You'll have to sit on that big flower-pot, Janet. The gardener must have taken our seventh box.'

Scamper began to bark. 'That's someone coming already,' said Peter. 'Shut the door, Janet, please. We'll have to ask the password as usual.'

Knock – knock!

'Password!' called Peter.

'Mint sauce!' said two voices.

'Enter!' said Peter, and Janet opened the door. 'Hello, George and Colin. You're jolly punctual.'

Knock – knock!

'Password!' shouted Peter. A cautious voice came in through the keyhole.

'I've forgotten. But I'm Pam, so you can let me in.'

'No, we can't. You know the rule,' said Peter, sternly.

'Think of lamb chops!' called Janet, before Peter could stop her.

A giggle was heard. 'Oh, yes – of course. MINT SAUCE.'

Janet opened the door, but Peter looked quite cross. 'How dare you remind Pam like that?' he demanded.

'Well, *you* reminded me!' said Janet, indignantly. 'You said, "Think of lamb chops", didn't you?'

'There's someone else coming,' said Peter, changing the subject hurriedly.

Knock– knock! 'Mint sauce,' said two voices.

'Come in!' shouted Peter, and in came Jack and Barbara together. Scamper greeted them with pleasure, and then everyone sat down and looked expectantly at Peter.

'Anything exciting?' asked Jack, eagerly.

'Yes – quite,' answered Peter. 'But what about that awful sister of yours, Jack? Is she anywhere about? This is quite an important meeting.'

'No. She's gone shopping with my mother,' said Jack. 'She doesn't even *know* there's a meeting on. So we're quite safe She won't come snooping round.'

'Have a ginger biscuit?' asked Janet, and the tin was handed round.

Peter cleared his throat. 'Well, now,' he began, 'it was my father who thought we should inquire into the matter I'm going to tell you about, so you can see it's quite important. It concerns a girl who has run away from her aunt's home, after stealing some money at school. She's been seen near here, at Belling Village, where her grandmother lives – but so far hasn't been to see her granny.'

'Oh – and I suppose it's up to the Secret Seven to keep a look-out for her – and find her!' said Jack. 'We ought to be able to do *that* all right. What's she like – and what are your plans, Peter?'

'That's just what this meeting is about,' said Peter. 'Now listen!'

Three

Mostly about Elizabeth

PETER explained everything clearly.

'The girl's name is Elizabeth Mary Wilhemina Sonning,' he said. 'Her parents live abroad, and she is a weekly boarder at school and spends her week-ends with an aunt. She has a brother who is away in France. She was accused of stealing money from her form-mistress's desk, and when the police went to speak to her aunt about it, she ran away.'

'What was she dressed in?' asked Pam.

'School uniform,' said Peter. 'Here's her photograph in it. Ordinary navy school coat, navy felt hat with school band round it, ordinary shoes, and stockings. It says here that she wore a gym tunic underneath, with a white blouse – well, really she's dressed just like Janet and Pam and Barbara when they're at school, it seems to me!'

'She might have taken some other clothes with her,' said Jack. 'Her Sunday coat or something.'

'No. Her aunt said that no other clothes were missing – only the ones she went in,' said Peter. 'You may be sure the aunt would look carefully, because it would be difficult to spot the girl if she were not in her school uniform.'

'Where's the description of what she's like?' asked Janet. 'It was in the evening paper last night, Peter.'

'Oh yes. Here it is,' said Peter, and began to read out loud. ' "Elizabeth can be recognized by her mass of soft, dark, curly hair, her brown eyes, straight eyebrows, and

scar down one arm. She is tall for her age, and strong. She swims well and is fond of horses." Well – there you are – do you think you'd spot her if you saw her?'

'We might,' said Colin, doubtfully. 'But lots of girls have dark, curly hair and brown eyes. If only the girl would wear short sleeves we might spot the scar – but that's the one thing she will certainly hide!'

'How do we set about looking for her?' asked George. 'Do we bike over to Belling Village and hunt all over the place?'

'That's what we've got to discuss,' said Peter. 'I don't actually think that just biking up and down the streets is going to be the slightest good – Elizabeth will be sure to find a hiding-place. She won't wander about in the day-time, I imagine – she'll lie low.'

'Where?' asked Pam.

'How do *I* know?' said Peter, who thought that Pam was sometimes very silly. 'Use your brains, Pam. Where would *you* hide if you ran away from home?'

'In a barn,' said Pam.

'In the woods under a thick bush,' said George.

'Wuff, wuff, wuff-wuff,' said Scamper, wagging his tail.

'What did you suggest – in a *kennel*?' said Peter. 'Thank you, Scamper – quite a good idea of yours.'

Everyone laughed, and Scamper looked pleased.

'I thought it would be sensible if we thoroughly explored Belling Village and round about,' said Peter. 'If Elizabeth has already actually been *seen* in Belling, she must be hiding *some*where near. I expect the police have already hunted pretty well everywhere, but we know better where to look than they do – because we know where *we'd* hide if we wanted to – but they wouldn't. Grown-ups seem to forget the things they did when they were young.'

'Yes, they do,' said George. 'But I *never* shall. I'm determined not to. What about the grandmother, Peter? Should one of us go to see her, do you think? She might have something helpful to say.'

'Yes, I think that's a good idea,' said Peter, considering it.

'Bags *I* don't go,' said Pam, at once. 'I wouldn't know what to say. I should just stand there and look silly.'

'Well, you'd find *that* quite easy,' said Colin, and Pam scowled at him.

'Now just you tell me what you –' she began, but Peter stopped the argument before it began.

'Shut up, you two. Jack and I will go, probably. And listen – there is another thing we might do.'

'What?' asked everyone.

'Well, this girl is fond of horses, it seems. We might go to the two or three stables we know of and see if any girl has been seen hanging around. She might even try to get a job at one.'

'That's a *good* idea,' said Janet, warmly. 'Well – there seems quite a lot we can do, Peter.'

'The next thing is to give each one of us a section of the countryside to hunt,' said Colin. 'It's no good us all going together – for one thing anyone in hiding would hear us coming and lie low. And for another thing we'd never cover all the countryside! What particular places must we search, Peter?'

'Well – you'll use your own common sense about that, of course,' said Peter. 'Anywhere that looks likely – a deserted shack – an empty caravan – a copse – anywhere in the woods where there are thick bushes – barns – sheds – even a hen-house!'

'Wuff, wuff, wuff-wuff,' put in Scamper.

'You mentioned a kennel before, Scamper, old thing,' said Peter. 'We'll leave *you* to examine those. Now, Secret Seven, there are two hours before dinner. Arrange between yourselves where you're going to search. Jack and I are going off to the grandmother's house. Everyone report back at half past two – SHARP! Now – get going!'

Four

Jumble for Mrs Sonning

PETER and Jack went out of the shed together. 'Do you know the address of the grandmother?' asked Jack.

'No, I don't,' said Peter. 'But I know her name is Sonning, the same as the girl's – so I vote we look it up in our telephone book.'

'Good idea,' said Jack. 'We'll get our bikes afterwards.' The two boys went down the path to the garden door, and Peter looked for the telephone book. He found it and began to hunt for the name of Sonning.

'What are you looking for, dear?' asked his mother, coming into the hall. 'Can't you find a number?'

'I was looking for the phone number of that runaway girl's grandmother,' said Peter. 'But she's not on the phone apparently.'

'But Peter, dear – you can't telephone her house and ask her questions about her granddaughter!' said his mother, quite shocked.

'I wasn't going to, Mother,' said Peter. 'I was going to call there with Jack – but I don't know her address.'

'I know it,' said his mother, surprisingly. 'She often runs jumble sales for Belling Women's Institute, and it was only last week that she wrote and asked me for some old clothes.'

'Some jumble?' said Peter, excited. 'Oh, Mother – what a chance for us! Can't we take some over to her, and say it's from you – and maybe she'll tell us a lot about Elizabeth, her granddaughter. We're looking for her, you know, just as Daddy suggested.'

'Oh dear – you and your Secret Seven!' said his mother. 'Very well – I'll give you some jumble, and you can say I've sent it by you. But you're to be polite and kind, and if she doesn't want to say a word about Elizabeth, you are NOT to ask questions.'

'All right, Mother. We'll be quite polite, really we will,' said Peter. 'Where's the jumble?'

'In those two boxes,' said his mother. 'I dare say you can strap them on the back of your bicycles if they won't go into your baskets. The address is "Bramble Cottage, Blackberry Lane".'

The two boys hurried off jubilantly with the jumble. 'Wasn't that a bit of luck?' said Peter. 'Come on – we've got a wonderful excuse for calling on the old lady!'

They rode off with Scamper running beside them, panting. They soon came to Belling Village, and asked for Blackberry Lane.

It was a little winding lane, with fields on one side and a wood on the other. Bramble Cottage was the last house in the lane, a pretty little place with tulips and wallflowers in the garden, and creepers climbing up the whitewashed walls.

'Here it is,' said Peter, seeing the name on the gate. 'Get your jumble, Jack.'

They carried the two cardboard boxes up the path, and rang the bell beside the green front door. They heard footsteps coming, and then someone in an overall opened the door and looked inquiringly at them.

She couldn't be the grandmother, Peter was certain. She looked a good deal too young.

'We have brought some jumble for Mrs Sonning's sale,' he said. 'May we speak to her, please? I have a message from my mother.'

'Come in,' said the woman, and led the way to a small sitting-room. 'Put the boxes down there, please. You can't see Mrs Sonning – she's in bed, not very well. I'm Miss Wardle, her companion, and *I'll* tell her you brought these.'

'I suppose she's very upset about her granddaughter,'

said Peter, plunging in at once. 'My mother was sorry to hear about it too.'

'Ah, yes – the old lady is very troubled,' said Miss Wardle. 'She's so fond of Elizabeth, and is longing for the child to come to her. She doesn't believe all that nonsense about stealing money. Neither do I!'

'Do you know Elizabeth, then?' asked Peter.

'Know her! I've known her since she was so high!' said Miss Wardle. 'And a nicer, more honest, straightforward child I've never seen. A bit of a rascal at times, but none the worse for that. Poor child – I can't bear to think of her hiding away somewhere, afraid to come out.'

'Do you think she's somewhere about here?' asked Jack. 'She has been seen in the district, hasn't she?'

'Yes – and, what's more, it's my belief she's been here, to this very house!' said Miss Wardle, lowering her voice. 'I haven't told Mrs Sonning about it, it would worry her. But some of my tarts went last night and a meat pie – and a tin of biscuits! And a rug off the backroom sofa!'

This was news indeed! Peter looked at Jack. Elizabeth must certainly be in the district!

'Why do you suppose she won't come to her grand-mother and stay with her instead of hiding away?' asked Peter. 'People usually hide when they feel guilty. But you say you don't believe Elizabeth *is* guilty of stealing that money!'

'That's true – I don't,' said Miss Wardle. 'But the pity of it is – the money was found in her chest of drawers! So what are you to believe?'

'Who's that, Emma, who's that?' a voice suddenly called from upstairs. 'Is there any news of Elizabeth?'

'That's Mrs Sonning. You must go,' said Miss Wardle, and ran up the stairs at once.

'Come on,' said Peter to Jack. 'We've got quite a lot of information! And on Monday we'll see if there's any more! I'll find another boxful of jumble, Jack – and we'll bring it to Miss Wardle and see if she has anything more to report – maybe another rug gone, or a pie! Come on, Scamper – we've done well!'

Five

Pam and Barbara are busy

Now how had the others been getting on? Well, Pam and Barbara had been having a very busy time. They had planned to explore the woods and the fields on the east side of Belling, while the boys and Janet explored the rest of the countryside – or as much as they could!

'There's an old shed in that field, look,' panted Barbara, as she toiled up a hill on her bicycle. 'Let's go and see if it looks as if someone is camping there.'

They left their bicycles by a gate and climbed into the field. The shed was in good repair – and the door was locked!

'Hm,' said Pam. 'Locked! I wonder why. Field sheds aren't usually locked. How can we look inside, Barbara?'

'There's a tiny window this side,' reported Barbara. 'But too high up to peep through. Let's look through the keyhole.'

There was nothing whatever to see through the keyhole, for the inside of the shed was pitch dark. It would have to be the window or nothing! Pam fetched her bicycle from the gate and proposed to stand on the saddle while Barbara held it steady. She was just about to stand on the saddle when a loud shout made her lose her balance in fright and fall off.

'Hey, you! What are you doing?'

The two girls turned round and saw a farm labourer leading a horse towards them. Pam couldn't think of any excuse but the truth.

'We – we were only just wondering what was in the shed,' she stammered. 'We weren't doing any harm.'

'Well, that's the shed where I lock up my tools,' said the man. 'Little nosy-parkers! If you were boys I'd give you a hiding!'

The girls left that field at top speed. Pam riding her bicycle over the bumpy clods! Goodness – what a cross fellow!

'We'd better be careful of the next shed we want to look into,' said Pam, as they cycled along. 'Look, there's an empty caravan – see, in that field there. That would be a good place for anyone to hide in. Now for goodness' sake let's be careful this time. I'll keep guard while you look inside. Buck up!'

Pam stood on guard near the dirty, broken-down old van, which looked as if no one had lived in it for years.

Barbara went cautiously up the steps and looked inside.

She beckoned to Pam in excitement.

'Pam! Someone *does* live here! There are a couple of dirty old rugs – or blankets – and a tin mug and plate – do come and look!'

Pam came up the steps too. 'Pooh!' she said, and held her nose. 'What a FRIGHTFUL smell! Come down, Barbara. You know jolly well you'd never hide in a place like that, nor any other schoolgirl either. I think I'm going to be sick.'

'You're right, I'd rather sleep in a ditch than in there,' said Barbara. 'Don't be sick, Pam. It's not worth it. Come on, let's get on with our job. We want to have plenty to report to the others this afternoon.'

Pam decided not to be sick after all, and they rode on again, keeping a sharp eye out for any kind of hiding-place. But except for a roadman's hut, they saw nothing else that was possible to hide in. They didn't even stop at the little hut, because the roadman himself was there, sitting in it and having some kind of snack.

'What about the woods?' asked Pam, at last. 'There's Thorney-Copse Wood – and it has plenty of thick bushes in it. We might go there. We've still got an hour to look round in.'

So they went to the nearby woods, and left their bicycles beside a tree. 'Now let's be as quiet as possible,' said Pam, in a low voice. 'You go that way, and I'll go this. Whistle twice if you see anything interesting.'

She went quietly in and out of the trees, looking behind any thick bush and even under them. But there was nothing at all interesting or exciting to be seen. Pam found an empty cigarette packet, and Barbara found a dirty handkerchief with J.P. on it, but neither of them felt that they were of any value in the hunt. Now if E.M.W.S. had been marked on the handkerchief, what a thrill!

And then Pam suddenly clutched hold of Barbara, making her jump violently, and hissed in her ear. 'Quiet! Somebody's coming, and it's a girl – look!'

They crept under a thick bush at once, and made little peep-holes through the leaves. Yes, it was a schoolgirl – in navy blue coming down a path towards their bush.

'Keep still – and then we'll follow her!' whispered Pam. 'I bet that's the girl we want!'

The girl's hat was pulled well down over her eyes. She walked boldly up to the bush – and then suddenly fell into it, almost squashing Pam and Barbara. She began to roar with laughter.

'Oh, it's Susie. Jack's horrible sister Susie!' cried Barbara, indignantly. 'Get off us, Susie – you've nearly squashed us flat. What did you do that for?'

'Well, you were lying in wait to jump out at me,

weren't you?' asked Susie. 'I spotted you crawling into the bush!'

'We were *not* lying in wait for you,' said Pam.

'Well,' said Susie, 'what were you doing then? Come on – you've *got* to tell me!'

Six

Up at the stables

PAM and Barbara glared at Susie. It was *just* like her to interfere. Pam rubbed her shoulder.

'You've given me a big bruise,' she said. 'And we shan't tell you a thing!'

'It's something to do with the Secret Seven, isn't it?' said Susie. 'Go on, tell me – I know it is. You've got some kind of secret on again, haven't you? Jack has gone off without saying a word to me. Tell me, and I'll help you.'

'Certainly not!' said Pam indignantly. 'We keep our secrets to ourselves!'

'Well – I'll get it out of Jack,' said the irritating Susie, and walked off, tipping her hat over her face once more. 'Good-bye – and don't lie in wait for me again!'

'Now she knows we're in the middle of another excitement,' said Barbara, brushing herself down. 'She's so sharp that I'm sure she'll find out what it is. I do hope we don't keep meeting her looking for Elizabeth too!'

'Time's getting on,' said Pam, looking at her watch. 'We'll just hunt in a few more places, and then we'll have to go home!'

They did quite a lot more hunting, and found an exciting hollow tree which, they decided, would have made a fine place for a runaway girl if she had happened to see it.

'We'll remember it for ourselves, in case we ever need a

place like this,' said Barbara. 'Now let's go home. We've nothing to report – except about Susie – but at least we've done our best. I wonder how Colin got on? He was going round the farms and looking into the barns.'

'And George and Janet were going to visit the riding stables in the district,' said Pam. 'That would be quite a nice job. I love stables.'

George and Janet thought it was quite a nice job too. They had looked up the riding stables in the district, and found that there were three.

'Belling Riding Stables,' said Janet. 'And Warner's Riding Stables – and Tiptree's. We'll go to all three, shall we?'

So off they went on their bicycles, feeling, as usual, very important to be on Secret Seven work again. They came to Tiptree's Stables first. Janet knew the man who ran it, for he was a friend of her father's.

He was rubbing down a horse and smiled at Janet and George. 'Well – come to have a look at my horses?' he said. 'I've a foal in there, look – Silver Star, she's called, and a bonny thing she is.'

They admired the lovely little foal. 'I do wish I worked at a stables,' said Janet, artfully. 'Do you ever let school-girls work here – perhaps in the school holidays, Mr Tiptree?'

The riding master laughed. 'No! I get plenty of help from my wife and two daughters – they're all mad about horses. They do all the work there is to do – I don't need anyone from outside. This is quite a family stables! Why – did you think you'd come and help? Your father has surely got plenty of horses for you to play about with?'

'Well, yes, he has,' said Janet, stroking the little foal. 'I only just wondered if you ever gave jobs to girls – lots of girls I know love horses and wish they could work in a stables.'

'Come on, Janet,' said George, seeing that they could get no useful information from Mr Tiptree. Obviously the runaway girl would not be able to get a job here, even if she wanted one.

'Thank you for showing us the foal, Mr Tiptree,' said Janet. 'I'll tell my father about her – he'll be interested.'

They rode off again, and George looked at his list of stables. 'We'll go to Warner's Stables next,' he said. 'That's not far from the old granny's house. It might be a good place for Elizabeth Sonning to hide in – or get a job at.'

'I hardly think she'd go anywhere so close, would she?' said Janet. 'She might be recognized. It's more likely she'd go farther off – to Belling Stables, the other side of the village. Still – we'll go to Warner's first.'

They rode up to the stables on the top of the next hill. Below them were spread fields of all kinds and shapes looking like a big patchwork quilt.

Warner's Stables were quite big, and looked busy as they came up to them. Some horses were going out with riders, and others were coming in. Nobody took much notice of the two children.

'Let's have a snoop round,' said Janet. 'And if we see any stable-girls, we'll have a good look at them.'

'Wouldn't Elizabeth have to wear riding things if she wanted a job at a stable?' said George. 'We know that she was wearing her school clothes when she left – she took no others.'

'Well – she might have borrowed some at the stables,' said Janet. 'Though that's rather unlikely, I think. Look – there's a stable-girl – see – cleaning out that stable.'

They stood and stared at the girl. Her back was towards them, and she was doing her job well. She turned round to fetch something, and at once they saw that it was not Elizabeth.

'Far too big!' said Janet, disappointed. 'Look – there are two stable-boys over there. Let's go and talk to them – we may learn something, you never know.'

Seven

Tom has some news

GEORGE and Janet made their way between the horses and their riders to where the two stable-boys were. One was carrying a great load of straw on his back. The other was helping a small girl down from a pony. They took no notice of George and Janet.

'Hello, Janet!' said the small girl, and Janet turned in surprise. It was Hilda, a little girl who went to her school, and was two forms below her in lessons.

'Hello, Hilda,' said Janet, feeling pleased to see her. Now she could pretend she was with her, and it wouldn't matter that she and George were not in riding clothes. Everyone would think they had come to meet Hilda.

'Thank you, Tom,' said Hilda to the boy who had helped her down. He took the pony off to a nearby stable. Hilda followed him, accompanied by Janet and George.

'I like the other boy best,' Hilda said. 'He talks to me, but this one won't. Come and see me give my pony some sugar. He's a darling.'

They walked over to the stable with her, following Tom and the pony. The other lad had gone into the same stable with his straw, and was now spreading it on the floor of a stall. He whistled as he worked, and had a merry look in his eye.

'You talk to this boy, and I'll talk to the other one,' said

George, in a low voice to Janet. 'Talk to Hilda too – find out if any new girl is here helping in any way – or if she has seen any strange girl wandering about, watching, as we are doing.'

'Right,' said Janet, and went to Tom and Hilda.

'It must be fun working with horses,' she said to the boy, who was now fastening the pony to the wall. He nodded.

'Not bad,' he said.

'It's funny that so many more girls ride than boys,' went on Janet. 'I can't see a single boy here except you and the other stable-boy. Are there any others?'

'No,' said the boy. 'Just us two.' He began to clean out the stall next to the little pony, turning his back on Hilda and Janet. Janet thought he was rather rude. So did Hilda.

'He's like that,' she whispered to Janet. 'The other boy, Harry, doesn't mind telling you anything. He's talking to George as if he's known him for years.

So he was. George was getting on very well indeed!

'Do they have many stable-girls here?' George asked, when he had a good chance. The burly fellow shook his head.

'Only one – and she's over there. One came the other day to ask for a job, but Mr Warner turned her down at once. Why, she wasn't any bigger than you! And yet she said she could handle this big cob over there.'

George pricked up his ears. He wasn't interested in the cob, but he was interested in this girl who had come for a job! Could it have been Elizabeth?

'What was she like?' he asked. Harry called across to the other stable-boy.

'Hey, Tom – what was that girl like who came and asked for a job the other day?'

'Was she brown-eyed?' asked George, eagerly. 'Had she masses of dark, fluffy hair? And did you notice if she had a scar down one of her arms?'

The stable-boy swung round sharply and stared at George. 'What girl's that?' he asked. 'Is she a friend of yours?'

'No, not exactly,' said George. 'It's — er — well, it's just someone we're looking out for. Do tell me, was this girl like my description of her?'

'I didn't see her,' said Tom, much to Janet's and George's disappointment. 'I wasn't here the day she came.'

'Oh, no – that's right,' said Harry. 'Well, I know she hadn't got dark hair – she had yellow hair, and she was lively as a monkey. Very cross too, when Mr Warner turned her down. She couldn't have been your friend.'

'I saw a girl like the one you described when I was in

Gorton the other day,' said Tom suddenly. 'Mass of fluffy brown hair, you said, didn't you – and a scar down one arm.'

'Did you? Did you *really* see her?' cried Janet, coming up, looking thrilled. Now they were really getting warm! 'How did you manage to see her scar?'

'Oh – she sat in a tea-shop, and it was hot there – so she took off her coat,' said Tom. 'I saw her scar then.'

'But hadn't she a long-sleeved school blouse on?' asked Janet, surprised.

'Maybe. But her sleeves must have been rolled up if so,' said Tom, and bent to his work again.

'Tom – this is really very important,' said George, joining in. 'Could you tell us anything she said – did she speak to you?'

'She said she was going to catch a train to London and see if she could fly to France to join a brother of hers,' said Tom, .to Janet's and George's surprise and excitement. Why, the girl *must* have been Elizabeth, then. A scar on her arm – and a brother in France! There was no doubt about it!

'Tom! I want you!' called a voice, and Mr Warner looked into the stable. 'Come and show this child how to saddle her horse.'

Tom went off, and Janet and George looked at one another, delighted. 'Well – we've got something to report to the meeting this afternoon!' said Janet. 'Come on, George – we needn't stay here any longer.'

Eight

Another meeting

EVERYONE was early for the two-thirty meeting, and the password was muttered five times as Janet and Peter opened and shut the door of the shed. Scamper barked a welcome to everyone. Then the door was locked and the meeting began.

'I hope everyone has something to report,' said Peter. 'I'll begin with my report. Well, Jack and I went to the grandmother's house, but the old lady wasn't well, so we didn't see her. We didn't find it difficult to ask questions, and her companion was quite friendly.'

'That was a bit of luck!' said George.

'It was,' said Peter. 'We learnt quite a few things – for instance, that Elizabeth is definitely hiding somewhere in the district – not far from her granny's, I should think – because she has got into the house at night and taken pies and things, and an old rug!'

George and Janet looked astonished. 'But, Peter—' began George and Janet together. Peter frowned. 'Please don't interrupt,' he said. 'You and Janet can have your say in a minute. Well, as I was saying — the old lady's companion, Miss Wardle – told us quite a lot about Elizabeth, and said that she was a very nice, straightforward girl.'

'She can't be!' interrupted Pam. 'You can't call a thief straightforward! She was only just *saying* that!'

'Be quiet,' said Peter, exasperated. 'The point I'm trying to make is that there's no doubt that Elizabeth is hiding somewhere near her grandmother's – and getting food from there. And she'll do that at night as often as she needs food! I suggest that we go and watch one night, and see if we can catch her. Jack and I are going to take some more jumble to the grandmother's on Monday, and if Elizabeth has been getting into the house again, we could perhaps watch that night.'

'Yes. Jolly good idea!' said Pam, Barbara, and Colin. George and Janet said nothing, but looked meaningly at one another.

'Well, that's my report – mine and Jack's,' said Peter. 'What about you, Colin?'

'Nothing to report at all,' said Colin, in a rather apologetic tone. 'I examined about six sheds, all kinds of barns, and wandered over a whole caravan colony the other side of Belling Hill – but didn't find out a thing. Not a thing. I'm sorry, Peter.'

'That's all right,' said Peter. 'You and Pam, Barbara – what's your report?'

'Well, nothing much, either,' said Barbara. 'We looked in a locked shed – or tried to – and got turned off by a man with a horse. And we found a terribly smelly old caravan with a rug inside and a tin cup and plate. And we hunted all through Thorney-Copse Wood, looking into and under bushes.'

'And that awful sister of Jack's was there, too,' said Pam. 'We saw her coming along, dressed in the same uniform as we wear – navy blue coat and hat – and we thought it might be the runaway girl, so we hid in a bush –

and Susie jumped right into it on purpose and fell on top of us – you should see the bruise I've got!'

'So *that's* why Susie was pestering the life out of me at dinner to find out what the Secret Seven are up to!' said Jack. 'You *are* a couple of idiots to make her think there is something up, you two. Now I shan't have a moment's peace. Susie is bound to find out what we're after – she's as sharp as a needle.'

'She certainly is,' said Peter, who had a healthy respect for Susie's sharpness. 'I wouldn't be a bit surprised if she's not snooping outside somewhere now, listening for all she's worth.'

'Scamper would bark,' began Janet – and just at that very moment Scamper *did* bark as a face looked in at the window of the shed! It was Susie, of course.

'Hello, Secret Seven,' she called. 'I *thought* you'd be here, Jack. I know what you're all up to. I found your newspaper cutting! Ha, ha.'

Peter looked furiously at Jack. 'Do you mean to say you left that newspaper report about?' he said.

'That's right, tick him off!' said the annoying Susie, pressing her face closer to the window. 'I say, you do look a lot of sweetie-pies sitting down there. Shall I tell you my news of Elizabeth Mary Wilhemina Sonning?'

Jack leapt up in a fury, flung open the door, and raced out with Scamper at his heels. The others went to the door.

Susie was a fast runner. She was running out of the gate, laughing, before Jack was half-way there. He knew it was no good chasing after her. He went back to the shed, red in the face.

'Do you suppose she heard what we were all saying?' asked Jack. Peter shook his head.

'No. Scamper would have barked. Susie could only just that moment have come. I must say it's very annoying. Now Susie will be hunting too. Blow! If she finds Elizabeth before we do, I shall be jolly furious.'

'She won't,' said George, bursting to tell what he had heard from Tom the stable-boy. 'You just wait till you hear what Janet and I have to report.'

Nine

Reports and plans

'GIVE your report, George and Janet,' said Peter. 'It sounds as if it may be an important one.'

'It is,' said Janet, proudly. 'You begin, George.'

'Well,' began George, 'Janet and I went to Tiptree Stables first, but as they don't employ anyone there except their own family, we knew Elizabeth wouldn't have got a job there. So we left at once and went on to Mr Warner's stables.'

'And we saw a stable-girl there, but she was much too big to be Elizabeth,' put in Janet.

'Then we saw two stable-boys – one a big, burly fellow called Harry, and the other smaller, called Tom. He was a bit surly, we thought, but Harry wasn't. He was nice. We asked him if any girl had been asking for a job at Mr Warner's, and one had, but she had yellow hair not brown, so we knew that was no good.'

'And when we told Harry what the girl was like that we wanted, the other boy, Tom, who was listening, suddenly said that *he* had seen a girl like the one we were describing – and she even had a scar down one arm!' cried Janet unable to resist joining in.

'What!' cried everyone, and sat up straight.

'This *is* news,' said Peter, delighted. 'Go on, George. Where had he seen Elizabeth – because it must be her if the description tallies.'

'He said he met her in a tea-shop in Gorton – that's not very far from here, is it? She was having tea, I suppose. It was hot and she had her coat off – that's how he noticed the scar down one arm. She talked to him.'

'What did she say?' demanded Peter, his eyes shining.

'She told him she was going to London to see if she could get a plane to fly to France to see her brother,' said Janet. 'She did really! So it *must* have been Elizabeth, mustn't it?'

'Yes. Of course it must,' said Peter, and the others nodded their heads. A brother in France – a scar on one arm – it *could* only be Elizabeth.

'Well, now you see why Janet and I don't think that Elizabeth is hiding anywhere in the district,' said George. 'She's probably hiding somewhere in London, trying to find out about planes.'

'Well – can you answer this question then, if that's so,' said Peter, looking suddenly puzzled. 'If Elizabeth is in London, waiting to fly to France, who is it who is taking pies and a rug from her grandmother's house at night?'

There was a deep silence. Everyone looked at Peter, even Scamper.

'I hadn't thought of that,' said Janet. 'Well, of course, George and I didn't know anything about the pies till you told us in your report, Peter. Blow! One of our reports is wrong somehow. If Elizabeth is hanging round her granny's house at night, she can't be going to fly to France!'

'She might have found that she hadn't enough money

to get to London and buy a seat on a plane,' said Jack. 'She might have changed her mind and gone to Belling, after all. She might even have hoped to get money from her grandmother's house. After all, if she had stolen once, she could easily do so again.'

'That's true,' said Peter. 'Yes – I think you're right, Jack. She may have made that plan at the beginning and then found she hadn't enough money – and so she came to this district. We know she was seen somewhere about here.'

There was another silence. The Seven were trying to sort things out in their minds. 'What about that girl who came to ask Mr Warner for a job – the one Harry told you about,' said Janet to George. 'He said she had golden hair, didn't he? Well, I suppose she might have had it dyed, mightn't she – I mean, that *might* have been Elizabeth, after all. I know my auntie once had her hair dyed golden when it was brown. So Elizabeth could have done the same, couldn't she?'

Nobody knew very much about hair being dyed, and Peter made up his mind that the next thing to do was to go and interview the two stable-boys himself. They might be able to tell him something they hadn't thought of telling Janet or George.

'I shall go and see those boys,' he said. 'What are they like to look at?'

'I told you Harry was big and burly, and the other smaller,' said George. 'They've both got dark hair, rather untidy. They ought to exchange riding-breeches too – Harry's are too small for him, and Tom's are too large! Wasn't it a bit of luck Tom meeting Elizabeth at Gorton –

now we know for certain she must be somewhere about, still wearing her school things.'

'Well, she's *got* to be somewhere near, or she couldn't raid her granny's house at night,' said Peter. 'Now, what do we do next? Tomorrow's Sunday, we can't do anything then. It will have to be Monday after school.'

'You and I will go to old Mrs Sonning's with some more jumble,' said Jack, 'and find out the latest news from *that* quarter.'

'And after that we'll go and see the stable-boys,' said Peter. 'The others can come too, so that it won't seem too noticeable, us asking questions. Meet here at five o'clock on Monday. Well – I *hope* we're on the trail – but it's not very easy at the moment!'

Ten

Miss Wardle has more news

SUNDAY passed rather slowly.

When Peter and Janet came back from morning church, Peter had an idea.

'Janet – George and I are going to take some more jumble to old Mrs Sonning tomorrow, you remember – to make an excuse for asking about Elizabeth again – so shall we hunt up some? What sort of things does Mother give for jumble? Old clothes mostly, I suppose.'

'Yes. But we can't give away any of our clothes without asking her,' said Janet. 'And she would want to know why we were doing it – she'd guess it was an excuse to go to old Mrs Sonning again, and she might not approve.'

'That's just what I was thinking,' said Peter. 'I know – let's turn out our cupboards and see if there's anything we can find that would do for jumble.'

They found plenty! It was astonishing what a lot of things they had which they had quite forgotten about and never used.

'Two packs of snap cards,' said Peter. 'A game of snakes and ladders – we've never even *used* it, because we always preferred our old game. And look here – a perfectly new ball! Shall we give that?'

'Well, jumble isn't really supposed to be *new* things,' said Janet. 'Let's give our old ball instead. And look, here are my old sandals I thought I'd left at the seaside! I can't get into them now – *they* can go.'

In the end they had quite a big box full of jumble and felt very pleased with themselves. They longed for Monday to come!

It came at last, and then there was morning school to get through, and afternoon school as well. They raced home to tea and were down in the shed just before five o'clock. All the Seven were there, very punctual indeed!

'Good,' said Peter, pleased. 'Well, Jack and I will bike to Bramble Cottage, and see if we can get any more news out of Miss Wardle, the companion, or Mrs Sonning, the granny. The rest of you can bike up to Warner's Stables and wait for us there. Chat to the stable-boys all you can. We'll join you later.'

They all set off, Peter with a neat box of 'jumble' tied to the back of his bicycle. They parted at the top of Blackberry Lane, and Jack and Peter went down the winding road, while the others rode up the hill to where Warner's Stables were, right at the top.

Peter and Jack left their bicycles at the gate of Bramble Cottage and went to the front door. They knocked, hoping that Miss Wardle would come, not old Mrs Sonning. Mrs Sonning might not be so willing to talk about Elizabeth as Miss Wardle was!

Thank goodness it was the companion who opened the door again. She seemed quite pleased to see them.

'Well now – don't say you've been kind enough to bring us some *more* jumble!' she said. 'Mrs Sonning was *so* pleased with the boxes you brought on Saturday. I'll give her these – she's still in bed, dear old lady.'

'Oh, I'm sorry,' said Peter. 'Hasn't she heard any more of her granddaughter?'

'Not a word,' said Miss Wardle 'The police say she seems to have disappeared completely – and yet she came here again last night – *and* the night before!'

This was indeed news! 'Did she?' asked Peter eagerly. 'Did you see her? Did she leave a note?'

'No. Not a note, not even a sign that she was here,' said Miss Wardle, 'except that more food was gone. How she got in beats me. Every door and window I made fast myself. She must have got a key to the side-door. That's the only one with no bolt.'

'What do the police say about that?' asked Jack.

'Nothing,' said Miss Wardle, rather indignantly. 'It's my belief they think I'm making it up, they take so little notice. Why don't they put a man to watch the house at night – they'd catch the poor child then, and what a relief it would be to the old lady to know she was safe!'

'They probably *do* put a man to watch,' said Peter, 'but I expect Elizabeth knows some way into the house that they don't. I bet she knows if there's a policeman about – and where he is and everything. *I* would! Why don't *you* watch, Miss Wardle?'

'What? Watch every door and window?' said the companion. 'Nobody could do that. And I'm not one to be able to keep awake all night, even if I had to.'

'Well – we'd better go,' said Peter. 'I *do* hope Elizabeth is soon found. It must be awful hiding away in some cold, lonely place all by herself, not daring to come home because she feels ashamed.'

They said good-bye and went. 'Well,' said Peter, as soon as they were out of the front gate, 'I know what *I'm* going to do tonight! I'm going to hide somewhere in the garden here! I bet I'll see Elizabeth if she comes – but I shan't tell the police. I'll try and get her to go and tell everything to her granny!'

'Good idea! I'll come too!' said Jack, thrilled. 'Let's go up to the stables now and find the others. I bet they'll want to come and watch as well!'

Eleven

Tom – and a bit of excitement

PETER and Jack saw the others as soon as they pushed open the tall double-gate and went into the big stable-yard. They had evidently been sent to fetch hay and straw, and looked very busy indeed, carrying it over their shoulders. The two stable-boys were there as well, help-ing.

'Hallo, Peter – hallo, Jack!' called Janet. 'Aren't we busy? We're having a lovely time. Mr Warner said we could take the ponies down to the field later on, with Harry and Tom, the stable-boys.'

'Good. I'll come too, with Jack,' said Peter, pleased. He loved anything to do with horses, and often helped old Jock, the horse-man, in his father's farm-stables. He went over to the two stable-boys. Harry grinned at him, but Tom just nodded. Peter looked at him keenly. So this was the boy who had actually seen Elizabeth!

'I say – I hear you saw that girl, Elizabeth Sonning, at Gorton the other day,' began Peter. 'That's jolly interest-ing. The police haven't found her yet – I should think her grandmother must be feeling ill with worry, wouldn't you?'

'What about the girl, then?' said Tom, in a gruff voice. 'I reckon she must be feeling pretty awful too.'

'Well, if she stole that money, she deserves to feel awful,' said Peter. 'The funny thing is that Miss Wardle,

who is the old lady's companion, says Elizabeth is an awfully nice girl, straightforward as anything! Here – let me
help you with that saddle.'

'Thanks,' said Tom. 'I feel interested in that girl –
seeing her in Gorton just by chance. I reckon she's in
France by now. She said she wanted to go to her
brother.'

'Well, she's *not* in France,' said Peter, struggling with
the heavy saddle. 'She goes each night to her granny's
house and takes things. Miss Wardle told me that. She
says she can't *think* how Elizabeth gets into the house –
everything's locked and fastened. She thought maybe the
girl might have a key to the side-door, which has no
bolt.'

Jack joined in then. 'And we thought we'd go and
watch the house ourselves tonight,' he said. 'We're sure *we*
should see her getting in, if she comes in the dark – and
we'd try and get her to go and talk to her old granny, who
loves her. We hate to think of a girl camping out somewhere all alone, feeling miserable.'

'Are you really going to watch tonight?' said Tom,
sounding surprised. Peter nodded. He hadn't wanted
Jack to tell a Secret Seven plan to the stableboy – that was
really *silly* of him, thought Peter, and gave him a stern
frown, which startled Jack very much.

'Well, if you're going to watch the house, I'd like to
come too,' said Tom, most surprisingly. 'I bet *I* could see
anyone creeping into a house at night. I'll come with
you.'

Peter hesitated. He wanted to say that Tom could certainly *not* come! But how could he prevent him if he

wanted to? It was just a nice little adventure to him, and possibly a chance to show how clever he was at spotting anyone breaking into a house!

'All right,' he said, at last. 'We shall be there at half past ten – not the girls – just the four boys. I'll give an owl-hoot when we arrive – and if you're there, hoot back.'

'I'll be there,' said Tom. 'And I suppose a policeman or two will, as well! Well, you stick up for me if I get seen by the police, and say I'm a friend of yours, not a burglar!'

'All right,' said Peter, wishing more than ever that Jack hadn't said so much. 'Do we take the ponies down to the fields now?'

Apparently they did, and a long trail of children riding

or leading the ponies went over the hill and down to the fields, bright in the evening sun.

After they had safely fastened in the tired ponies, the Seven, with Tom and Harry, walked back to the stables. Tom looked tired and spoke very little. Harry cracked jokes and slapped the other stable-boy on the back several times. Peter whispered to Tom when he had a chance.

'Don't forget the owl-hoot!' Tom nodded and turned away. The children shouted good-bye and fetched their bicycles, riding them down the hill-path.

In the distance they saw someone climbing over a stile –

someone with a suit-case – someone in a navy blue coat and hat – someone who looked round and then, seeming scared, ran hurriedly down the road.

'Look!' said Colin, pointing. 'Is that Elizabeth – with a suit-case, too! Quick, let's follow!'

They rode along the path, bumping up and down as they went, for it was very rough. They came to the stile. By it lay something white.

Janet picked it up. 'A handkerchief!' she said. 'And I say – LOOK! It's got E in the corner, embroidered in green! It *was* Elizabeth! Her hiding-place *is* somewhere near here. Quick, let's follow her.'

They lifted their bicycles over the stile into the road and looked to see if they could spy a running figure in navy blue.

'There she is – at the corner – by that old cottage!' shouted George. 'If only we can get her to be friends and come with us! Ring your bells, all of you, so that she'll hear us coming!'

Twelve

How very annoying!

THE whole Seven cycled as fast as they could after the disappearing figure in navy blue, ringing their bells loudly to attract her attention.

The figure reached the corner, and vanished round it. When they came to it, the girl was nowhere to be seen. The Seven dismounted from their bicycles and looked at one another.

'Wherever has she gone? She's nowhere down the road!' said Janet. 'She must have slipped into some hiding-place. But I can't see any near by.'

'Yes, look – there's that ruined old cottage,' said Colin, pointing. 'Can't you see it – among that little thicket of trees. I bet she's there!'

'We'll go and look,' said George, and, putting their bicycles beside the hedge, they squeezed through a gap and ran over to the old stone cottage. It had very little roof left, and there were only two rooms below and one above. A broken stone stairway went up in one corner to the room above.

'There's nobody here!' said Pam, surprised. 'Oh, but look – there's an old stone stairway. Perhaps she's up there!'

George ran up – and gave a shout. 'The girl isn't here – but her suit-case is! And it's got E.M.W.S. on it! It *was* Elizabeth we saw!'

Everyone tore up the stairs in a hurry. They looked at
the cheap little suitcase on the dirty floor. Yes – it certainly had E.M.W.S. printed on it in black.

'Elizabeth Mary Wilhemina Sonning,' said Barbara,
touching the initials. 'But where *is* Elizabeth?' She called
loudly. 'Elizabeth! Where are you?'

There was no reply. 'That's queer,' said Janet. 'There
really isn't anywhere for her to hide here. Why did she
throw her case up these stairs and then rush away. She
might guess we'd find it. Where *is* she? ELIZABETH!'

'I'm going to open the case,' said Peter. 'I feel there's
something peculiar about all this. I hope it isn't locked.'

It wasn't. It snapped open easily enough. The Seven
crowded round to look inside. One small box was there,
and nothing else. It was tied up with string.

'Perhaps this is the money she stole!' said Colin. 'Gosh –
look! It's got "THE MONEY" printed on it in big letters.
Open the box, Peter.'

Peter undid the string and opened the box. Inside was a
smaller one, also tied with string. He undid that, and
inside found once again another box. He looked puzzled.

It seemed strange to put money inside so many boxes!

He opened the third box – and inside that was a card, laid on its face. Peter picked it up and turned it over. He stared at it as if he couldn't believe his eyes!

'What does it say? What does it say?' cried Pam, trying to see.

Peter flung it down on the floor and stamped on it, looking very angry. 'It says *"Lots and lots of love from Susie!"* OH! I'd like to slap her! Making us chase after her – leaving that silly hanky by the stile – and making us undo all those boxes!'

The Secret Seven were very, very angry, especially Jack. 'How *dare* she play a trick like that!' he said. 'Just wait till I get home. I'll have something to say to her!'

'Where's she gone?' said Barbara. 'I didn't see her after we turned the corner. She must have had her bicycle hidden somewhere here.'

'She planned it all very well,' said George. 'I must say she's jolly clever. Gosh – I really *did* think we'd got hold of Elizabeth that time!'

'Susie must have laughed like anything when she printed the initials E.M.W.S. on that cheap old suit-case,' said Jack. 'I recognize it now – it's been up in our loft for ages.'

'Well, come on – let's get home,' said Janet. 'I'm tired of talking about Susie.'

They left the little ruined cottage and rode away. Peter began to arrange the night's meeting with George, Jack, and Colin. The girls were sad that they could not come too.

'You always leave us out of these night adventures,'

complained Janet. 'I do so wish we were coming. It will be so exciting to wait in that dark garden – let me see – there will be five of you counting that boy Tom – though I really do think it's a pity to have him, too.'

'There may be a policeman or two as well,' said George. 'I vote we get there before they do – or they'll get rather a shock when they hear a whole collection of people taking up their positions here and there in the garden!'

Everyone laughed. 'Don't you DARE to let anything out to Susie about tonight,' Peter warned Jack. 'We can't have her ruining everything. I do wonder how Elizabeth gets into the house. She must have an extra key.'

They arranged to meet at ten past ten at the corner, and bicycle all together to Belling. 'We'll hide our bikes under the nearby hedge and get into the garden at the back,' planned Peter. 'Remember to hoot if there's any danger.'

'This is awfully exciting,' said Jack. 'I only hope Susie doesn't hear me getting up and going downstairs.'

'Jack – if you do anything silly so that Susie follows you, I'll dismiss you from the Secret Seven!' said Peter – and he REALLY meant it!

Thirteen

Waiting and watching

THAT night Peter, Jack, George and Colin slipped silently out of their houses. Jack was very much afraid that Susie might hear him, but when he put his ear to her door, he could hear gentle little snores. Good – she was asleep! He remembered Peter's threat to dismiss him from the Secret Seven if he wasn't careful about Susie, and he felt very glad to hear those snores!

The boys met together and then cycled quickly over to the grandmother's house in Belling. They met nobody at all, not even a policeman, and were very thankful. The four of them dismounted quietly and put their bicycles into the hedge beyond Bramble Cottage. The cottage was in complete darkness.

'The only person to hoot is *me*,' whispered Peter. 'If we all hoot when we hear or see something interesting or suspicious, it would sound as if the garden was *full* of owls – and any policeman would be jolly suspicious!'

'All right,' whispered back George. 'Can we choose our own hiding-places? What about two of us going to hide in the garden at the front of the house, and two at the back?'

'No – two at the back, one in the front – you, Colin – and one at the side where the side-door is,' said Peter, in a low voice. 'Don't forget that Miss Wardle said she thought

Elizabeth might have a key to that door – and there are no bolts there on the inside!'

'Oh, yes!' said Jack. 'I'll go and hide in the hedge beside the garden door, Peter. There isn't any door on the fourth side. We shall be watching every door there is – and every window.'

'It's very dark,' said Peter, looking up at the sky. 'There's no moon, and it's a cloudy night, so there are no stars either. We shall have to keep our ears wide open, because it may be pretty difficult to see anything.'

'Our eyes will soon get used to the darkness,' said Colin.

'I say – listen, what's that?' He clutched at Peter and made him jump.

A slight noise came from near by, and then a shadow loomed up. A voice spoke. 'It's me – Tom. I was waiting here, and I heard you. Where are you hiding?'

They told him. 'Well, I think *I'll* climb up a tree,' said Tom, in a low voice. 'That will be a very good place to watch from – or listen from! I don't think any policemen are about. I've been here for some time.'

'Hoot if you hear anyone coming,' Peter reminded him. 'I'll hoot back. But only you or I will hoot.'

'I'll find a tree to climb,' whispered Tom. 'See – that one over there, near the wall. I shall have a good view from there – if only the clouds clear and the stars shine out!'

The four went to find their own hiding-places, feeling pleasantly excited. This *was* fun! They heard Tom climbing his tree. Then there was silence. Peter was snuggled into a bush, from where he could keep good watch.

A sudden screech made everyone jump, and their hearts beat fast. Whatever was it? Then a white shadow swept round the dark garden, and everyone heaved a sigh of relief.

'Only a barn-owl!' thought Peter. 'Goodness – it made me jump. Good thing it doesn't hoot, only screeches – or we would all of us have thought that someone was coming!'

Nothing happened for a while – then a low, quavering hoot came across the garden. 'Hoo! Hoo-hoo-hoo-hoooooooo!'

'That's Tom!' thought Peter, and he and the others in

hiding stiffened, and listened hard, trying to see through the darkness.

Then someone brushed by Peter's bush and he crouched back in fright. He heard a little cough – a man's cough. It must be a policeman who had come along so quietly that no one but Tom had heard him. Peter waited a few seconds till he was sure that the man had found a hiding-place, and then he hooted too.

'Hoo! Hoo-hoo-hoo-hooooooo!'

Now everyone must guess that at least one policeman was in the garden! Peter's heart began to thump. Suddenly things seemed very strange and very exciting – all the dark shadows around, and so many people waiting! He half hoped that Elizabeth would not come to her granny's house that night. It would be so frightening for her to be surrounded suddenly by complete strangers!

Then suddenly he stared in amazement. Was that a *light* he saw in one of the upstairs rooms of the house? A light like that made by a torch? Yes – it was! He could see the beam moving here and there behind the drawn curtains!

Elizabeth must be there – she must have got in somehow, in spite of everyone watching! Or could it be Miss Wardle creeping about with a torch? No – surely she would switch on a light!

Peter gave a hoot again. 'Hoooo! Hoo-hoo-hoo-hooooooooo!' That would make certain that everyone was on guard. If Elizabeth had got in, then she would have to get out – and surely one of them would see her!

The light in the upstairs room disappeared – and reappeared again in another room. Peter thought it was the kitchen. Perhaps the hungry runaway girl was looking for food again?

How HAD she got in? But, more important still – where was she going to come out?

Fourteen

A real mystery!

THE light from the torch inside the house moved here and there. Then it disappeared completely, as if it had been switched off. All the watchers listened, and strained their eyes in the darkness. Now Elizabeth would be leaving the house, and they must stop her. What door – or what window – would she creep from?

Nothing happened. No door opened. No window creaked or rattled. For ten whole minutes the watchers stood silent and tense. Then a man's voice called from somewhere in the garden.

'Will! Seen anyone?'

To Peter's intense surprise another's man's voice answered. 'No. Not a thing. The kid must be still in the house. We'll knock up Miss Wardle and search.'

So there were *two* policemen in the garden then! How very quiet the other one had been! The boys were most surprised. *Now* what should they do? They watched the policemen switch on torches and heard them go to the front door of the house.

Peter hooted once more, and the others, realizing that he wanted them, left their hiding-places and came cautiously to find him. Tom slid down the tree and joined them too.

'The policemen didn't hear or see anyone – any more than we did!' said Peter. 'We could only have seen what

they saw – a light in the downstairs of the house. Tom, did *you* see anything else?'

'Not a thing,' said Tom. 'Look – I'll slip off, I think. The police don't know me, and they might wonder what I'm doing here with you. So long!'

He disappeared into the night and left the four boys together. They went near to the front door, at which the policemen had rung a minute ago. Keeping in the dark shadows. The door was being opened cautiously by a very scared Miss Wardle, dressed in a long green dressing-gown, her hair in pins.

'Oh – it's you!' the boys heard her say to the police. 'Come in I'm afraid I was asleep, although I said I'd try and keep awake tonight. Do you want me to go and see if anything is taken?'

'Well, Miss Wardle, we know that *someone* was in your house just now,' said one of the policemen. 'We saw the light of a torch in two rooms. One of us would like to come in and search, please – the other will stay out here in case the girl – if it is the girl – tries to make a run for it. We haven't seen her come out – or go in either for that matter! But we did see the light of her torch.'

'Oh, I see. Well, come in, then,' said Miss Wardle. 'But please make no noise, or you'll scare the old lady. Come into the kitchen – I can soon tell if food is gone again.'

The policeman disappeared into the cottage with Miss Wardle, leaving the other man on guard in the garden. The four boys watched from the safety of the shadows. Surely Elizabeth must be in the house? She couldn't have left by any door or window without being seen or heard! They watched lights going on in each room, as Miss

Wardle and the policeman searched.

After what seemed like a very long time, they heard voices in the hall. Miss Wardle came to the door with the policeman.

'Nothing to report, Will,' said the policeman to the man left on guard. 'Nobody's in the house. Miss Wardle even went into the old lady's room to make sure the girl hadn't crept in there, feeling that she was cornered.'

'Well – nobody's come *out* of the house,' said Will, sounding surprised. 'Has anything been taken?'

'Yes – more food. Nothing else,' said the first policeman. 'Queer, isn't it? How could anyone have got in under our very eyes and ears – taken food – and got out again without being heard or seen going away? Well – thanks, Miss Wardle. Sorry to have been such a nuisance for nothing. How that girl – and it *must* be the girl – gets in and out like this beats me. And where she's hiding beats me too. We've combed the countryside for her! Well – her brother's coming over to this country tomorrow – not that *he* can do much, if we can't!'

The police departed. The front door shut. The light went off in the hall, and then one appeared upstairs. Then that went out too. Miss Wardle was presumably safely in bed again.

'What do you make of it, Peter?' whispered Jack. 'Peculiar, isn't it?'

'Yes. I can't understand it,' said Peter. 'I mean – there were us four hiding here – and two policemen – and Tom up the tree – and yet not one of us saw Elizabeth getting in and out — and not one of us even *heard* her.'

'And yet she must have come here, into this garden,'

said Jack. 'She broke in somewhere – or unlocked a door –
she even put on her torch in the house to see what she
could take – and then she got out again, with us all watching and listening – and disappeared. No – I don't understand it either.'

'Come on – let's go home and sleep on it,' said Peter. 'I
feel quite tired now, with all the waiting and watching –
and the excitement – and now the disappointment. Poor
Elizabeth – what must she be feeling, having to scrounge
food at night, and hide away in the daytime? She must be
very miserable.'

'Well – maybe her brother can help,' said Colin. 'He'll
be here tomorrow. Come on – I'm going home!'

Fifteen

Crosspatches

THE four boys belonging to the Secret Seven overslept the next morning. They were so tired from their long watch the night before! Janet was cross when Peter wouldn't wake, because she was longing to know what happened!

'Gosh – I'll be terribly late for school,' groaned Peter, leaping out of bed. 'You might have waked me before, Janet.'

'Well, I squeezed a sponge of cold water over you, and yelled in your ear, and pulled all the clothes off!' said Janet indignantly. 'And Scamper barked his head off. What *more* would you like me to do? And what happened last night?'

'Nothing. Absolutely nothing!' said Peter, dressing hurriedly. 'I mean, we didn't get Elizabeth – she got into the house, took what she wanted, and got out again – and disappeared. And although there were seven people altogether in the garden, watching, nobody saw her. So you see – nothing happened. ALL RIGHT, MOTHER! I'M JUST COMING.'

He tore downstairs with his mother still calling him, ate his breakfast standing up, and then cycled to school at top speed. He yelled to Janet as he left her at the corner.

'Meeting tonight at five-thirty. Tell Pam and Barbara!'

The meeting was not very thrilling. After such high

hopes of something really exciting happening the night before, everyone felt flat. Pam made them all cross by saying that if *she* had hidden in the garden she would certainly have heard or seen Elizabeth creeping by.

'You must have fallen asleep,' she said. 'You really must. I mean – *seven* of you there! And nobody heard a thing! I bet you fell asleep.'

'Be quiet,' said Peter crossly. 'You don't know what you're talking about, Pam. Now don't start again. BE QUIET, I say!'

'Well,' said Pam, obstinately, 'all I can say is that if Elizabeth *really* didn't get in or out, and it seems like that to me, or you'd have heard her – then she must be hiding in some jolly good place *inside* the house.'

'The police searched all over it,' said Peter. 'I did think of that bright idea myself – but I gave it up when the policeman hunted all through the cottage last night without finding Elizabeth. After all, it's only a small place – no cellars – no attics. We did hear *one* thing of interest, though. The brother who's in France is arriving in this country today. Maybe he'll have something to say that will be of help.'

'Well – why don't you go and see him, then?' said Pam, who was in a very persistent mood that day. 'You could tell him what *you* know – about Tom the stable-boy seeing Elizabeth in Gorton, for instance.'

'H'm. That's the first sensible remark you've made, Pam,' said Peter. He turned to Jack. 'Will you come with me, Jack? I'd like to see the brother, I must say.'

'Wuff-wuff-wuff!' said Scamper, suddenly.

'*Now* what's the matter?' said Peter, whose late night

had made him decidedly impatient that day. 'What's Scamper barking for? If it's Susie I'll have a few sharp words to say to her about playing that fat-headed trick on us with the suit-case!'

It *was* Susie. She stood grinning at the door when Peter opened it. 'Mint Sauce!' she said promptly. 'Let me in. I've some clues – great big ones. I know where Elizabeth is and what she's doing. I . . .'

'You do NOT!' yelled a furious Peter, and called for Jack. 'Jack – pull her by the hair all the way home. Pam, Barbara, Janet – get hold of her frock and pull too. Come on! Get going!'

And for once in a way the cheeky Susie was taken by surprise and found herself being dragged to the gate, and not very gently either!

'All right!' she yelled, kicking and hitting out as vigorously as she could. 'I shan't tell you my big clues. But you'll see I'm right! And I know your password, see! Mint sauce, Mint sauce, Mint sauce!'

She disappeared up the lane and the Seven went back

to the shed, feeling better for the excitement. 'Now we shall have to alter our password,' said Peter, in disgust. 'How did Susie know it, Jack? Have you been saying it in your sleep, or something?'

'No,' said Jack, still angry. 'She must have hidden somewhere near the shed and heard us saying it. Blow Susie! You don't think she really *does* know something, do you?'

'How can she?' said Peter. 'And why can't you keep her in order? If Janet behaved like that I'd jolly well spank her.'

'You would *not*,' said Janet, indignantly. 'You just try it!'

'Gosh – we really are crosspatches today!' said Barbara, surprised. 'The boys must be tired after their late night! Well – have we any plans?'

'Only that Jack and I will go and see Elizabeth's

brother, if he's arrived at the grandmother's,' said Peter, calming down. 'He'll be sure to go there, because his sister is known to be somewhere near. Come on, Jack – I'm fed up with this meeting. Let's go!'

Sixteen

Unexpected news

PETER and Jack arrived at Bramble Cottage on their bicycles, and at once heard voices there. They put their cycles by the gate and looked over the hedge.

Three people were sitting in deck-chairs in the little garden, enjoying the warm evening sunshine. One was Miss Wardle – one was an old lady, obviously the grandmother – and one was a youth of about eighteen, looking very worried.

'He must be the brother,' said Peter. 'Good, he's arrived! Come on. We'll go up the front path, and if Miss Wardle sees us, she'll call us and we'll go over and talk.'

Miss Wardle did see them, and recognized them at once. 'Oh,' she said to the old lady beside her, 'those are the two nice boys who brought all that jumble. Come here, boys – I'm sure Mrs Sonning would like to thank you.'

Peter and Jack walked over. 'Good evening,' said Peter, politely. 'I do hope you have news of your granddaughter, Mrs Sonning.'

'No. We haven't,' said the old lady, and to Peter's alarm, a tear rolled down her cheek. 'This is my grandson, Charles, her brother. He's come over from France to see if he can help, because Elizabeth is very fond of him. If she knows he is here, she may come out of hiding.'

'We met a boy the other day who saw her in Gorton.'

said Peter. 'She must have been on her way here then.'

'What!' said the boy Charles. 'Someone actually saw her in *Gorton*! But that's *not* on the way here. Who was this boy?'

'One of the stable-boys up at Warner's Stables there,' said Peter, pointing up the hill. 'He said Elizabeth told him she was going to France to see you.'

'But she didn't know where I *was* in France,' said Charles. 'I've been travelling around all the time! Even the police only got in touch with me with great difficulty! I'm certain that Elizabeth wouldn't have been mad enough to try to find me when she didn't even know what part of France I was in!'

'Well,' said Peter, 'that's what *Tom* said she told him, and he couldn't very well have made it up, because he had never met her before!'

'I'll go and see him,' said Charles, and got up – but just then the telephone bell shrilled out, the noise coming clearly into the garden.

'Answer it, Charles, there's a dear,' said old Mrs Sonning, and the boy went indoors. Peter and Jack waited patiently for him, and were immensely surprised to see him come running out again at top speed, his eyes shining and his face aglow.

'Granny! It was Elizabeth's headmistress. She . . .

'Oh – has the child gone back to school – or gone back to her aunt?' said the old lady.

'No! But all that upset about the stolen money is cleared up!' said Charles, taking his grandmother's hand. 'It *wasn't* Elizabeth who took it, of course. The girl who stole it got frightened when the papers kept reporting that Elizabeth hadn't been found, and she suddenly owned up.'

'Who *was* the girl?' said Miss Wardle, indignantly.

'I'm afraid it was the one supposed to be Elizabeth's best friend,' said Charles. 'Lucy Howell – she came here to stay with Elizabeth last year, Granny. She saw the cash-box in the desk and took it on the spur of the moment, without even opening it. She hid it somewhere, waiting for a chance to break it open. She didn't realize that there was about twenty pounds in it, and she was horrified when the police were called in about it.'

'I should think so!' said Mrs Sonning. 'I never did like

Lucy – a sly little thing I thought she was. I was sorry that she was Elizabeth's friend.'

'Well, apparently Lucy was annoyed with Elizabeth and very jealous of her just then, because Elizabeth was ahead of her in marks and doing better at games – and what did she do but take the cash-box and put it into Elizabeth's chest of drawers! When the boarders' trunks and chests were searched – Elizabeth is a weekly boarder as you know – the cash-box was found – still unopened! Elizabeth had gone home for the week-end to Aunt Rose's, and the police went there to question her.'

'Poor Elizabeth!' said Mrs Sonning. 'But didn't she deny taking the money?'

'Yes, of course – but she wasn't believed. Most unfortunately she had actually been in the form-room where the money had stupidly been left, doing some homework all by herself, and had been seen there. Aunt Rose was very upset – and poor Elizabeth felt there was nothing to do but run away! I expect she thought she might have to go to prison or something!'

'Poor child! But now she can come back with her name cleared!' said Mrs Sonning. 'What a dreadful thing to happen to someone like Elizabeth. She's as straight as can be.'

'Yes. But how are we going to let her know that everything is all right?' asked Miss Wardle. 'We don't even know where the child is!'

'No. That's true,' said Charles, worried. 'But we *must* find her! She took only enough money with her to pay her railway fare down here apparently – that's all she had. She wouldn't have enough to buy food or anything else.

She's hiding somewhere, all alone, worried and miserable – thinking that we're all ashamed of her!'

'Don't,' said old Mrs Sonning, and began to weep into her handkerchief. 'Such a dear, good child – always so kind. Charles, we must find her – we must!'

'Well – the first thing to do is for me to go up and see this stable-boy who met Elizabeth in Gorton,' said Charles, getting up. 'Will you take me up to him, you two boys?'

'Yes,' said Peter and Jack, who had been listening to the conversation with much interest. 'We'll take you now. I say – we are glad everything's cleared up!'

Seventeen

A funny business altogether

PETER, Jack, and Charles went to the gate at the bottom of the little garden, and up the hill to Warner's Stables, the two boys wheeling their bicycles. They liked Charles. He reminded them of someone, but they couldn't think who it was.

'Where's Tom?' Peter called to Harry, when they came to the stables. He was saddling a horse.

'Somewhere about,' he shouted back. 'Over there, I think.'

'You see if Tom is over yonder, and I'll go into the stables and see if he's there,' said Peter. Charles went with Jack, and Peter looked into the stables. At the far end he saw Tom, cleaning out one of the stalls.

'Hey, Tom!' called Peter. 'There's someone wants to see you.'

'Who?' shouted back Tom.

'You remember meeting that girl Elizabeth?' said Peter. 'Well, it's her brother, Charles. He's come over from France, he's so upset, and . . .'

He stopped, because Tom had suddenly flung down his rake, and had shot past him at top speed. He tore out of the door, and Peter stared in surprise. When Peter got to the stable door himself, there was no sign of Tom! He saw Jack and Charles coming towards him, and called to them.

'Did you see Tom? He tore out of here just now, good-ness knows why!'

'We saw someone racing off,' said Jack. 'Blow! Just as we wanted him. Didn't you tell him someone wanted to see him?'

'Yes, of course. I don't know if he heard me or not, but he suddenly flung down his fork and dashed off without a word!' said Peter, puzzled.

Harry, the other stable-boy, came up with the big stable-girl. 'Don't take any notice of Tom,' he said. 'He's a bit queer! Isn't he, Kate?'

The stable-girl nodded. 'Hasn't got much to say for himself,' she said. 'Funny boy – a bit potty, *I* think!'

'But where did he go?' said Peter. 'Do you know where he lives? We could go to his home, and then our friend here could ask him a few things he wants to know.'

Neither Harry nor the girl knew where Tom lived, so Jack and Peter gave it up. 'Sorry,' they said to Charles and Peter added: 'We could come here again tomorrow, if you like. Not that Tom can really tell you anything of importance. He may even have made it all up about meeting Elizabeth. He may have read about her in the papers, and just invented the whole meeting! He really *is* a bit queer, I think.'

'Well – thank you,' said Charles, who looked worried again. 'I'll go back. My poor old granny won't be herself again till we find Elizabeth. My parents haven't been told yet, but they'll have to be cabled tomorrow, and asked to come home. Dad's out in China on a most important job, and we didn't want to worry him at first. Apparently the police thought they would soon find my sister.'

'Yes – with no money – and wearing her school clothes it *ought* to have been easy to spot her,' said Jack. 'Well – good-bye – and good luck!'

The boys rode off down the hill. 'I'm jolly glad Elizabeth didn't steal that money after all,' said Peter. 'Though we've never met her, I thought it was rather queer that anyone said to be so honest and straightforward should have done such a thing. And now I've seen that old granny, and her nice brother Charles – he *is* nice, isn't he, Jack? – I see even more clearly that Elizabeth couldn't have been a thief.'

'It's a funny business altogether,' said Jack. 'And it's not cleared up yet, Peter – not till Elizabeth's found. Remember, *she* doesn't know th t the real thief has owned up!'

'I know,' said Peter. 'Well – we'll have another Secret Seven meeting tomorrow night, the same time as today, Jack. We'll tell the others at school tomorrow. We'll have to report this evening's happenings, and see if there's anything further we can do.'

'Right!' said Jack. 'See you tomorrow!' and with a jingling of bicycle bells the two parted, each thinking the same thing. 'What a pity Elizabeth doesn't know that her name is cleared!'

Next evening the Secret Seven gathered in the meeting shed as usual, anxious to hear what Jack and Peter had to say. They were all very thrilled to hear about the brother Charles – and the exciting telephone call that had come while Jack and Peter were there.

'What a pity that boy Tom didn't stop and speak to Charles,' said Colin, puzzled. 'Do you suppose he made up that tale about meeting Elizabeth, and was afraid of being found out in his fairy-tale by Charles?'

'*I* tell you what!' said George, suddenly. 'I believe he knows where Elizabeth is! That's why he acts so queerly! That's why he ran off like that – to warn her that her brother was there!'

'You may be right, George,' said Peter, considering the matter. 'Yes – perhaps he *does* know where she is! Well – all the more reason why we should go up tomorrow and see him! We'll ask him straight out if he knows where the girl is – and watch his face. He's sure to give himself away if he *does* know where she is – even if he swears he doesn't!'

'We'll tell Charles to come too,' said Jack. 'If *he* thinks Tom knows his sister's hiding-place, I've no doubt he'll be able to make him tell it!'

'Right,' said Peter. 'Well – tomorrow may be exciting. We'll just see!'

Eighteen

Peter goes mad

THE next evening the Seven took their bicycles and went riding to Warner's Stables once more, leaving a message at Bramble Cottage for Charles to follow, if he wished. He was out when they called.

Harry and the stable-girl were carting straw about the yard, but Tom was nowhere to be seen.

'He asked if he could work down in the fields today,' said Harry. 'Not in the stables. You could bike down to them, if you want him. He's a bit touchy today, is old Tom!'

'If someone called Charles comes along, tell him where we are,' said Peter. 'That's the boy who was with us yesterday.'

They rode down to the fields, and saw Tom in the distance exercising ponies round the meadow. They shouted to him and waved.

He stopped and looked hard at them all. Then he waved back and came cantering over.

'Sorry I'm busy,' he said. 'Is there anything you want?'

'Yes!' said Peter, putting his bicycle by the gate and climbing over the top bar. 'Tom – I want to ask you a question. Do you know where Elizabeth Sonning is hiding? *Do* you?'

A frightened look came into Tom's face. 'Why should I

know that?' he said. 'Don't be crazy!' And with that he kicked his heels against the pony's side and galloped off!

'He does know! He does!' said Jack. 'And he won't tell.' He turned to Peter and looked suddenly astonished. 'Why, Peter – what on earth's the matter? Why are you looking like that?'

Peter did indeed look queer – astonished – bewildered – as if someone had knocked him on the head. Jack shook him, quite scared.

'Peter! What is it?'

'Gosh – of *course* he knows where Elizabeth is!' said Peter. 'Nobody in the world knows better where Elizabeth hides out! Nobody!'

'Peter!' cried everyone, wondering if he had suddenly gone mad. What in the world did he mean?

He didn't answer, but did something very surprising. He lifted his bicycle over the gate into the field, mounted it and rode over the grass after Tom, who was still cantering along, on the pony.

The Seven stared open-mouthed. No doubt about it – Peter had gone off his head! Now he was shouting at the top of his voice.

'Come here, you fathead! Everything's all right! Elizabeth! COME HERE, I say! I've got good news for you! Elizabeth! ELIZABETH!'

'Mad,' said Jack, looking quite scared. They all stood and watched, really amazed.

Now Peter was cycling quite near to Tom and his rather frightened pony, and he was still shouting.

'Everything's all right, I tell you! Lucy Howell confessed *she* took the money! Everyone knows it wasn't you! WILL you stop, you ass, and listen to me?'

And at last the pony stopped, and the rider allowed Peter to cycle up and jump off by its side. The six by the gate poured into the field to hear what was happening.

Peter was out of breath, but he still talked. 'You're Elizabeth! I know you are! I *knew* your brother reminded me of someone – and I suddenly saw the likeness just now at the gate! Elizabeth, it's all right. Your name's cleared. And look – there's your brother at the gate. Come now – you *are* Elizabeth, aren't you?'

Tears began to fall down the girl's face. 'Yes – I *am* Elizabeth Sonning! Oh, is it true that Lucy said she took the money? I thought she had – but I wasn't sure. Nobody will think me a thief any more?'

'Nobody,' said Peter. 'My word, you're a plucky kid, aren't you – getting a job as a stable-boy, and working hard like this! Where did you hide at night? How . . . ?'

'Oh – there's Charles!' cried Elizabeth, suddenly, though the Seven still couldn't help thinking of her as Tom, of course! The girl galloped her pony over to Charles, shouting to him: 'Charles! Charles! Oh, I'm so glad to see you!'

She almost fell off her pony into his arms, and the two hugged one another tightly. The Seven went over to them, feeling excited and pleased. What a surprising ending to the problem they had been puzzling over so long!

'Well, you monkey!' said Charles, who suddenly looked much younger. 'What have you got to say for yourself? Bringing me over from France like this – having everyone hunting for you? Where have you been hiding? How did you get in and out of Granny's house? Why . . . ?'

'Oh, Charles – I'll answer all your questions!' said Elizabeth, half-crying and half-laughing. 'But let's go to Granny's, do let's. I do want to hug her, I do want to tell her everything's all right!'

'Come on, then,' said Charles, putting his arm round his sister. He turned to the Seven. 'You kids can come too,' he said. 'We've a lot to thank you for – and I'm longing to know how you spotted that this dirty, untidy, smelly stable-boy was no other than my naughty little sister Elizabeth.'

Nineteen

A jolly good finish

THEY all went out of the field, and took the path that led down to Bramble Cottage. The Seven were very thrilled to be in at the finish. To their great disgust they met Susie on her bicycle, riding along with a friend.

'Hallo!' she called cheekily. 'Solved your silly mystery yet?'

'Yes!' said Jack. 'And that boy Tom was Elizabeth – dressed up like a stable-boy! *You'd* never have thought of that in a hundred years!'

'Oh, but I knew it!' said the aggravating Susie. 'Shan't tell you how! But I knew it!' And away she went, waving her cheeky hand at them.

'She's a terrible fibber,' said Janet. 'I suppose she *couldn't* have guessed, could she, Jack?'

'I wouldn't put it past her,' said Jack, with a groan. 'Anyway, she'll keep on and on saying she knew. *Why* did I tell her just now?'

'Goodness knows,' said Peter. 'You'd better safety-pin your mouth, Jack! Well – here we are at the cottage. Won't the old granny be pleased?'

She was! She hugged the brown-faced, short-haired girl and kissed her and fondled her, happy tears streaming down her face.

Miss Wardle rushed indoors and brought out biscuits

and lemonade for everyone. Scamper, who was there as usual, of course, was delighted to have two fine biscuits presented to him.

'Elizabeth! Now where did you hide? And are those *my* riding-breeches?' asked Charles, pulling at them. 'Where did you get them?'

'From your chest of drawers here,' said Elizabeth. 'I knew nobody would miss them. They're rather big for me, though. And I've made them very dirty! I hid in the hay-loft at the stables each night, with just a rug to cover me. I was quite warm and cosy.'

'So you *did* take that rug!' said Miss Wardle. 'I thought so! And all that food too, I suppose?'

'Yes. You see, I'd no money left after paying my fare down here,' said Elizabeth. 'At least, I had fivepence, that's all. So I had to get a job – but you're only paid once a week, so I had to have food till my wages were due – I couldn't go without eating!'

'You poor child!' said Miss Wardle. 'Bless you, I knew you were innocent, I knew you weren't a thief! Yes, and I cooked special tarts and pies for you, my little dear, and left them out, hoping you'd come and take them.'

'Oh – thank you!' said Elizabeth. 'I did wonder why there was such a *lot* of food in the larder – and food I especially liked!'

'Why did you tell us that you had met – well, met *yourself* in Gorton, and all that?' asked Peter, puzzled.

'Only to put you off the scent,' said Elizabeth. 'I thought if people imagined I was off to France to find Charles, they wouldn't guess I was hiding near Granny's. I had to come near Granny's because of getting food, you see – and, anyway, I wanted to *feel* I was near somebody belonging to me, I was so miserable.'

'How did you get into the house, Elizabeth?' said Miss Wardle, and Charles chimed in with:

'Yes – how did you?'

And Peter added, 'Why, the other night we all watched here in the garden – but, how very funny, you were here too, Elizabeth, pretending to watch for yourself – you were Tom, up that tree! *Were* you up the tree?'

Elizabeth laughed. 'Yes, of course. That tree has a branch that goes to the bathroom window – and I know how to open the window from the outside and slip in – I'll show you, it's quite easy if you have a pocket-knife. But I'm getting too large to squeeze through it now, really! It really made me laugh to think of everyone watching and waiting – and there was I, up the tree, waiting to slip through the window. I got a lovely lot of food that night – did you see my torch shining in the downstairs rooms? And I was just sliding down the tree again when I heard the police knocking on the front door.'

'And you told us not to tell the police you were there – because you knew your pockets were full of food!' said Peter, with a chuckle. 'Yes, I think your brother's right. You really are a monkey.'

'But I was a very, very good stable-boy,' said Elizabeth, earnestly. 'Granny, Mr Warner said he was very pleased with me, and he even promised me a rise in wages if I went on working so hard! Can I go on being a stable-boy? It's nicer than being at school.'

'Certainly not!' said her grandmother, smiling. 'You'll go back to school and be welcomed there by everyone –

and you'll work hard and be top of the exams, although you've missed a week and a half!'

'But what *I* want to know is – how did *you*, Peter, realize so suddenly that Tom the stable-boy was Elizabeth?' asked Charles.

'Well – I suddenly saw the likeness between you,' said Peter. 'And then somehow the bits of the jigsaw all fell into place, if you know what I mean! And I was so afraid that Elizabeth would run off again when she saw you, as she did when she heard you were at the stables yesterday, that I just felt I had to cycle at top speed after her pony and yell at her!'

'I was never so surprised in my life as when you came at me and my pony at sixty miles an hour on your bike, yelling at the top of your voice,' said Elizabeth. 'But I'm glad you did. Granny, I'm coming here for the holidays, aren't I? Can I have these children to play sometimes?'

'Of course!' said her grandmother. 'I shall always be glad to see them. There's only one thing I'm sad about Elizabeth – your hair! *What* a pity you hacked it short like that. It was so soft and pretty!'

'I had to, Granny,' said Elizabeth. 'I did it with your nail scissors when I came one night to take Charles's riding-breeches to wear – and I took his jersey too, though it's so dirty now I don't expect he recognizes it! Oh, Granny – I'm so very happy. You can't *think* how different I feel!'

'We'd better go,' said Peter to the others, in a low voice. 'Let's leave them all to be happy together. Come on, say good-bye.'

They said good-bye, and Scamper gravely shook paws

as well. Then away they went on their bicycles, Scamper running beside them.

'What a jolly fine finish!' said Jack. 'Who would have thought it would end like that? I feel rather happy myself! When's the next meeting, Peter?'

'Tomorrow – and we'll have a celebration to mark our success!' said Peter. 'Everyone must bring some food or drink. And we'll have to think of a new password, of course. What shall it be?'

'Stable-boy!' said Jack at once.

Well, it's quite a good one – but I mustn't tell you if it's the *right* one. Knock on the door of the shed, say 'Stable-boy!' and see if the Secret Seven let you in!

SECRET SEVEN ON THE TRAIL

CONTENTS

One

The Secret Seven meet

'MUMMY, have you got anything we could have to drink?' asked Janet. 'And to eat too?'

'But you've only *just* finished your breakfast!' said Mummy in surprise. 'And you each had two sausages. You can't possibly want anything more yet.'

'Well, we're having the very last meeting of the Secret Seven this morning,' said Janet. 'Down in the shed. We don't think it's worth while meeting when we all go back to school, nothing exciting ever happens then.'

'We're going to meet again when the Christmas holidays come,' said Peter. 'Aren't we, Scamper, old boy?'

The golden spaniel wagged his tail hard, and gave a small bark.

'He says, he hopes he can come to the last meeting too,' said Janet. 'Of course you can, Scamper.'

'He didn't say that,' said Peter, grinning. 'He said that if there were going to be snacks of any kind at this meeting, he'd like to join in!'

'Woof,' agreed Scamper, and put his paw up on Peter's knee.

'I'll give you lemons, and some sugar, and you can make your own lemonade,' said Mummy. 'You like doing that, don't you? And you can go and see if there are any rock-buns left in the tin in the larder. They'll be stale, but I know you don't mind that!'

'Oh, thanks, Mummy,' said Janet. 'Come on Peter. We'd better get the things now, because the others will be here soon!'

They ran off to the larder, Scamper panting behind. Rock-buns! Stale or not, Scamper liked those as much as the children did.

Janet took some lemons, and went to get the sugar from her mother. Peter emptied the stale rock-buns on to a plate, and the two of them, followed by Scamper, went down to the shed. Janet had the lemon-squeezer and a big jug of water. It was fun to make lemonade.

They pushed open the shed door. On it were the letters S.S. in green – S.S. for the Secret Seven!

'Our Secret Society has been going for some time now,' said Janet, beginning to squeeze a lemon. 'I'm not a bit tired of it, are you, Peter?'

'Good gracious, no!' said Peter. 'Why, think of all the adventures we've had, and the exciting things we've done! But I do think it's sensible not to bother about the Secret Seven meetings till the hols. For one thing, in this Christmas term the days get dark very quickly, and we have to be indoors.'

'Yes, and nothing much happens then,' said Janet. 'Oh, Scamper – you won't like that squeezed out lemon-skin, you silly dog! Drop it!'

Scamper dropped it. He certainly didn't like it! He sat with his tongue hanging out, looking most disgusted. Peter glanced at his watch.

'Nearly time for the others to come,' he said. 'I hope they'll agree to this being the last meeting till Christmas. We'd better collect all the badges from them, and put them in a safe place. If we don't, someone is bound to lose one.'

'Or that silly sister of Jack's will take it and wear it herself,' said Janet. 'What's her name – Susie? Aren't you glad I'm not annoying to you, like Susie is to Jack, Peter?'

'Well, you're pretty annoying sometimes,' said Peter, and immediately got a squirt of lemon-juice in his eye from an angry Janet! 'Oh, don't do that. Don't you know that lemon-juice smarts like anything? Stop it, Janet!'

Janet stopped it. 'I'd better not waste the juice,' she said. 'Ah, here comes someone.'

Scamper barked as somebody walked up the path and rapped on the door.

'Password!' called Peter, who never opened the door to anyone until the correct password was called.

'Pickled onions!' said a voice, and giggled.

That was the latest password of the Secret Seven, suggested by Colin, whose mother had been pickling onions on the day of the last meeting they had had. It was such a silly password that everyone had laughed, and Peter had said they would have it till they thought of a better one.

'Got your badge?' said Peter, opening the door.

Outside stood Barbara. She displayed her badge proudly. 'It's a new one,' she said. 'My old one's got so dirty, so I made this.'

'Very good,' said Peter. 'Come in. Look, here come three others.'

He shut the door again, and Barbara sat down on a

box beside Janet, and watched her stirring the lemonade. Rat-a-tat! Scamper barked as knocking came at
the door again.

'Password!' called out Peter, Janet and Barbara
together.

'Pickled onions!' yelled back everyone. Peter flung
open the door and scowled.

'How MANY times am I to tell you not to yell out the
password!' he said. 'Now everyone in hearing distance
has heard it.'

'Well, you all yelled out PASSWORD at the tops of
your voices,' said Jack. 'Anyway, we can easily choose
a new one.' He looked slyly at George, who had come in
with him. 'George thought it was pickled cabbage, and
we had to tell him it wasn't.'

'Well, of all the –' began Peter, but just then another knock came on the door and Scamper growled.

'Password!' called Peter.

'Pickled onions!' came his mother's voice, and she laughed. 'If that *is* a password! I've brought you some home-made peppermints, just to help the last meeting along.'

'Oh. Thanks, Mummy,' said Janet, and opened the door. She took the peppermints and gave them to Peter. Peter frowned round, when his mother had gone.

'There you are, you see,' he said. 'It just happened to be my mother who heard the password, but it might have been anybody. Now who's still missing?'

'There's me here, and you, George, Jack, Barbara and Pam,' said Janet. 'Colin's missing. Oh, here he comes.'

Rat-tat! Scamper gave a little welcoming bark. He knew every S.S. member quite well. Colin gave the password and was admitted. Now the Secret Seven were complete.

'Good,' said Peter. 'Sit down, Colin. We'll get down to business as soon as Janet pours out the lemonade. Buck up, Janet!'

Two

No more meetings till Christmas!

JANET poured out mugs of the lemonade, and Peter handed round the rock-buns.

'A bit stale,' he said, 'but nice and curranty. Two each and one for old Scamper. Sorry, Scamper; but, after all, you're not a *real* member of the Secret Seven, or you could have two.'

'He couldn't,' said Jack. 'There are only fifteen buns. And anyway, I *always* count him in as a real member.'

'You can't. We're the Secret *Seven,* and Scamper makes eight,' said Peter. 'But he can always come with us. Now listen, this is to be the last meeting, and –'

There were surprised cries at once.

'The *last* meeting! Why, what's happening?'

'The *last* one! Surely you're not going to stop the Secret Seven?'

'Oh but, Peter – surely you're not meaning –'

'Just let me *speak,*' said Peter. 'It's to be the last meeting till the holidays come again. Tomorrow all of us boys go back to school, and the girls go to their school the day after. Nothing ever happens in term-time, and anyway we're too busy to look for adventure, so –'

'But something *might* happen,' said Colin. 'You just never know. I think it's a silly idea to stop the Secret Seven for the term-time. I do really.'

302

'So do I,' said Pam. 'I like belonging to it, and wearing my badge, and remembering the password.'

'Well, you can still wear your badges if you like,' said Peter, 'though I *had* thought of collecting them today, as we're all wearing them, and keeping them till our meeting next hols.'

'I'm not giving *mine* up,' said Jack, firmly. 'And you needn't be afraid I'll let my sister Susie get it, either, because I've got a perfectly good hiding-place for it.'

'And suppose, just *suppose*, something turned up in term-time,' said Colin, earnestly. 'Suppose one of us happened on something queer, something that ought to be looked into. What would we do if the Secret Seven was disbanded till Christmas?'

'Nothing ever turns up in term-time,' repeated Peter, who liked getting his own way. 'And anyway I've got to work jolly hard this term. My father wasn't at all keen on my last report.'

'All right. You work hard, and keep out of the Society till Christmas,' said Jack. 'I'll run it with Janet. It can be the Secret Six till then. S.S. will stand for that as much as for Secret Seven.'

That didn't please Peter at all. He frowned. 'No,' he said. 'I'm the head. But seeing that you all seem to disagree with me, I'll say this. We won't have any *regular* meetings, like we have been having, but only call one if anything *does* happen to turn up. And you'll see I'm right. Nothing will happen!'

'We keep our badges, then, and have a password?' said Colin. 'We're still a very live Society, even if nothing happens? And we call a meeting at once if something does?'

'Yes,' said everyone, looking at Peter. They loved being the Secret Seven. It made them feel important, even if, as Colin said, nothing happened for them to look into.

'All right,' said Peter. 'What about a new password?'

Everyone thought hard. Jack looked at Scamper, who seemed to be thinking too. 'What about Scamper's name?' he said. ' "Scamper" would be a good password.'

'It wouldn't,' said Janet. 'Every time anyone gave the password Scamper would think he was being called!'

'Let's have *my* dog's name – Rover,' said Pam.

'No, have my aunt's dog's name,' said Jack. 'Cheeky Charlie. That's a good password.'

'Yes! Cheeky Charlie! We'll have that,' said Peter.

'Nobody would ever think of that for a password. Right – Cheeky Charlie it is!'

The rock-buns were passed round for the second time. Scamper eyed them longingly. He had had his. Pam took pity on him and gave him half hers, and Barbara did the same.

Scamper then fixed his eyes mournfully on Jack, who quickly gave him a large piece of his bun too.

'Well!' said Peter. 'Scamper's had more than any real member of the Secret Seven! He'll be thinking he can run the whole Society soon!'

'Wuff,' said Scamper, thumping his tail on the ground, and looking at Peter's bun.

The lemonade was finished. The last crumb of cake had been licked up by Scamper. The sun came out and shone down through the shed window.

'Come on, let's go out and play,' said Peter, getting up. 'School tomorrow! Well, these have been jolly good hols. Now, Secret Seven, you all know the password, don't you? You probably won't have to use it till the Christmas holidays, so just make up your minds to remember it.'

Three

The Famous Five

SCHOOL began for the boys next day, and they all trooped
off with their satchels and bags. The girls went off the
day after. All the Secret Seven wore their little badges
with S.S. embroidered on the button. It was fun to see the
other children looking enviously at them, wishing they
could have one too.

'No, you can't,' said Janet, when the other girls asked
her if they could join. 'It's a *Secret* Society. I'm not
supposed even to talk about it.'

'Well, I don't see why you can't make it a bit bigger
and let *us* come in,' said the others.

'You can't have more than seven in our Society,' said
Janet. 'And we've got seven. You go and make Secret
Societies of your own!'

That was an unfortunate thing to say! Kate and Susie,
who was Jack's tiresome sister, immediately went off to
make a Society of their own! How very annoying!

They got Harry, Jeff and Sam as well as themselves.
Five of them. And then, to the intense annoyance of the
Secret Seven, these five appeared at school with badges
of their own!

On the buttons they wore were embroidered two
letters, not S.S., of course, but F.F. Everyone crowded
round to ask what F.F. meant.

'It means "Famous Five",' said Susie. 'We've named

ourselves after the Famous Five in the "Five" books!
Much better idea than "Secret Seven".'

Susie was very irritating to poor Jack. 'You haven't
got nearly such a good Society as *we* have,' she said.
'Our badges are bigger, we've got a splendid password,
which I wouldn't *dream* of telling you, and we have a
secret sign, too. *You* haven't got that!'

'What's your secret sign?' said Jack, crossly. '*I've* never
seen you make it.'

'Of course not. I tell you it's a *secret* one!' said Susie.
'And we're meeting every single Saturday morning. And,
what's more, we've got an adventure going already!'

'I don't believe you,' said Jack. 'Anyway, you're just
a copy-cat. It was *our* idea! You're mean.'

'Well, you wouldn't let me belong to your silly Secret
Seven,' said Susie, annoyingly. 'Now I belong to the
Famous Five, and I tell you, we've got an adventure
already!'

Jack didn't know whether to believe her or not. He
thought Susie must be the most tiresome sister in the
world. He wished he had one like Janet. He went
gloomily to Peter and told him all that Susie had said.

'Don't take any notice of her,' said Peter. 'Famous
Five indeed! They'll soon get tired of meeting and playing about.'

The Famous Five Society was very annoying to the
Secret Seven that term. The members wore their big
badges every single day. Kate and Susie huddled together
in corners at break each morning and talked in excited
whispers, as if something really *was* happening.

Harry, Jeff and Sam did the same at their school,

which annoyed Peter, Colin, Jack and George very much. They met in the summer-house in Jack's garden, and Susie actually ordered Jack to keep out of the garden when the 'Famous Five' held their meetings in the summer-house!

'As if I shall keep out of my own garden!' said Jack, indignantly, to Peter. 'But I say, Peter, I believe they really *have* got hold of something, you know. I think something *is* up. Wouldn't it be awful if *they* had an adventure and we didn't? Susie would crow like anything.'

Peter thought about this. 'It's up to you to find out about it,' he said, at last. 'After all, they've stolen our idea, and they're doing it to annoy us. You try and find out what's up, Jack. We'll soon put a stop to it!'

So Jack went to hide in a bush at the back of the summer-house when he heard that Susie had planned another meeting there for that Saturday morning. But unfortunately Susie was looking out of the bedroom window just then, and saw him squeezing into the laurel bush!

She gazed down in rage, and then suddenly she smiled. She sped downstairs to meet the other four at the front gate, instead of waiting for them to go down to the summer-house.

They all came together, and Susie began to whisper excitedly.

'Jack's going to try and find out what we're doing! He's hidden himself in the laurel bush at the back of the summer-house to listen to all we say!'

'I'll go and pull him out,' said Harry at once.

'No, don't,' said Susie. 'I've got a better idea. Let's go

down to the summer-house, whisper the password so that
he can't hear it, and then begin to talk as we really *had*
found an adventure!'

'But why?' said Kate.

'You're silly! Don't you see that Jack will believe it all,
and if we mention places such as that old house up on the
hill, Tigger's Barn, he'll tell the Secret Seven, and –'

'And they'll all go and investigate it and find there's
nothing there!' said Kate, giggling. 'What fun!'

'Yes. And we can mention names too. We'll talk about
Stumpy Dick, and – Twisty Tom, and make Jack think
we're right in the very middle of something,' said Susie.

'And we could go to Tigger's Barn ourselves and wait

till the Secret Seven come, and have a good laugh at them!' said Jeff, grinning. 'Come on, let's go down to the summer-house now, Susie. Jack will be wondering why we are so late.'

'No giggling, anybody!' Susie warned them, 'and just back me up in all I say. And be as solemn as you can. I'll go down first, and you can all come one by one, and don't forget to *whisper* the password, because he mustn't hear *that.*'

She sped down the garden and into the summer-house. Out of the corner of her eye she saw the laurel bush where poor Jack had hidden himself very uncomfortably. Susie grinned to herself. Aha! She was going to have a fine revenge on Jack for keeping her out of *his* Secret Society!

One by one the others came to the summer-house. They whispered the password, much to Jack's annoyance. He would dearly have loved to pass it on to the Secret Seven! But he couldn't hear a word.

However, he heard plenty when the meeting really began. He couldn't help it, of course, because the Famous Five talked so loudly. Jack didn't guess that it was done on purpose, so that he might hear every word.

He was simply amazed at what the Famous Five said. Why, they seemed to be in the very middle of a Most Exciting Adventure!

Four

Susie tells a tale

SUSIE led the talking. She was a good talker, and was determined to puzzle Jack as much as she could.

'I've found out where those rogues are meeting,' she said. 'It's an important piece of news, so please listen. I've tracked them down at last!'

Jack could hardly believe his ears. He listened hard.

'Tell us, Susie,' said Harry, playing up well.

'It's at Tigger's Barn,' said Susie, enjoying herself. 'That old, deserted house up on the hill. A tumbledown old place, just right for rogues to meet in. Far away from anywhere.'

'Oh yes. I know it,' said Jeff.

'Well, Stumpy Dick and Twisty Tom will both be there,' said Susie.

There were 'oooohs' and 'ahs' from her listeners, and Jack very nearly said 'Ooooh' too. Stumpy Dick and Twisty Tom – good gracious! What *had* the Famous Five got on to?

'They're planning something we must find out about,' said Susie, raising her voice a little, to make sure that Jack could hear. 'And we've simply *got* to do something.

So one or two of us must go to Tigger's Barn at the right time and hide ourselves.'

'I'll go with you, Susie,' said Jeff at once.

Jack felt surprised when he heard that. Jeff was a very timid boy, and not at all likely to go and hide in a deserted place like Tigger's Barn. He listened hard.

'All right. You and I will go together,' said Susie. 'It will be dangerous, but what do we care for that? We are the Famous Five!'

'Hurrah!' said Kate and Sam.

'When do we go?' said Jeff.

'Well,' said Susie, 'I *think* they will meet there on Tuesday night. Can you come with me then, Jeff?'

'Certainly,' said Jeff, who would never have *dreamed* of going to Tigger's Barn at night if Susie's tale had been true.

Jack, out in the bush, felt more and more surprised. He also felt a great respect for the Famous Five. My word! They were as good as the Secret Seven! Fancy their getting on to an adventure like this! What a good thing he had managed to hide and hear about it!

He longed to go to Peter and tell him all he had heard. He wondered how his sister Susie knew anything about this affair. Blow Susie! It was just like her to make a Secret Society and then find an adventure for it.

'Suppose Stumpy Dick discovers you?' said Kate.

'I shall knock him to the ground,' said Jeff in a very valiant voice.

This was going a bit too far. Not even the Famous Five could imagine Jeff facing up to anyone. Kate gave a sudden giggle.

That set Sam off, and he gave one of his extraordinary snorts. Susie frowned. If the meeting began to giggle and snort like this, Jack would certainly know it wasn't serious. That would never do.

She frowned heavily at the others. 'Shut up!' she whispered. 'If we begin to giggle Jack won't believe a word.'

'I c-c-can't help it,' said Kate, who never could stop giggling once she began. 'Oh, Sam, please don't snort again!'

'Sh!' said Susie, angrily. 'Don't spoil it all.' Then she raised her voice again so that Jack could hear. 'Well, Famous Five, that's all for today. Meet again when you get your orders, and remember, don't say a word to ANY-ONE about Tigger's Barn. This is OUR adventure!'

'I bet the Secret Seven wish they could hear about this,' said Jeff, in a loud voice. 'It makes me laugh to think they don't know anything.'

He laughed, and that was the signal for everyone to let themselves go. Kate giggled again, Sam snorted, Susie roared, and so did Harry. They all thought of Jack out in the laurel bush, drinking in every word of their ridiculous story, and then they laughed all the more. Jack listened crossly. How dare they laugh at the Secret Seven like that?

'Come on,' said Susie, at last. 'This meeting is over. Let's go and get a ball and have a game. I wonder where Jack is? He might like to play too.'

As they all knew quite well where Jack was, this made them laugh again, and they went up the garden path in a very good temper. What a joke to play on a member of the Secret Seven! Would he rush off at once and call a meeting? Would the Secret Seven go to Tigger's Barn on Tuesday night in the dark?

'Susie, you don't *really* mean to go up to Tigger's Barn on Tuesday night, do you?' said Jeff, as they went up the path.

'Well, I did think of it at first,' said Susie. 'But it would be silly to. It's a long way, and it's dark at night now, and anyway, the Secret Seven might not go, and it would be awfully silly for any of us to go and hide there for nothing!'

'Yes, it would,' said Jeff, much relieved. 'But you'll be able to see if Jack does, won't you, Susie? If he slips off somewhere on Tuesday night, won't we have a laugh!'

'We certainly will!' said Susie. 'Oh, I *do* hope he does! I'll tell him it was all a trick, when he comes back, and won't he be FURIOUS!'

Five

Jack tells the news

JACK crept carefully out of the laurel bush as soon as he felt sure that the others were safely out of the way. He dusted himself down and looked round. Nobody was in sight.

He debated with himself what to do. Was it important enough to call a meeting of the Secret Seven? No – he would go and find Peter and tell him first. Peter could decide whether to have a meeting or not.

On the way to Peter's house Jack met George. 'Hallo!' said George, 'you look very solemn! What's up? Have you had a row at home or something?'

'No,' said Jack. 'But I've just found out that the Famous Five are in the middle of something. I heard Susie telling them, down in our summer-house. I was in the laurel bush outside.'

'Is it important?' asked George. 'I mean, your sister Susie's a bit of a nuisance, isn't she? You don't want to pay too much attention to her. She's conceited enough already.'

'Yes, I know,' said Jack. 'But she's clever, you know. And after all, *we* managed to get into a good many adventures, didn't we? And there's really no reason why the Famous Five shouldn't, too, if they keep their eyes and ears open. Listen, and I'll tell you what I heard.'

He told George, and George was most impressed.
'Tigger's Barn!' he said. 'Well, that *would* be a good
meeting-place for rogues who wanted to meet without
being seen. But how did Susie get hold of the names of
the men? I say, Jack, it would be absolutely *maddening*
if the Famous Five hit on something important before
we did!'

'That's what *I* think,' said Jack. 'Especially as Susie's
the ring-leader. She's always trying to boss me, and she
would be worse than ever if her silly Society discovered
some gang or plot. Let's find Peter, shall we? I was on
the way to him when I met you.'

'I'll go with you, then,' said George. 'I'm sure Peter
will think it's important. Come on!'

So two solemn boys walked up the path to Peter's house,
and went round the back to find him. He was chopping
up firewood, one of his Saturday morning jobs. He was
very pleased to see Jack and George.

'Oh, hallo,' he said, putting down his chopper. 'Now
I can knock off for a bit. Chopping wood is fine for about
five minutes, but an awful bore after that. My mother
doesn't like me to do it, because she thinks I'll chop my
fingers off, but Dad's hard-hearted and makes me do it
each Saturday.'

'Peter,' said Jack, 'I've got some news.'

'Oh, what?' asked Peter. 'Tell me.'

So Jack told him about how he had hidden in the laurel
bush and overheard a meeting of the Famous Five.
'They've got a password, of course,' he said, 'but I
couldn't hear it. However, they forgot to whisper once
they had said the password, and I heard every word.'

He told Peter what he had heard, but Peter didn't take it seriously. He was most annoying.

He listened to the end, and then he threw back his head and laughed. 'Oh Jack! Surely you didn't fall for all that nonsense? Susie must have been pretending. I expect that's what they do at their silly meetings – pretend they are in the middle of an adventure, and kid themselves they're clever.'

'But it all sounded absolutely serious,' said Jack, beginning to feel annoyed. 'I mean, they had no idea I was listening, they all seemed quite serious. And Jeff was ready to go and investigate on Tuesday evening!'

'What, *Jeff! Can* you imagine that little coward of a Jeff going to look for a *mouse*, let alone Stumpy Dick and the other fellow, whatever his name is!' said Peter, laughing again. 'He'd run a mile before he'd go to Tigger's Barn at night. That sister of yours was just putting up a bit of make-believe, Jack, silly kid's stuff, like pretending to play at Red Indians or something, that's all.'

'Then you don't think it's worth while calling a meeting of the Secret Seven and asking some of us to go to Tigger's Barn on Tuesday night?' said Jack, in a hurt voice.

'No, I don't,' said Peter. 'I'm not such a fathead as to believe in Susie's fairy-tales.'

'But suppose the Famous Five go, and discover something *we* ought to discover?' said George.

'Well, if Jack sees Susie and Jeff creeping off somewhere on Tuesday evening, he can follow them,' said Peter, still grinning. 'But they won't go! You'll see I'm right. It's all make-believe!'

'All right,' said Jack, getting up. 'If that's what you think there's no use in talking about it any longer. But you'll be sorry if you find you ought to have called a meeting and didn't, Peter! Susie may be a nuisance, but she's jolly clever, *too* clever, and I wouldn't be a bit surprised if the Famous Five weren't beginning an adventure *we* ought to have!'

Peter began to chop wood again, still smiling in a most superior way. Jack marched off, his head in the air, very cross. George went with him. They said nothing for a little while, and then George looked doubtfully at Jack.

'Peter's very certain about it all, isn't he?' he said. 'Do you think he's right? After all, he's the chief of the Secret Seven. We ought to obey.'

'Look here, George. I'm going to wait and see what Susie does on Tuesday evening,' said Jack. 'If she stays at home, I'll know Peter's right, and it's all make-believe on her part. But if she goes off by herself, or Jeff comes to call for her, I'll know there's something up, and I'll follow them!'

'That's a good idea,' said George. 'I'll come with you, if you like.'

'I shan't know what time they'll go, though, if they *do* go,' said Jack. 'I know, you come to tea with me on Tuesday, George. Then we can follow Susie and Jeff at once, if they slip off. And if they don't go out, then we'll know it's nonsense and I'll apologize to Peter the next morning for being such a fathead.'

'Right,' said George, pleased. 'I'll come to tea on Tuesday, then, and we'll keep a close watch on Susie. I'm glad I haven't got a sister like that! You never know what she's up to!'

When Jack got home, he went straight to his mother. 'Mother,' he said, 'may I have George to tea on Tuesday, please?'

Susie was there, reading in a corner. She pricked up her ears at once, and grinned in delight. She guessed that Jack and George meant to follow her and Jeff – if they went! All right, she would take the joke a little farther.

'Oh, that reminds me, Mother,' she said. 'Could I have *Jeff* to tea on Tuesday too? It's rather important! I can? Thank you very much!'

Six

Susie's little trick

JACK was pleased when he heard Susie asking for Jeff to come to tea on Tuesday.

'That just proves it!' he said to himself. 'They will slip off to Tigger's Barn together. Peter was quite wrong! Let me see. Tuesday is the evening Mother goes to a Committee Meeting, so Susie and Jeff can go off without anyone bothering. And so can I! Aha! George and I will be on their track all right.'

Jack told George, who agreed that it did look as if there really was something in all that had been said at the meeting of the Famous Five.

'We'll keep a jolly good watch on Susie and Jeff, and follow them at once,' said George. 'They'll be most annoyed to find we are with them in Tigger's Barn! We'd better take a torch, Jack. It will be dark.'

'Not awfully dark,' said Jack. 'There will be a moon. But it might be cloudy so we certainly will take a torch.'

Susie told Jeff, with many giggles, that Jack had asked George to tea on Tuesday. 'So I've asked for you to come too,' she said. 'And after tea, Jeff, you and I will slip out secretly, and make Jack and George think we are off to Tigger's Barn, but really and truly we will only be hiding somewhere, and we'll go back and play as soon as we are certain Jack and George have gone off to try and follow us to Tigger's Barn! Oh, dear, they'll go all the way there, and won't find a thing, except a horrid old tumble-down house!'

'It will serve them right!' said Jeff. 'All I can say is that I'm jolly glad *I'm* not going off to that lonely place at night.'

Tuesday afternoon came, and with it came Jeff and George after school, on their way to tea with Jack and Susie. The two boys walked with Jack, who pretended to be astonished that Jeff should go to tea with Susie.

'Going to play with her dolls?' he asked. 'Or perhaps you're going to spring-clean the dolls' house?'

Jeff went red. 'Don't be a fathead,' he said. 'I've got my new railway set with me. We're going to play with that.'

'But it takes ages to set out on the floor,' said Jack, surprised.

'Well, what of it?' said Jeff, scowling. Then he re-membered that Jack and George thought that he and Susie were going off to Tigger's Barn, and would naturally imagine that he wouldn't have time to play such a lengthy game as trains. He grinned to himself. Let Jack be puzzled! It would do him good!

They all had a very good tea, and then went to the playroom upstairs. Jeff began to set out his railway lines. Jack and George would have liked to help, but they were afraid that Susie might point out that Jeff was *her* guest, not theirs. Susie had a very sharp tongue when she liked!

So they contented themselves with trying to make a rather complicated model aeroplane, keeping a sharp eye on Susie and Jeff all the time.

Very soon Jack's mother put her head in at the door.

'Well, I'm off to my Committee Meeting,' she said. 'You must both go home at eight o'clock, Jeff and George – and Jack, if I'm not back in time for your supper, make yourself something, and then go and have your baths.'

'Right, Mother,' said Jack. 'Come and say good-night to us when you get back.'

As soon as her mother had gone, Susie went all mysterious. She winked at Jeff, who winked back. Jack saw the winks, of course. They meant him to! He was on the alert at once. Ah, those two were probably going to slip out into the night!

'Jeff, come and see the new clock we've got downstairs,' said Susie. 'It has a little man who comes out at the top and strikes a hammer on an anvil to mark every quarter of an hour. It is nearly a quarter past seven, let's go and watch him come out.'

'Right,' said Jeff, and the two went out, nudging each other, and laughing.

'There they go,' said George. 'Do we follow them straightaway?'

Jack went to the door. 'They've gone downstairs,' he said. 'They will get their coats out of the hall cupboard. We'll give them a minute to put them on, then we'll get ours. We shall hear the front door bang, I expect. It won't take us a minute to follow them.'

In about a minute they heard the front door being opened, and then it shut rather quietly, as if it was not really meant to be heard.

'Did you hear that?' asked Jack. 'They shut it very quietly. Come on, we'll pull on our coats and follow. We don't want to track them too closely, or they'll see us. We

will jolly well surprise them when they get to Tigger's Barn, though!'

They put on their coats, and opened the front door. It was fairly light outside because of the rising moon. They took a torch with them, in case the clouds became thick.

There was no sign of Jeff and Susie.

'They have gone at top speed, I should think!' said Jack, closing the door behind him. 'Come on, we know the way to Tigger's Barn, even if we don't spot Jeff and Susie in front of us.'

They went down the garden path. They did not hear the giggles that followed them! Jeff and Susie were hiding behind the big hall curtains, and were now watching Jack and George going down the path. They clutched one another as they laughed. What a fine joke they had played on the two boys!

Seven

At Tigger's Barn

JACK and George had no idea at all that they had left Jeff and Susie behind them in the hall. They quite imagined that the two were well in front of them, hurrying to Tigger's Barn! They hurried too, but, rather to their surprise, they did not see any children in front, however much they strained their eyes in the moonlit night.

'Well, all I can say is they must have taken bicycles,' said George, at last. 'They *couldn't* have gone so quickly. Has Susie a bike, Jack?'

'Oh yes, and I bet she's lent Jeff mine,' said Jack, crossly. 'They'll be at Tigger's Barn ages before us. I hope the meeting of those men isn't over before we get there. I don't want Susie and Jeff to hear everything without us hearing it too!'

Tigger's Barn was about a mile away. It was up on a lonely hill, hemmed in by trees. Once it had been part of a farmhouse, which had been burnt down one night. Tigger's Barn was now only a tumbledown shell of a house, used by tramps who needed shelter, by jackdaws who nested in the one remaining enormous chimney, and by a big tawny owl who used it to sleep in during the daytime.

Children had played in it until they had been forbidden to in case the old walls gave way. Jack and George had

once explored it with Peter, but an old tramp had risen up from a corner and shouted at them so loudly that they had fled away.

The two boys trudged on. They came to the hill and walked up the narrow lane that led to Tigger's Barn. Still there was no sign of Jeff or Susie. Well, if they had taken bicycles, they would certainly be at Tigger's Barn by now!

They came to the old building at last. It stood there in the rather dim moonlight, looking forlorn and bony, with part of its roof missing, and its one great chimney sticking up into the night sky.

'Here we are,' whispered Jack. 'Walk quietly, because we don't want to let Jeff and Susie know we're here, or those men either, if they've come already! But everything is very quiet. I don't think the men are here.'

They kept in the shadow of a great yew hedge, and made their way on tiptoe to the back of the house. There was a front door and a back door, and both were locked, but as no window had glass in, it was easy enough for anyone to get inside the tumbledown place if they wanted to.

Jack clambered in through a downstairs window. A scuttling noise startled him, and he clutched George and made him jump.

'Don't grab me like that,' complained George, in a whisper. 'It was only a rat hurrying away. You nearly made me yell when you grabbed me so suddenly.'

'Sh!' said Jack. 'What's that?'

They listened. Something was moving high up in the great chimney that towered from the hearth in the broken-down room they were in.

'Maybe it's the owl,' said George, at last. 'Yes, listen to it hooting.'

A quavering hoot came to their ears. But it didn't really sound as if it came from the chimney. It seemed to come from outside the house, in the overgrown garden. Then an answering hoot came, but it didn't sound at all like an owl.

'Jack,' whispered George, his mouth close to Jack's ear, 'that's not an owl. It's men signalling to one another. They *are* meeting here! But where are Susie and Jeff?'

'I don't know. Hidden safely somewhere, I expect,' said Jack, suddenly feeling a bit shaky at the knees. 'We'd better hide too. Those men will be here in half a minute.'

'There's a good hiding-place over there in the hearth,' whispered George. 'We can stand there in the darkness, right under the big chimney. Come on, quick. I'm sure I can hear footsteps outside.'

The two boys ran silently to the hearth. Tramps had made fires there from time to time, and a heap of ashes half-filled the hearth. The boys stood ankle-deep in them, hardly daring to breathe.

Then a torch suddenly shone out, and raked the room with its beam. Jack and George pressed close together, hoping they did not show in the great hearth.

They heard the sound of someone climbing in through the same window they had come in by. Then a voice spoke to someone outside.

'Come on in. Nobody's here. Larry hasn't come yet. Give him the signal, Zeb, in case he's waiting about for it now.'

Somebody gave a quavering hoot again. 'Ooooo-oo-oo! Ooooo, ooo-oo-oo!'

An answering call came from some way away, and after about half a minute another man climbed in. Now there were three.

The two boys held their breath. Good gracious! They were right in the middle of something very queer! Why were these men meeting at this tumbledown place? Who were they and what were they doing?

Where were Susie and Jeff, too? Were they listening and watching as well?

'Come into the next room,' said the man who had first spoken. 'There are boxes there to sit on, and a light won't shine out there as much as it does from this room. Come on, Larry – here, Zeb, shine your torch in front.'

Eight

An uncomfortable time

THE two boys were half-glad, half-sorry that the men had gone into another room. Glad because they were now not afraid of being found, but sorry because it was now impossible to hear clearly what the men were saying.

They could hear a murmur from the next room.

Jack nudged George. 'I'm going to creep across the floor and go to the door. Perhaps I can hear what they are saying then,' he whispered.

'No, don't,' said George, in alarm. 'We'll be discovered. You're sure to make a noise!'

'I've got rubber-soled shoes on. I shan't make a sound,' whispered back Jack. 'You stay here, George. I DO wonder where Susie and Jeff are. I hope I don't bump into them anywhere.'

Jack made his way very quietly to the doorway that led to the next room. There was a broken door still hanging there, and he could peep through the crack. He saw the three men in the room beyond, sitting on old boxes, intently studying a map of some kind, and talking in low voices.

If only he could hear what they said! He tried to see what the men were like, but it was too dark. He could only hear their voices, one an educated voice speaking clearly and firmly, and the other two rough and common.

Jack hadn't the slightest idea what they were talking about. Loading and unloading. Six-two or maybe seven-ten. Points, points, points. There mustn't be a moon. Darkness, fog, mist. Points. Fog. Six-two, but it might go as long as seven-twenty. And again, points, points, points.

What in the world could they be discussing? It was maddening to hear odd words like this that made no sense. Jack strained his ears to try and make out more, but it was no use, he couldn't. He decided to edge a little nearer.

He leaned against something that gave way behind him. It was a cupboard door! Before he could stop himself Jack fell inside, landing with a soft thud. The door closed on him with a little click. He sat there, alarmed and astonished, not daring to move.

'What was that?' said one of the men.

They all listened, and at that moment a big rat ran silently round the room, keeping to the wall. One of the men picked it out in the light of his torch.

'Rats,' he said. 'This place is alive with them. That's what we heard.'

'I'm not sure,' said the man with the clear voice. Switch off that light, Zeb. Sit quietly for a bit and listen.'

The light was switched off. The men sat in utter silence, listening. Another rat scuttered over the floor.

Jack sat absolutely still in the cupboard, fearful that the men might come to find out who had made a noise. George stood in the hearth of the next room, wondering what had happened. There was such dead silence now, and darkness too!

The owl awoke in the chimney above him, and stirred

once more. Night-time! It must go hunting. It gave one soft hoot and dropped down the chimney to make its way out through the bare window.

It was as startled to find George standing at the bottom of the chimney as George was startled to feel the owl brushing his cheek. It flew silently out of the window, a big moving shadow in the dimness.

George couldn't bear it. He must get out of this chimneyplace, he must! Something else might fall down on him and touch his face softly. Where was Jack? How mean of him to go off and leave him with things that lived in chimneys! And Jack had the torch with him too. George would have given anything to flick on the light of a torch.

He crept out of the hearth, and stood in the middle of the floor, wondering what to do. What *was* Jack doing? He had said he was going to the doorway that led to the next room, to see if he could hear what the men said. But were the men there now? There wasn't a sound to be heard.

Perhaps they have slipped out of another window and gone, thought poor George. If so why doesn't Jack come back? It's too bad of him. I can't bear this much longer.

He moved over to the doorway, putting out his hands to feel if Jack was there. No, he wasn't. The next room was in black darkness, and he couldn't see a thing there. There was also complete silence. Where *was* everyone?

George felt his legs giving way at the knees. This horrible old tumbledown place! Why ever had he listened to Jack and come here with him? He was sure that Jeff and Susie hadn't been fatheads enough to come here at night.

He didn't dare to call out. Perhaps Jack was somewhere nearby, scared too. What about the Secret Seven password? What was it now? Cheeky Charlie!

If I whisper Cheeky Charlie, Jack will know it's me, he thought. It's our password. He'll know it's me, and he'll answer.

So he stood at the doorway and whispered: 'Cheeky Charlie! Cheeky Charlie!'

No answer. He tried again, a little louder this time, 'Cheeky Charlie!'

And then a torch snapped on, and caught him directly in its beam. A voice spoke to him harshly.

'What's all this? What do you know about Charlie? Come right into the room, boy, and answer my question.'

Nine

Very peculiar

GEORGE was extremely astonished. Why, the men were still there! Then where was Jack? What had happened to him? He stood there in the beam of the torch, gaping.

'Come on in,' said the voice, impatiently. 'We heard you saying "Cheeky Charlie". Have you got a message from him?'

George gaped still more. A message from him? From Cheeky Charlie? Why, that was only a password! Just the name of a dog! What did the man mean?

'*Will* you come into the room?' said the man, again. 'What's the matter with you, boy? Are you scared? We shan't eat a messenger from Charlie.'

George went slowly into the room, his mind suddenly working at top speed. A messenger from Charlie. Could there be someone called Charlie, Cheeky Charlie? Did these men think he had come from him? How very extraordinary!

'There won't be no message from Charlie,' said the man called Zeb. 'Why should there be? He's waiting for news from *us*, isn't he? Here, boy – did Charlie send you to ask for news?'

George could do nothing but nod his head. He didn't want to have to explain anything at all. These men appeared to think he had come to find them to get news for someone called Charlie. Perhaps if he let them give him the message, they would let him go without any further questions.

'Can't think why Charlie uses such a dumb kid to send out,' grumbled Zeb. 'Got a pencil, Larry? I'll scribble a message.'

'A kid that can't open his mouth and speak a word is just the right messenger for us,' said the man with the clear voice. 'Tell Charlie what we've decided, Zeb. Don't forget that he's to mark the tarpaulin with white lines at one corner.'

Zeb scribbled something in a note-book by the light of a torch. He tore out the page and folded it over. 'Here you are,' he said to George. 'Take this to Charlie, and don't you go calling him Cheeky Charlie, see? Little boys that are saucy get their ears boxed! His friends can call him what they like, but not you.'

'Oh, leave the kid alone,' said Larry. 'Where's Charlie now, kid? At Dalling's or at Hammond's?'

George didn't know what to answer. 'Dalling's,' he said at last, not knowing in the least what it meant.

Larry tossed him ten pence. 'Clear off!' he said. 'You're scared stiff of this place, aren't you? Want me to take you down the hill?'

This was the last thing that poor George wanted. He shook his head.

The men got up. 'Well, if you want company, we're all going now. If not, buzz off.'

George buzzed off, but not very far. He went back again into the other room, thankful to see that the moon had come out again, and had lighted it enough for him to make his way quickly to the window. He clambered

out awkwardly, because his legs were shaking and were not easy to manage.

He made for a thick bush and flung himself into the middle. If those men really were going, he could wait till they were gone. Then he could go back and find Jack. WHAT had happened to Jack? He seemed to have disappeared completely.

The men went cautiously out of Tigger's Barn, keeping their voices low. The owl flew over their heads, giving a sudden hoot that startled them. Then George heard them laugh. Their footsteps went quietly down the hill.

He heaved a sigh of relief. Then he scrambled out of the bush and went back into the house. He stood debating what to do. Should he try the password again? It had had surprising results last time, so perhaps this time it would be better just to call Jack's name.

But before he could do so, a voice came out of the doorway that led to the further room.

'Cheeky Charlie!' it said, in a piercing whisper.

George stood stock still, and didn't answer. Was it Jack saying that password? Or was it somebody else who knew the real Cheeky Charlie, whoever he might be?

Then a light flashed on and caught him in its beam. But this time, thank goodness, it was Jack's torch, and Jack himself gave an exclamation of relief.

'It *is* you, George! Why in the world didn't you answer when I said the password? You must have known it was me.'

'Oh, Jack! Where were you? I've had a frightful time!' said George. 'You shouldn't have gone off and left me like that. Where have you been?'

'I was listening to those men, and fell into this cupboard,' said Jack. 'It shut on me, and I couldn't hear another word. I didn't dare to move in case those men came to look for me. But at last I opened the door, and when I couldn't hear anything, I wondered where *you* were! So I whispered the password.'

'Oh, I see,' said George, thankfully. 'So you didn't hear what happened to *me*? The men discovered me – and –'

'*Discovered* you! What did they do?' said Jack, in the greatest astonishment.

'It's really awfully peculiar,' said George. 'You see, *I* whispered the password too, hoping *you* would hear it. But the *men* heard me whispering "Cheeky Charlie", and they called me in and asked me if I was a messenger from him.'

Jack didn't follow this, and it took George a little time to explain to him that the three men seemed really to think that someone they knew, who actually *was* called Cheeky Charlie, was using George for a messenger!

'And they gave *me* a message for him,' said George. 'In a note. I've got it in my pocket.'

'No! Have you really!' said Jack, suddenly excited. 'I *say*, this is thrilling. We might be in the middle of an adventure again. Let's see the note.'

'No. Let's go home and then read it,' said George. 'I want to get out of this tumbledown old place, I don't like it a bit. Something came down the chimney on me, and I nearly had a fit. Come on, Jack, I want to go.'

'Yes, but wait,' said Jack, suddenly remembering. 'What about Susie and Jeff? They must be somewhere here too. We ought to look for them.'

'We'll have to find out how they knew there was to be a meeting here tonight,' said George. 'Let's call them, Jack. Honestly, there's nobody else here now. *I'm* going to call them anyway!'

So he shouted loudly: 'JEFF! SUSIE! COME ON OUT, WHEREVER YOU ARE!'

His voice echoed through the old house, but nobody stirred, nobody answered.

'I'll go through the place with the torch,' said Jack, and the two boys went bravely into each broken-down, bare room, flashing the light all round.

There was no one to be seen. Jack suddenly felt anxious. Susie was his sister. Boys must always look after their sisters, yes, even the most tiresome of sisters! What had happened to Susie?

'George, we must go back home as quickly as ever we can, and tell Mother that Susie's disappeared,' he said. 'And Jeff has too. Come on quick! Something may have happened to them.'

They went back to Jack's house as quickly as ever they could. As they ran to the front gate, Jack saw his mother coming back from her meeting. He rushed to her.

'Mother! Susie's missing! She's gone! Oh, Mother, she went to Tigger's Barn, and now she isn't there!'

His mother looked at him in alarm. She opened the front door quickly and went in, followed by the two boys.

'Now tell me quickly,' she said. 'What do you mean? Why did Susie go out? When –'

A door was flung open upstairs and a merry voice called out: 'Hallo, Mother! Is that you? Come and see Jeff's railway going! And don't scold us because it's so late; we've been waiting for Jack and George to come back.' ·

'Why, that's Susie,' said her mother, in surprise. 'What did you mean, Jack, about Susie disappearing. What a silly joke!'

Sure enough, there were Susie and Jeff upstairs, with the whole floor laid out with railway lines!

Jack stared at Susie in surprise and indignation. Hadn't she gone out, then? She grinned at him wickedly.

'Sucks to you!' she said rudely. 'Who came spying on our Famous Five meeting? Who heard all sorts of things and believed them? Who's been all the way to Tigger's Barn in the dark? Who's a silly-billy, who's a –'

Jack rushed at her in a rage. She dodged behind her mother, laughing.

'Now, Jack, now!' said his mother. 'Stop that, please. What has been happening? Susie, go to bed. Jeff, clear up your lines. It's time for you to go. Your mother will be telephoning to ask why you are not home. JACK! Did you hear what I said? Leave Susie alone.'

Jeff went to take up his lines, and George helped him. Both boys were scared of Jack's mother when she was cross. Susie ran to her room and slammed the door.

'She's a wicked girl,' raged Jack, 'she – she – she –'

'Go and turn on the bath-water,' said his mother, sharply. 'You can both go without your supper now. I WILL NOT have this behaviour.'

George and Jeff disappeared out of the house as quickly as they could, carrying the boxes of railway things. George completely forgot what he had in his pocket – a pencilled note to someone called Cheeky Charlie, which he hadn't even read! Well, well, well!

Ten

Call a meeting!

GEORGE went quickly along the road with Jeff. Jeff
chuckled.

'I say, you and Jack fell for our little trick beautifully,
didn't you? Susie's clever, she laid her plan well. We all
talked at the tops of our voices so that Jack would be sure
to hear. We knew he was hiding in the laurel bush.'

George said nothing. He was angry that Susie and the
Famous Five should have played a trick like that on the
Secret Seven – angry that Jack had been so easily taken
in – but, dear me, what curious results that trick had had!

Susie had mentioned Tigger's Barn just to make Jack
and the Secret Seven think that the Famous Five had got
hold of something that was going on there, and had talked
about a make-believe Stumpy Dick and Twisty Tom. And
lo and behold, something *was* going on there, not between
Stumpy Dick and Twisty Tom, but between three
mysterious fellows called Zeb, Larry, and had he heard
the other man's name? No, he hadn't.

'You're quiet, George,' said Jeff, chuckling again.
'How did you enjoy your visit to Tigger's Barn? I bet
it was a bit frightening!'

'It was,' said George, truthfully, and said no more.
He wanted to think about everything carefully, to sort

out all he had heard, to try and piece together what had happened. It was all jumbled up in his mind.

One thing's certain, he thought, suddenly. We'll have to call a meeting of the Secret Seven. How queer that the Famous Five should have played a silly joke on us and led us to Something Big – another adventure, I'm sure. Susie's an idiot, but she's done the Secret Seven a jolly good turn!

As soon as George got home he felt in his pocket for the note that Zeb had given him. He felt round anxiously. It would have been too dreadful if he had lost it!

But he hadn't. His fingers closed over the folded piece of paper. He took it out, his hand trembling with excitement. He opened it, and read it by the light of his bedroom lamp.

Dear Charlie,

Everything's ready and going O.K. Can't see that anything can go wrong, but a fog would be very welcome as you can guess! Larry's looking after the points, we've arranged that. Don't forget the lorry, and get the tarpaulin truck cover marked with white at one corner. That'll save time in looking for the right load. It's clever of you to send out this load by truck, and collect it by lorry!

All the best,
Zeb

George couldn't make head or tail of this. What in the world was it all about? There was a plot of some kind, that was clear, but what did everything else mean?

George went to the telephone. Perhaps Peter wouldn't yet be in bed. He really MUST get on to him and tell him something important had happened.

Peter was just going to bed. He came to the telephone in surprise, when his mother called him to it.

'Hallo! What's up?'

'Peter, I can't stop to tell you everything now, but we went to Tigger's Barn, Jack and I, and my word, there *is* something going on. We had quite an adventure, and –'

'You don't mean to tell me that that tale of Susie's was true!' said Peter, disbelievingly.

'No. At least, it was all made-up on her part, as you said, but all the same, something *is* going on at Tigger's Barn, Peter, something Susie didn't know about, of course, because she only mentioned the place in fun. But it's serious, Peter. You must call a meeting of the Secret Seven tomorrow evening after tea.'

There was a pause.

'Right,' said Peter, at last. 'I will. This is jolly queer, George. Don't tell me anything more over the phone, because I don't want Mother asking me too many questions. I'll tell Janet to tell Pam and Barbara there's a meeting tomorrow evening at five o'clock in our shed, and we'll tell Colin and Jack. Golly! This sounds pretty mysterious.'

'You just wait till you hear the whole story!' said George. 'You'll be amazed.'

He put down the receiver, and got ready for bed, quite forgetting that he had had no supper. He couldn't stop thinking about the happenings of the evening. How queer that the password of the Secret Seven should be Cheeky

Charlie, and there should be a real fellow called by that name!

And how extraordinary that Susie's bit of make-believe should suddenly have come true without her knowing it! Something *was* going on at Tigger's Barn!

He got into bed and lay awake for a long time. Jack was also lying awake thinking. He was excited. He wished he hadn't been shut up in that silly cupboard, when he might have been listening all the time. Still, George seemed to have got quite a lot of information.

The Secret Seven were very thrilled the next day. It was difficult not to let the Famous Five see that they had something exciting on hand, but Peter had strictly forbidden anyone to talk about the matter at school, just in *case* that tiresome Susie, with her long ears, got to hear of it.

'We don't want the Famous Five trailing us around,' said Peter. 'Just wait till this evening, all of you, and then we'll really get going!'

At five o'clock every single member of the Secret Seven was in the shed in Peter's garden. All of them had raced home quickly after afternoon school, gobbled their teas, and come rushing to the meeting.

The password was whispered quickly, as one after another passed into the shed, each wearing the badge with S.S. on. 'Cheeky Charlie, Cheeky Charlie, Cheeky Charlie.'

Jack and George had had little time to exchange more than a few words with one another. They were bursting to tell their strange story!

'Now, we're all here,' said Peter. 'Scamper, sit by the

door and keep guard. Bark if you hear anything at all. This is a most important meeting.'

Scamper got up and went solemnly to the door. He sat down by it, listening, looking very serious.

'Oh, do buck up, Peter,' said Pam. 'I can't wait a minute more to hear what it's all about!'

'All right, all right,' said Peter. 'You know that we weren't going to call another meeting till the Christmas hols, unless something urgent happened. Well, it's happened. Jack, you start off with the story, please.'

Jack was only too ready to tell it. He described how he had hidden in the laurel bush to overhear what the Famous Five said at their meeting in the summer-house. He repeated the ridiculous make-up that Susie had invented to deceive the Secret Seven, and to send them off on a wild-goose chase just to make fun of them.

He told them how Peter had laughed at the story and said it *was* a make-up of Susie's, but how he and George had decided to go to Tigger's Barn just in case it wasn't.

'But I was right,' interrupted Peter. 'It *was* a make-up, but just by chance there was some truth in it, too, though Susie didn't know.'

George took up the tale. He told the others how he and Jack had gone to Tigger's Barn, thinking that Susie and Jeff were in front of them. And then came the thrilling part of their adventure in the old tumbledown house!

Everyone listened intently, the girls holding their breath when George came to the bit where the three men arrived.

Then Jack told how he went to the doorway to listen, and fell into the cupboard, and George told how he had gone to look for Jack, and had said the password, Cheeky Charlie, which had had such surprising results.

'Do you mean to say, there actually *is* a man called Cheeky Charlie?' asked Barbara, in amazement. 'Our password is only the name of a dog. Just fancy there being a *man* called that, too! My goodness!'

'Don't interrupt,' said Peter. 'Go on, both of you.'

Everyone sat up with wide eyes when George told how the men had thought he was a messenger from Cheeky Charlie, and when he told them about the note they had given him, and produced it from his pocket, the Secret Seven were speechless with excitement!

The note was passed from hand to hand. Peter rapped on a box at last.

'We've all seen the note now,' he said. 'And we've heard Jack and George tell what happened last night. It's quite clear that we've hit on something queer again. Do the Secret Seven think we should try and solve this new mystery?'

Everyone yelled and rapped on boxes, and Scamper barked in excitement too.

'Right,' said Peter. 'I agree too. But we have got to be very, very careful this time, or else the Famous Five will try and interfere, and they might spoil everything. Nobody – NOBODY – must say a single word about this to anyone in the world. Is that agreed?'

It was. Scamper came up and laid a big paw on Peter's knee, as if he thoroughly agreed too.

'Go back to the door, Scamper,' said Peter. 'We depend on you to give us warning if any of those tiresome Famous Five come snooping round. On guard, Scamper.'

Scamper trotted back to his place by the door obediently. The Seven crowded more closely together, and began a grand discussion.

'First, let's sort out all the things that Jack and George heard,' said Peter. 'Then we'll try and make out what they mean. At the moment I'm in a muddle about everything and haven't the slightest idea what the men are going to do.'

'Right,' said Jack. 'Well, as I told you, I heard the men talking, but their voices were very low, and I could only catch words now and again.'

'What words were they?' asked Peter. 'Tell us carefully.'

'Well, they kept saying something about "loading and unloading",' said Jack. 'And they kept on and on mentioning "points".'

'What sort of points?' asked Peter.

Jack shook his head, completely at a loss.

'I've no idea. They mentioned figures too. They said "six-two" quite a lot of times, and then they said "maybe seven-ten". And they said there mustn't be a moon, and I heard them talk about darkness, fog, and mist. Honestly, I couldn't make head or tail of it. I only know they must have been discussing some plan.'

'What else did you hear?' asked Janet.

'Nothing,' answered Jack. 'I fell into the cupboard then, and when the door shut on me I couldn't hear another word.'

'And all *I* can add is that the men asked me if Cheeky Charlie was at Dalling's or Hammond's,' said George. 'But goodness knows what *that* meant.'

'Perhaps they are the name of a workshop or works of

some kind,' suggested Colin. 'We could find out.'

'Yes. We might be able to trace those,' said Peter. 'Now, this note. Whatever can it mean? It's got the word "points" here again. And they talk about trucks and lorries. It's plain that there's some robbery planned, I think. But what kind? They want fog, too. Well, that's understandable, I suppose.'

'Shall we take the note to the police?' said Barbara, suddenly gripped by a bright idea.

'Oh no! Not yet!' said George. 'It's *my* note and I'd like to see if we can't do something about it ourselves before we tell any grown-ups. After all, we've managed lots of affairs very well so far. I don't see why we shouldn't be able to do something about this one too.'

'I'm all for trying,' said Peter. 'It's jolly exciting. And we've got quite a lot to go on, really. We know the names of three of the four men – Zeb, which is probably short for Zebedee, a most unusual name; and Larry, probably short for Laurence; and Cheeky Charlie, who is perhaps the boss.'

'Yes, and we know he's at Dalling's or Hammond's,' said Jack. 'What do we do first, Peter?'

Scamper suddenly began to bark wildly and scrape at the door.

'Not another word!' said Peter, sharply. 'There's someone outside!'

Eleven

Any ideas?

PETER opened the door. Scamper tore out, barking. Then he stopped by a bush and wagged his tail. The Secret Seven ran to him.

A pair of feet showed at the bottom of the bush. Jack gave a shout of rage and pushed into the bush. He dragged someone out – Susie!

'How dare you!' he yelled. 'Coming here and listening! How dare you, Susie?'

'Let me go,' said Susie. 'I like you asking me how I dare! I'm only copying what *you* did on Saturday! Who hid in the laurel bush, and –'

'How did you know we were having a meeting?' demanded Jack, shaking Susie.

'I just followed you,' said Susie, grinning. 'But I didn't hear anything because I didn't dare to go near the door, in case Scamper barked. I did a sudden sneeze, though, and he must have heard me. What are you calling a meeting about?'

'As if we'd tell you!' said Peter, crossly. 'Go on home, Susie. Go on! Jack, take her home. The meeting is over.'

'Blow!' said Jack. 'All right. Come on, Susie. And if I have any nonsense from you, I'll pull your hair till you yell!'

Jack went off with Susie. Peter faced round to the others and spoke in a low voice.

'Listen. All of you think hard about what has been said, and give me or Janet any good ideas tomorrow. It's no good going on with this meeting. Somebody else belonging to the Famous Five might come snooping round too.'

'Right,' said the Secret Seven, and went home, excited and very much puzzled. *How* could they think of anything that would help to piece together the jumble of words they knew? Points. Six-two, seven-ten. Fog, mist, darkness. Dalling's. Hammond's.

Each of them tried to think of some good idea. Barbara could think of nothing at all. Pam tried asking her father about Dalling's or Hammond's. He didn't know either of them. Pam felt awkward when he asked her why she wanted to know, and didn't go on with the subject.

Colin decided that a robbery was going to be done one dark and foggy night, and that the goods were to be unloaded from a lorry somewhere. He couldn't imagine why they were to be sent in a truck. All the boys thought exactly the same thing, but, as Peter said, it wasn't much help because they didn't know what date, what place, or what lorry!

Then Jack had quite a good idea. He thought it would be helpful if they tried to find a man called Zebedee, because surely he must be the Zeb at Tigger's Barn. There couldn't be *many* Zebedees in the district!

'All right, Jack. It's a good *idea*,' said Peter. 'You can do the finding out for us. Produce this Zeb, and that may be the first step.'

'Yes, but how shall I find out?' said Jack. 'I can't go round asking every man I meet if he's called Zeb.'

'No. That's why I said it was a good *idea*,' said Peter, grinning. 'But that's about all it is. It's an impossible thing to do, you see; so that's why it will remain just a good idea and nothing else. Finding the only Zebedee in the district would be like looking for a needle in a haystack.'

'I shouldn't like to have to do *that*,' said Janet, who was with them. 'Peter and I have got about the only good idea, I think, Jack.'

'What's that?' asked Jack.

'Well, we looked in our telephone directory at home to see if any firm called Dalling or Hammond was there,' said Janet. 'But there wasn't, so we thought they must be somewhere farther off, not in our district at all. Our telephone book only gives the names of people in this area, you see.'

'And now we're going to the post-office to look in the big telephone directories there,' said Peter. 'They give the names of districts much farther away. Like to come with us?'

Jack went with them. They came to the post-office and went in. Peter took up two telephone books, one with the D's in and one with the H's. '

'Now I'll look for Dalling,' he said, and thumbed through the D's. The other two leaned over him, looking down the D's too.

'Dale, Dale, Dale, Dales, Dalgleish, Daling, Dalish, Dallas, DALLING!' read Peter, his finger following down the list of names. 'Here it is – Dalling. Oh, there are three

Dallings! Blow!'

'There's a Mrs A. Dalling, Rose Cottage, Hubley,' said Janet. 'And E. A. Dalling, of Manor House, Tallington, and Messrs. E. Dalling, Manufacturers of Lead Goods. Well – which would be the right Dalling? The manufacturers, I suppose.'

'Yes,' said Peter, sounding excited. 'Now for the H's. Where are they? In the other book. Here we are – Hall, Hall – goodness, what a lot of people are called Hall! Hallet, Ham, Hamm, Hammers, Hamming, Hammond, Hammond, Hammond, Hammond – oh, LOOK!'

They all looked. Peter was pointing to the fourth name of Hammond. 'Hammond and Co.' Ltd. Lead manufacturers. Petlington.'

'There you are,' said Peter, triumphantly. 'Two firms dealing in lead, one called Hammond, one called Dalling.

Cheeky Charlie must be something to do with both.'

'Lead!' said Jack. 'It's very valuable nowadays, isn't it? I'm always reading about thieves going and stealing it off church roofs. I don't know why churches so often have lead roofs, but they seem to.'

'It looks as if Cheeky Charlie might be going to send a load of lead off somewhere in a truck, and Zeb and the others are going to stop it, and take the lead,' said Peter. 'As you say, it's very valuable, Jack.'

'Charlie must have quite a high position if he's in both firms,' said Janet. 'Oh, dear – I do wonder what his real name is! Cheeky Charlie! I wonder why they call him that?'

'Because he's bold and has got plenty of cheek, I expect,' said Peter. 'If only Hammond's and Dalling's weren't so far away! We could go and snoop round there and see if we could hear of anyone called Cheeky Charlie.'

'They're miles away,' said Jack, looking at the addresses. 'Well, we've been quite clever, but I don't see that we've got very much farther, really. We just know that Dalling's and Hammond's are firms that deal in lead, which is very valuable stuff, but that's all!'

'Yes. It doesn't take us very far,' said Peter, shutting up the directory. 'We'll have to think a bit harder. Come on, let's go and buy some sweets. Sucking a bit of toffee always seems to help my thinking!'

Twelve

A game – and a brain-wave!

ANOTHER day went by, and Saturday came. A meeting was called for that morning, but nobody had much to say. In fact, it was rather a dull meeting after the excitement of the last one. The Seven sat in the shed eating biscuits provided by Jack's mother, and Scamper was at the door, on guard as usual.

It was raining outside. The Seven looked out dismally.

'No good going for a walk, or having a game of football,' said Peter. 'Let's stay here in the shed and play a game.'

'Fetch your railway set, Peter,' said Janet. 'And I'll fetch the farm set. We could set out the lines here in the midst of the toy trees and farm buildings, looking as if they were real countryside. We've got simply heaps of farm stuff.'

'Oh yes. Let's do that,' said Pam. 'I love your farm set. It's the nicest and biggest I've ever seen. Do get it! We girls could set it out, and the boys could put up the railway.'

'It's a jolly good thing to do on a rainy morning like this,' said Jack, pleased. 'I wanted to help Jeff with *his* fine railway the other day, when George came to tea with me, but he was Susie's guest, and she wouldn't have

354

let us join in for anything. You know, she's very suspicious that we're working on something, Peter. She keeps on and on at me to tell her if anything happened at Tigger's Barn that night.'

'Well, just shut her up,' said Peter. 'Scamper, you needn't watch the door any more. You can come and join us, old fellow. The meeting's over.'

Scamper was pleased. He ran round everyone, wagging his tail. Peter fetched his railway set, and Janet and Pam went to get the big farm set. It had absolutely everything, from animals and farm men to trees, fences, troughs and sties!

They all began to put up the two sets – the boys putting together the lines, and girls setting out a proper little countryside, with trees, fences, animals and farm buildings. It really was fun.

Peter suddenly looked up at the window. He had noticed a movement there. He saw a face looking in, and leapt up with such a fierce yell that everyone jumped in alarm.

'It's Jeff,' he cried. 'I wonder if he's snooping round for the Famous Five. After him, Scamper!'

But Jeff had taken to his heels, and, even if Scamper had caught him, nothing would have happened, because the spaniel knew Jeff well and liked him.

'It doesn't really matter Jeff looking in,' said Janet. 'All he'd see would be us having a very peaceful game! Let him stand out in the rain and look in if he wants to!'

The railway lines were ready at last. The three beautiful clockwork engines were attached to their line of trucks. Two were passenger trains and one was a goods train.

'I'll manage one train, you can do another train, Colin, and you can have a third one, Jack,' said Peter. 'Janet, you do the signals. You're good at those. And, George, you work the points. We mustn't have an accident. You can always switch one of the trains on to another line, if two look like crashing.'

'Right. I'll manage the points,' said George, pleased. 'I like doing those. I love seeing a train being switched off a main-line into a siding.'

The engines were wound up and set going. They tore round the floor, and George switched them cleverly from one line to another when it seemed there might be an accident.

And, in the middle of all this, Janet suddenly sat up straight, and said in a loud voice: 'WELL, I NEVER!'

The others looked at her.

'What's the matter?' said Peter. 'Well, I never *what*? Why are you looking as if you are going to burst?'

'Points!' said Janet, excitedly. 'Points!' And she waved her hand to where George was sitting working the points, switching the trains from one line to another. 'Oh Peter, don't be so *stupid*! Don't you remember? Those men at Tigger's Barn talked about *points*. Jack said they kept *on* mentioning them. Well, I bet they were *points on some railway line*!'

There was a short silence. Then everyone spoke at once. 'Yes! It could be! Why didn't we think of it before? Of course! Points on the railway!'

The game stopped at once and an eager discussion began.

'Why should they use the points? It must be because

they want to switch a train on to another line.'

'Yes, a train that contains something they want to steal – lead, probably!'

'Then it's a goods train. One of the trucks must be carrying the lead they want to steal!'

'The tarpaulin! Would that be covering up the load? Don't you remember? It had to be marked with white at the corner, so that the men would know it.'

'Yes! They wouldn't have to waste time then looking into every truck to see which was the right one. Sometimes there are thirty or forty trucks on a goods train. The white marks on the tarpaulin would tell them at once they had the right truck!'

'Woof,' said Scamper, joining in the general excitement.

Peter turned to him. 'Hey, Scamper, on guard at the door again, old fellow!' he said, at once. 'The meeting's begun again! On guard!'

Scamper went on guard. The Secret Seven drew close together, suddenly very excited. To think that one simple word had set their brains working like this, and put them on the right track at once!

'You are really clever, Janet,' said Jack, and Janet beamed.

'Oh, anyone might have thought of it,' she said. 'It just rang a bell in my mind somehow, when you kept saying "points". Oh, Peter, where are these points, do you think?'

Peter was following out another idea in his mind. 'I've thought of something else,' he said, his eyes shining. 'Those figures the men kept saying. Six-two, seven-ten.

Couldn't they be the times of trains?'

'Oh *yes*! Like when we say Daddy's going to catch the six-twenty home, or the seven-twelve!' cried Pam. 'Six-two – there must be a train that starts somewhere at six-two. Or arrives somewhere then.'

'And they want a foggy or misty, dark night, because then it would be easy to switch the train into some siding,' said Jack. 'A foggy night would be marvellous for them. The engine-driver couldn't possibly see that his train had been switched off on the wrong line. He'd go on till he came to some signal, and the men would be there ready to take the lead from the marked truck –'

'And they'd deal with the surprised engine-driver, and the guard too, I suppose,' said Colin.

There was a silence after this. It suddenly dawned on the Seven that there must be quite a big gang engaged in this particular robbery.

'I think we ought to tell somebody,' said Pam.

Peter shook his head. 'No. Let's find out more if we can. And I'm sure we can now! For instance, let's get a time-table and see if there's a train that arrives anywhere at two minutes past six – 6.2.'

'That's no good,' said Jack, at once. 'Goods trains aren't in the time-tables.'

'Oh no. I forgot that,' said Peter. 'Well, what about one or two of us boys going down to the station and asking a few questions about goods trains and what time they come in, and where from? We know where the firms of Dalling and Hammond are. Where was it now – Petlington, wasn't it?'

'Yes,' said Janet. 'That's a good idea of yours to go

down to the station, Peter. It's stopped raining. Why don't you go now?'

'I will,' said Peter. 'You come with me, Colin. Jack and George have had plenty of excitement so far, but you haven't had very much. Come on down to the station with me.'

So off went the two boys, looking rather thrilled. They really were on the trail now!

Peter and Colin arrived at the station just as a train was coming in. They watched it. Two porters were on the platform, and a man stood with them in dirty blue overalls. He had been working on the line, and had hopped up on to the platform when the train came rumbling in.

The boys waited till the train had gone out. Then they went up to one of the porters.

'Are there any goods trains coming through?' asked Peter. 'We like watching them.'

'There's one in fifteen minutes' time,' said the porter.

'Is it a very long one?' said Colin. 'I once counted forty-seven trucks pulled by a goods engine.'

'The longest one comes in here in the evening,' said the porter. 'How many trucks do you reckon it has as a rule, Zeb?'

The man in dirty overalls rubbed a black hand over his face, and pushed back his cap. 'Well, maybe thirty, maybe forty. It depends.'

The boys looked at one another. *Zeb!* The porter had called the linesman *Zeb!* Could it be – could it *possibly* be the same Zeb that had met the other two men at Tigger's Barn?

They looked at him. He wasn't much to look at, certainly, a thin, mean-faced little man, very dirty, and with hair much too long. Zeb! It was such an unusual name that the boys felt sure they must be face to face with the Zeb who had been up at the old tumbledown house.

'Er – what time does this goods train come in the evening?' asked Peter, finding his tongue again at last.

'It comes in about six o'clock twice a week,' said Zeb. 'Six-two, it's supposed to be here, but sometimes it's late.'

'Where does it come from?' asked Colin.

'Plenty of places!' said Zeb. 'Turleigh, Idlesston, Hayley, Garton, Petlington. . . .'

'Petlington!' said Colin, before he could stop himself. That was the place where the firms of Dalling and Hammond were. Peter scowled at him, and Colin hurried to

cover up his mistake in calling attention to the town they
were so interested in.

'Petlington, yes, go on, where else?' said Colin.

The linesman gave him another string of names, and
the boys listened. But they had learnt already a good deal
of what they wanted to know.

The 6.2 was a goods train, that came in twice a week,
and Petlington was one of the places it came from, probably with a truck or two added there, full of lead goods
from Hammond's and Dalling's! Lead pipes? Sheets of
lead? The boys had no idea, and it didn't really matter.
It was lead, anyway, valuable lead, they were sure of
that! Lead sent off by Cheeky Charlie for his firms.

'We've been playing with my model railway this morning,' said Peter, suddenly thinking of a way to ask about
points and switches. 'It's a fine one, it's got points to
switch my trains from one line to another. Jolly good they
are too, as good as real points!'

'Ah, you want to ask my mate about *them*,' said Zeb.
'He's got plenty to deal with. He uses them to switch the
goods trains from one part of the line to another. They
often have to go into sidings, you know.'

'Does he switch the 6.2 into a siding?' said Peter. 'Or
does it go straight through on the main-line?'

'Straight through,' said Zeb. 'No, Larry only switches
the goods trains that have to be unloaded near here. The
6.2 goes right on to Swindon. You'll see it this evening
if you come down.'

Peter had given a quick look at Colin to see if he had
noticed the name of Zeb's mate – Larry! Zeb and
Larry – what an enormous piece of luck! Colin gave a

quick wink at Peter. Yes, he had noticed all right! He
began to look excited.

'I wish we could see Larry working the points,' said
Peter. 'It must be fun. I expect the switches are quite
different from the ones on my railway lines at home.'

Zeb laughed. 'You bet they are! Ours take some
moving! Look, would you like to walk along the line with
me, and I'll show you some switches that send a train off
into a siding? It's about a mile up the line.'

Peter took a look at his watch. He would be very late
for his dinner, but this was really important. Why, he
might see the very points that Larry was going to use one
dark, foggy night!

'Look out the kids don't get knocked down by a train,'
the porter warned Zeb, as the linesman took the two boys
down on to the track with him.

The boys looked at him with scorn. As if they couldn't
tell when a train was coming!

It seemed a very long way up the line. Zeb had a job
of work not far from the points. He left his tools by the
side of the line he was to repair, and took the boys to
where a number of lines crossed one another. He explained how the points worked.

'You pull this lever for that line, see? Watch how the
rails move so that they lead to that other line over there,
instead of letting the train keep on this line.'

Colin and Peter did a little pulling of levers themselves,
and they found it exceptionally hard work.

'Does the 6.2 come on this line?' asked Peter, innocently.

'Yes. But it goes straight on; it doesn't get switched to

one side,' said Zeb. 'It never has goods for this district; it goes on to Swindon. Now don't you ever mess about on the railway by yourselves, or the police will be after you straight away!'

'We won't,' promised the two boys.

'Well, I must get on with my job,' said Zeb, not sounding as if he wanted to at all. 'So long! Hope I've told you what you wanted to know.'

He certainly had, much, much more than he imagined. Colin and Peter could hardly believe their luck. They made their way to the side of the line, and stood there for a while.

'We ought really to go and explore the siding,' said Peter. 'But we're so frightfully late. Blow! We forgot to ask what evenings the goods train comes in from Petlington!'

'Let's get back, and come again this afternoon,' said Colin. 'I'm frightfully hungry. We can find out the two days the goods train comes through when we're here this afternoon, and explore the siding too.'

They left the railway and went to the road. They were both so excited that they could hardly stop talking. 'Fancy bumping into Zeb! Zeb himself! And hearing about Larry in charge of the points! Why, everything's as plain as can be. What a good thing Janet had the brain-wave this morning about points! My goodness, we're in luck's way!'

'We'll be back this afternoon as soon as we can,' said Peter. 'I vote the whole lot of us go. My word, this *is* getting exciting!'

Thirteen

An exciting afternoon

BOTH Peter's mother and Colin's were very angry when they arrived back so late for their dinner. Janet was so full of curiosity to know what had happened that she could hardly wait till Peter had finished. He kept frowning at her as he gobbled down his hot stew, afraid that she would ask some awkward questions.

He sent her round to collect the Secret Seven, and they all arrived in a very short time, though Colin was late because he had to finish his dinner.

Peter told them everything, and they listened, thrilled. Well, what a tale! To meet Zeb like that, and to have him telling them so much that they wanted to know!

'Little did he know why we asked him so many questions!' said Colin, with a grin. 'I must say he was quite nice to us, though he's a mean-looking fellow with shifty eyes.'

'This afternoon we will all go to the siding,' said Peter. 'We'll find out what days that goods train comes along, too.'

So off they went. First they went to the station and found the porter again. He had nothing much to do and was pleased to talk to them. He told them tales of this, that and the other on the railway, and gradually Peter guided him to the subject of goods trains.

'Here comes one,' said the porter. 'It won't stop at the station, though – no passengers to get on or off, you see. Want to count the trucks? It's not a very long train.'

Most of the trucks were open ones, and they carried all kinds of things, coal, bricks, machinery, crates. The train rumbled by slowly, and the Seven counted thirty-two trucks.

'I'd rather like to see that goods train Zeb told us about,' said Peter to the porter. 'The one that comes from Petlington and beyond, the 6.2, I think he said. It's sometimes a very long one, isn't it?'

'Yes. Well, you'd have to come on Tuesday or Friday,' said the porter. 'But it's dark then, so you won't see much. Look, the guard of that last goods train is waving to you!'

They waved back. The goods train got smaller and smaller in the distance and at last disappeared.

'I wonder things aren't stolen out of those open trucks,' said Peter, innocently.

'Oh, they are,' said the porter. 'There's been a whole lot of stealing lately, yes, even a car taken out of one truck, though you mightn't believe it! Some gang at work, they say. Beats me how they do it! Well, you kids, I must go and do a spot of work. So long!'

The Seven wandered off. They walked by the side of the track for about a mile until they came to where the points were that Zeb had explained that morning.

Peter pointed them out. 'That's where they plan to switch the goods train off to a side-line,' he said. 'I wish we knew which evening. I think it must be soon, though, because that note George got said that everything was ready and going O.K.'

They followed the side-line, walking by the side of the railway. The line meandered off all by itself and finally came into a little goods yard, which seemed to be completely deserted at that moment.

Big gates led into the goods yard. They were open to let in lorries that came to take the goods unloaded from trucks sent down the side-line. But only empty trucks stood on the little line now, and not a soul was about. It was plain that no goods train was expected for some time.

'This is a very lonely little place,' said Colin. 'If a goods train was diverted down here, nobody would hear it or see it, except those who would be waiting for it! I bet there will be a lorry creeping in here some evening, ready to take the lead sheets or pipes or whatever they are, from

the truck whose tarpaulin is marked with white lines!'

'What about coming here on Tuesday evening, just in *case* that's the night they've arranged?' said Jack, suddenly. 'Not the girls. Only us boys. Then, if we saw anything happening, we could telephone the police. And before Zeb and Larry and the other two could finish their unloading we could get the police here. I say, wouldn't that be a thrill?'

'I don't know. I think really we ought to get in touch with that big Inspector we like,' said Peter. 'We know quite enough now to be sure of what we say. The only thing we *don't* know is whether it's this Tuesday or if it's to be later on.'

They stood together, arguing, and nobody saw a burly policeman sauntering in through the open gates. He stared when he saw the children, and stood watching them.

'I'd like to see those points,' said Colin, getting tired of the argument. 'Show me them, Peter. We'll look out for trains.'

Peter forgot that children were not allowed to trespass on the railway lines. He set off up the side-line with the others, walking in the middle of the lines on his way to the points.

A loud voice hailed them. 'Hey, you kids there! What do you think you're doing, trespassing like that? You come back here. I've got something to say to you.'

'Let's run!' said Pam, in a panic. 'Don't let him catch us.'

'No. We can't run,' said Peter. 'I forgot we ought not to walk on the lines like this. Come back and explain, and if we say we're sorry, we'll be all right!'

So he led all the Seven back into the goods yard. The policeman came up to them, frowning.

'Now you look here,' he said; 'there's been too much nonsense from children on the railways lately. I've a good mind to take all your names and addresses and make a complaint to your parents about you.'

'But we weren't doing a thing!' said Peter, indignantly. 'We're sorry we trespassed, but honestly we weren't doing a scrap of harm.'

'What are you doing in this here goods yard?' said the policeman. 'Up to some mischief, I'll be bound!'

'We're not,' said Peter.

'Well, what *did* you come here for, then,' said the policeman. 'Go on, tell me. You didn't come here for nothing.'

'Tell him,' said Barbara, frightened and almost crying.

The policeman became very suspicious at once when he heard that there was something to tell. 'Oho! So there *was* something you were after!' he said. 'Now you just tell me, or I'll take your names and addresses!'

Peter wasn't going to tell this bad-tempered fellow anything. For one thing, he wouldn't believe the extraordinary tale that the Secret Seven had to tell, and for another, Peter wasn't going to give all his secrets away! No, if he was going to tell anyone, he would tell his father, or the Inspector they all liked so much!

It ended in the big policeman losing his temper thoroughly and taking down all their names and addresses, one by one. It was really maddening. To think they had come there to help to catch a gang of clever thieves, and had had their names taken for trespassing!

'I'll get told off if my father hears about this,' said Colin, dolefully. 'Oh, Peter, let's tell our nice Inspector everything, before that policeman goes round to our parents.'

But Peter was angry and obstinate. 'No!' he said. 'We'll settle this affair ourselves, and the police can come in at the last moment, when we've done everything, yes, that horrid fellow, too, who took our names. Think of his face if he has to come along to this goods yard one night to catch thieves *we've* tracked down, instead of him! I'll feel jolly pleased to crow over him!'

'I'd like to come, too, on that night,' said Janet.

'Well you won't,' said Peter, very much the head of the Secret Seven at that moment. 'No girls at all. Look at Barbara crying over a policeman taking her name and address! What use would *she* be on an evening with dangerous things going on? No, we four boys will go, nobody else, and that's that!'

Fourteen

Tuesday evening at last!

THERE was a meeting the next morning to talk over everything and to make arrangements for Tuesday. It was a proper November day, and a mist hung everywhere.

'My father says there will be a fog before tomorrow,' announced Peter. 'If so those fellows are going to be lucky on Tuesday. I don't expect the driver of the engine will even guess his train's on the side-line when the points send him there! He won't be able to see a thing.'

'I wish Tuesday would buck up and come,' said Jack. 'Susie *knows* there's something up, and she and her Famous Five are just *longing* to know what it is! Won't she be wild when she knows that it was her silly trick that put us on to all this?'

'Yes. I guess that will be the end of the Famous Five,' said Colin. 'I say, Peter, look here. I managed to get hold of a railway map. My father had one. It shows the lines from Petlington, and all the points and everything. Jack, do you think it could have been a map like this that Zeb and Larry and the other man were looking at in Tigger's Barn?'

'Yes. It may have been,' said Jack. 'I bet those fellows have played this kind of game before. They know the railway so well. Oh, I do wish Tuesday would come!'

Tuesday did come at last. Not one of the Secret Seven could do good work at school that day. They kept on and on thinking of the coming night. Peter looked out of the window a hundred times that morning!

'Dad was right,' he thought. 'The fog did come down, a real November fog. And tonight it will be so thick that there will be fog-signals on the railways. We shall hear them go off.'

The four boys had arranged to meet after tea, with Scamper. Peter thought it would be a good thing to take him with them in case anything went wrong.

They all had torches. Peter felt to see if he had any sweets in his pocket to share with his friends. He had! Jolly good! He shivered with excitement.

He nearly didn't go with the others, because his mother saw him putting his coat on, and was horrified to think that he was going out into the fog.

'You'll get lost,' she said. 'You mustn't go.'

'I'm meeting the others,' said Peter, desperately. 'I *must* go, Mummy.'

'I really can't let you,' said his mother. 'Well – not unless you take Scamper with you. He'll know the way home if you don't!'

'Oh, I'm taking Scamper, of *course*,' said Peter thankfully, and escaped at once, Scamper at his heels. He met the others at his gate and they set off.

The thick fog swirled round them, and their torches could hardly pierce it. Then they heard the bang-bang of the fog-signals on the railway.

'I bet Zeb and the rest are pleased with this fog!' said

Colin. 'Look, there's the fence that runs beside the railway. If we keep close to that we can't lose our way.'

They arrived at the goods yard about five minutes to six, and went cautiously in at the gates, which were open. All the boys had rubber-soled shoes on, and they carefully switched off their torches as they went quietly into the goods yard.

They heard the sound of a lorry's engine throbbing, and stopped. Voices came to them, low voices, and then they saw a lantern held by someone.

'The gang are here, and the lorry sent by Cheeky Charlie!' whispered Jack. 'You can just see it over there. I bet it's got the name of Hammond or Dalling on it!'

'It *was* this Tuesday,' said Colin, in relief. 'I did hope we hadn't come all the way here in this fog for nothing.'

Bang! Bang-bang!

More fog-signals went off and yet more. The boys knew when trains were running over the main-line some distance away because of the sudden explosions of the fog-signals, warning the drivers to look out for the real signals or to go slowly.

'What's the time?' whispered George.

'It's about half-past six now,' whispered back Peter. 'The 6.2 is late because of the fog. It may be along any time now, or it may be very late, of course.'

BANG! Another fog-signal went off in the next few minutes. The boys wondered if it had gone off under the wheels of the late goods train.

It had. The driver put his head out of his train and looked for the signal. It shone green. He could go on. He went on slowly, not knowing he was on the wrong line!

Larry was there at the points, well-hidden by the darkness and the fog, and he had switched the goods train carefully on to the little side-line!

The goods train left the main-line. It would not go through the station tonight, it would only go into the little goods yard, where silent men awaited it. Larry switched the levers again, so that the next train would go safely on to the main-line. He did not want half a dozen trains on the side-line together! Then he ran down the single-line after the slow-moving train.

'It's coming! I can hear it,' whispered Peter suddenly, and he caught hold of Jack's arm. 'Let's go over there by that shed. We can see everything without being seen. Come on!'

Rumble-rumble-rumble! The goods train came nearer. The red eye of a lamp gleamed in the fog. Now what was going to happen?

Fifteen

In the goods yard

A FOG-SIGNAL went off just where the gang wanted the train to stop. Bang!

The engine pulled up at once, and the trucks behind clang-clanged as they bumped into one another. A hurried talk had gone on between Zeb, Larry and four other men by the coach. The boys could hear every word.

'We'll tell him he's on the wrong line. We'll pretend to be surprised to see him there. Larry, you tell him he'd better stay on this side-line till the fog clears and he can get orders and go back. Take him off to that shed and hot up some tea or something. Keep him there while we do the job!'

The others nodded.

Peter whispered to Jack: 'They're going to tell the engine-driver that he's run off the main-line by mistake into this side-line, and then take him off out of the way, the guard too, I expect. There won't be any fighting, which is a good thing.'

'Sh!' said Jack. 'Look, the engine-driver is jumping down. He's lost, I expect! Doesn't know where he is!'

'Hey, there, engine-driver, you're on the side-line!' called Larry's voice, and he ran up to the engine, a lamp swaying in his hand. 'You ought to be on the main-line, running through the station.'

'Ay, I should be,' said the driver, puzzled. 'There must have been some mistake at the points. Am I safe here, mate?'

'Safe as can be!' called back Larry, cheerily. 'Don't you worry! You're in a goods yard, well out of the way of main-line traffic. Better not move till you get orders, this fog's terrible!'

'Good thing I got on to a side-line, that's all I can say,' said the driver. The guard came up at that moment from the last van, and joined in the conversation. He thought it peculiar.

'Someone making a mess of the points,' he grumbled. 'Now we'll be here for the night, and my missus is expecting me for supper.'

'Well, you may be home for breakfast if the fog clears,' said the driver, comfortingly.

The guard didn't think so. He was very gloomy.

'Well, mates, come along to this shed,' said Larry. 'There's an oil-stove there, and we'll light up and have a cup of something hot. Don't you worry about telephoning for orders. I'll do all that.'

'Who are you?' asked the gloomy guard.

'Who, me? I'm in charge of this yard,' said Larry, most untruthfully. 'Don't you worry now. It's a blessing you got on to this side-line. I bet your orders will be to stay here for the night. I'll have to find a shake-down somewhere for you.'

They all disappeared into the shed. A glow soon came from the window. Peter daringly peeped in, and saw the three men round an oil stove, and a kettle on top to boil water for tea.

Then things moved remarkably quickly. Zeb disappeared down the side-line to look for the truck covered by the tarpaulin with white marks. It was the seventh one, as he informed the others when he came back.

'We'll start up the lorry, and take it to the truck,' he said. 'Fortunately it's just where the yard begins, so we shan't have to carry the stuff far. Good thing, too, because it's heavy.'

The lorry was started up, and ran cautiously up the yard to the far end. There it stopped, presumably by the seventh truck. The four boys went silently through the fog and watched what happened for a minute or two.

The men were untying the tarpaulin by the light of a railway lantern. Soon it was entirely off. Jack could see the white paint at one corner that had marked it for the men.

Then began a pulling and tugging and panting as the men hauled up the goods inside. What were they? The boys couldn't see.

'Sheets of lead, I think,' whispered Colin. 'Peter, when are we going to telephone the police? Don't you think we'd better do that now?'

'Yes,' whispered back Peter. 'Come on. There's a telephone in that little brick building over there. I noticed telephone wires going to the chimney there this afternoon. One of the windows is a bit open. We'll get in there. Where's Scamper? Oh, there you are. Now, not a sound, old boy!'

Scamper had behaved perfectly. Not a bark, not a whine had come from him, though he was very puzzled by the evening's happenings. He trotted at Peter's heels as the four boys went to telephone.

They had to pass the lorry on the way. Peter stopped dead and listened. No one was in the lorry. The men were still unloading the truck.

To the astonishment of the other three, he left them, leapt up into the driving seat and down again.

'Whatever are you doing?' whispered Jack.

'I took the key that turns on the engine!' said Peter, excited. 'Now they can't drive the lorry away!'

'Golly!' said the others, lost in admiration at Peter's quickness. 'You *are* smart, Peter!'

They went to the little stone building. The door was locked, but, as Peter said, a window was open just a little. It was easy to force it up. In went Peter and flashed his torch round quickly to find the telephone. Ah yes, there it was. Good!

He switched off his torch and picked up the receiver. He heard the operator's voice.

'Number, please?'

'Police station – quickly!' said Peter.

And in two seconds a voice came again. 'Police station here.'

'Is the Inspector there, please?' asked Peter, urgently. 'Please tell him it's Peter, and I want to speak to him quickly.'

This peculiar message was passed on to the Inspector, who happened to be in the room. He came to the telephone at once.

'Yes, yes? Peter who? Oh *you*, Peter! What's up?'

Peter told him. 'Sir, I can't tell you all the details now,

but the 6.2 goods train has been switched off the main-line on to the side-line here, near Kepley, where there's a goods yard. And there is a gang of men unloading lead from one of the waggons into a lorry nearby. I think a man called Cheeky Charlie is in charge of things, sir.'

'Cheeky Charlie! Chee – How do *you* know anything about that fellow?' cried the Inspector, filled with amazement. 'All right, don't waste time telling me now. I'll send men out straight away. Look out for them, and look out for yourselves too. That gang is dangerous. Cheeky Charlie, well, my word!'

Sixteen

Hurrah for the Secret Seven!

It seemed a long time before any police cars came. The four boys were so excited that they could not keep still. Peter felt as if he really must go and see how the gang was getting on.

He crept out into the yard, and made his way to the lorry. It was dark there, and quiet. He crept forward, and suddenly bumped into someone standing still beside it.

The someone gave a shout and caught him. 'Here, who's this? What are you doing?'

Then a light was flashed on him, and Zeb's voice said: 'You! The kid who was asking questions the other day! What are you up to?'

He shook Peter so roughly that the boy almost fell over. And then Scamper came flying up!

'Grrrrrrr!' He flew at Zeb and nipped him sharply on the leg. Zeb gave a yell. Two of the other men came running up. 'What's the matter? What's up?'

'A boy – and a dog!' growled Zeb. 'We'd better get going. Is the unloading finished? That kid may give the alarm.'

'Where is he? Why didn't you hang on to him?' said one of the men, angrily.

'The dog bit me, and I had to let the boy go,' said Zeb, rubbing his leg. 'They've both disappeared into the fog. Come on, hurry, I've got the wind up now.'

Peter had shot back to the others, alarmed at being so nearly caught. He bent down and fondled Scamper. 'Good boy!' he whispered. 'Brave dog! Well done, Scamper!'

Scamper wagged his tail, pleased. He didn't understand in the least why Peter should have brought him to this peculiar place in a thick fog, but he was quite happy to be with him anywhere.

'When's that police car coming?' whispered Colin, shivering as much with excitement as with cold.

'Soon, I expect,' whispered back Peter. 'Ah, here it comes – no, two of them!'

The sound of cars coming down the road that led to the goods yards was plainly to be heard. They came slowly, because of the fog. They would have got there very much more quickly if the evening had been clear.

They came into the yard and stopped. Peter ran to the first one. It was driven by the Inspector, and had four policemen in it. The second car was close behind, and policemen in plain clothes tumbled swiftly out of it.

'Sir! You've come just in time!' said Peter. 'Their lorry is over there. They've loaded it now. You'll catch them just at the right moment!'

The police ran over to the dark shape in the fog, the big lorry. Zeb, Larry, Cheeky Charlie and the other men were all in it, with the load of lead behind, but try as Zeb would he could not find the starting-key of the lorry!

'Start her up quickly, you ninny!' said Cheeky

Charlie. 'The police are here! Drive the lorry at them if they try to stop us!'

'The key's gone. It must have dropped down,' wailed Zeb, and flashed a torch on to the floor below the steering-wheel. But it was not a bit of good looking there, of course. It was safely in Peter's pocket!

The police closed round the silent lorry. 'Game's up, Charlie,' said the Inspector's stern voice. 'You coming quietly, or not? We've got you right on the spot!'

'You wouldn't have, if we could have got this lorry to move!' shouted Zeb, angrily. 'Who's got the key? That's what I want to know. Who's got it?'

'I have,' called Peter. 'I took it out myself so that you couldn't get away in the lorry!'

'Good boy! Smart fellow!' said a nearby policeman,

admiringly, and gave the delighted Peter a thump on the back.

The fog suddenly thinned, and the scene became clearer in the light of many torches and lamps. The engine-driver, the fireman and the guard came out of the shed in amazement, wondering what was happening. They had been left comfortably there by Zeb, drinking tea and playing cards.

The gang made no fuss. It wasn't worth it, with so many strong men around! They were bundled into the police cars, which drove away at a faster speed than they had come, thanks to the thinning of the fog!

'I'll walk back with you,' said the Inspector's cheerful voice. 'There's no room in the cars for me now. There's a bit of a squash there at the moment!'

He told the engine-driver to report what had happened to his headquarters by telephone, and left the astonished man, and the equally astonished fireman and guard, to look after themselves and their train.

Then he and the four boys trudged back to Peter's house. How amazed his mother was when she opened the door and found four of them with the big Inspector!

'Oh dear, what have they been up to now?' she said. 'A policeman has just been round complaining about Peter trespassing on the railway the other day, with his friends. Oh, don't say he's done anything terribly wrong!'

'Well, he's certainly been trespassing on the railway again,' said the Inspector, with a broad smile, 'but what he's done this time is terribly right, not terribly wrong. Let me come in and tell you.'

So, with a very excited Janet listening, the tale of that evening was told.

'And, you see,' finished the Inspector, 'we've got our hands on Cheeky Charlie at last. He's the boss of this gang that robs the goods trucks all over the place. A clever fellow, but not *quite* so clever as the Secret Seven!'

The Inspector left at last, beaming, full of admiration once more for the Secret Seven. Peter turned to the others.

'Tomorrow,' he said solemnly, but with his face glowing – 'tomorrow we call a meeting of the Secret Seven – and we ask the Famous Five to come along too!'

'But why?' said Janet, surprised.

'Just so that we can tell them how the Secret Seven manage their affairs!' said Peter. 'And to thank them for putting us on the track of this most exciting adventure!'

'Ha! Susie won't like that!' said Jack.

'She certainly won't,' said Janet. 'Famous Five indeed! This will be the end of *them*!'

'Up with the Secret Seven!' said Jack, grinning. 'Hurrah for us – hip-hip-hurrah!'

FUN FOR THE
SECRET SEVEN

CONTENTS

One

A meeting, please!

'PETER! Peter, where are you?' shouted Janet, racing up the stairs.

'Here – in my room,' called Peter, appearing at his door and looking very cross. 'I'm tidying it up. Dad looked in this morning, and wanted to know if I *liked* living in a pigsty! He said the pigs were tidier than I am!'

'Well – he was about right,' said Janet, looking round the room. 'Do you *ever* pick anything up when you drop it? Goodness, what's this mess on the carpet – something stuck to it?'

'Oh – so *that's* where my nougat went!' said Peter, scraping a sticky mess off the carpet. 'Good thing Dad didn't tread on that – it would have stuck to his shoe for ages!'

Janet gave a delighted chuckle. 'You really are dreadfully untidy, Peter,' she said. 'I suppose I'd better tidy up your room for you before Daddy comes back again.'

'What did you want me for?' asked Peter, still scraping. 'Ooh – it's horrid, this. What a waste of a nice bar of nougat.'

'Listen, Peter – a note came through the letter-box just now. It's addressed to "Peter, Head of the Secret Seven". So it's for you. Who is it from, do you suppose?'

'Oh, one of the others wants something, I expect. Maybe a meeting of the Seven for some reason,' said Peter, tearing open the envelope. 'Yes – it's from Jack. Listen. He says:

' "*Dear Peter,*

"Will you call a meeting? I have had a strange request for help from Bob Smith. He's in our form at school, you know. He didn't say much except that he needs our help badly. He's pretty upset. Perhaps the Secret Seven can help him – he's a decent little fellow. Anyway – isn't it about time we met again, before we all forget we're the Secret Seven?

"Jack." '

'Oh dear!' said Janet. 'He sounds rather high and mighty, doesn't he? I suppose you ought to call the meetings more often, Peter. They're great fun.'

'Well, after all, so many of us go away during the summer holidays, it's hardly *worth* holding meetings then,' said Peter, rather red in the face. 'I wonder what's up with Bob Smith – and why he wants *our* help.'

'We've only got a week or so before the autumn term begins,' said Janet. 'You'll have to be quick about the meeting if we want to get all the members there.'

'Right,' said Peter. 'I'll scribble three notices of our next meeting, and you scribble two, Janet.'

So up they went to the playroom, and when Mother looked in to see why in the world they were both so

quiet, she found them busily writing out the notes. She looked over Peter's shoulder, and read what he had written.

Please come to a meeting in the shed at half past two this afternoon. No one admitted without the password. We have to discuss something important. Bob Smith will be at the meeting. I shall ask him five minutes later than anyone else, in case he overhears the password. Wear your badge else you won't be allowed in.

Peter

'Well!' said Mother, in surprise. 'Whatever does Bob Smith want help for? I think . . .'

'Oh, Mother – you shouldn't have read that bit,' said Janet. 'It might be something secret. It *will* be fun to have another meeting! Peter – do you remember the password?'

'Of course!' said Peter. 'But I bet *you* don't.'

'No – I don't,' said Janet. She grinned at Peter's solemn face. 'It's all right. I've written it down in my diary, so all I have to do is to look it up. Ha! Ha! You were sure I'd forgotten it. *You* tell me what it is – I bet you don't remember, either!'

'Yes, I do,' said Peter, crossly. 'As if the head of the Secret Seven could forget his own password! It's Scamper's name – just "Scamper". Easy!'

'Thanks!' said Janet, with a grin. 'Now I shan't have to look it up. Lovely password – Scamper!'

'Wuff!' said a surprised voice, and Scamper raised his head from the floor, where he had been lying waiting for the others to take him for a walk. He leapt up and ran to Peter, putting his lovely golden head on the boy's knee. Peter patted the soft, silky head. 'You coming to the meeting too, Scamper? All right. Half past two sharp. So don't go rabbiting after dinner, because you won't be let into the meeting-shed if you're late!'

Scamper gave a small whine, and licked Peter's hand. How *could* he be late when he was going with the two children?

'Did you remember to tell Jack in your note that he could bring Bob Smith to the meeting?' asked Janet.

'Yes. But he's to tell Bob to come five minutes *after* us, so that he doesn't hear the password, and so that we can ask Jack what's up with Bob, before we see him,' said Peter, folding up the last of his notes. 'Come on, now – we must deliver these at once, so that the others have plenty of notice about the meeting.'

They were soon on their way and went the round of Peterswood, popping the notes into various letterboxes. 'I do hope everyone will be able to come!' said Janet. 'Shall we take something to eat and drink? It's much more fun then.'

'Yes. Mother will help with that,' said Peter. 'I'll buy some sweets too. Luckily I've got some pocket-money left.'

'Well, NOT nougat, then,' said Janet, firmly. 'Even Scamper is tired of licking up dropped pieces. Buy some boiled sweets. They take ages to suck, and every-one likes them. Oh, I *am* glad we're to be the Secret Seven again! Come on, Scamper! We haven't finished yet!'

It wasn't long before all the notes had been de-livered. They caused quite a bit of excitement. As soon as one had been dropped into Jack's letter-box and he had run to pick it up, he read it and raced after the two children going out of his front gate.

'Hey! I say! Are we *really* going to have a Secret Seven meeting this afternoon? Three cheers! I thought the Secret Seven had gone west!'

'Then you were a fat-head,' said Peter, 'As soon as I had your note I arranged a meeting at once. We're all back from holiday now, and it will be fun. Bring Bob

Smith with you, as I said in my letter. We'll try to help him if we can.'

'I don't really know what's up,' said Jack. 'He didn't tell me. But I do know he's been going around looking pretty miserable. I bet we *can* help him!'

'See you at the meeting, then,' said Peter. 'I suppose you've lost your badge as usual?'

'I have *not*!' said Jack, indignantly. 'Just because I lost it once, you think I'm going to lose it always! And *I* didn't lose it then; my sister Susie took it, as you very well know.'

'Well, don't shout at me,' said Peter, grinning, 'else that awful sister of yours will hear you and try to come to the meeting with Binkie, that silly, giggly, twitchy-nosed friend of hers.'

'They're both going to a party,' said Jack, thankfully. 'So they'll be well out of the way. I do wonder what old Bob wants to tell us, don't you?'

'Well, we'll soon find out,' said Peter. 'By the way, Bob is to wait outside till we're ready to have him in. I put that in the note. Leave him some way off so that he can't hear what our password is.'

'Right,' said Jack. 'I've got the password written on the back of the calendar in my room. It's . . .'

'Well, don't shout it out, or Scamper will come rushing to you!' said Peter, with a chuckle. 'So long, Jack!'

When Peter and Janet had delivered all the notes, and had a little talk with each delighted member, they went home, *just* in time for dinner! The gong sounded as they went in at the garden door.

'Wash your hands, quick!' said Janet. 'I'll wash mine with you to save time. Put the bottle of boiled sweets where we can see them in case we forget them. All right, Mother – we're coming! JUST coming!'

Scamper raced into the dining-room with them, hungry as a hunter. Where was his bowl of meat? Ah, there it was. Good old Cookie, she had got him JUST the kind of meat he liked best. Soon he and the two children were all eating hungrily. Mother laughed.

'Anyone would think that you two and Scamper hadn't had a meal for weeks!' she said. 'Scamper – don't gobble so. You'll choke! There – I knew you would!'

However, Scamper went on gobbling and had finished his dinner almost before the children had eaten three mouthfuls. He went to his rug and lay down, yawning. Ah – that was good! He wouldn't mind eating another whole plateful! He thought it was a pity that nobody ever offered him a second helping. He shut his eyes sleepily.

'Hey – don't you fall asleep, Scamper! You have to come to a Secret Seven meeting after we've finished dinner,' called Peter.

'Woof!' said Scamper, sleepily. He shut one eye and kept the other open.

'Funny to be half asleep and half awake like that,' said Janet. 'What's in that package over there, Mother?'

'Just a few new-made buns for the hungry Secret Seven!' said Mother, smiling. 'I made them this morning.'

'Mother, you're a pet,' said Janet, and gave her a hug. 'I don't know why food tastes so nice when we all sit in the shed and talk. But it does.'

'I've some boiled sweets too,' Peter told his mother. 'And I dare say one or two of the others will bring something. Golly – it *will* be fun to have a meeting again.'

At a quarter past two Peter and Janet left the house with Scamper, and went down to the meeting-shed. They carried the buns, the sweets, and four bottles of ginger beer.

'Let's hope one of the others brings something to drink too,' said Peter. 'Four bottles of fizz won't go far between seven of us on this hot afternoon.'

'Eight, you mean. Bob will be there,' said Janet. 'Nine, with Scamper!'

'Woof!' said Scamper, agreeing, his tail wagging hard.

Nobody had yet arrived at the shed. There it stood, the letters S.S. on the door. Janet pushed it open and looked inside. The shed was quite tidy, but it needed a dusting. She took the duster from a shelf and flicked it round the seats and little table. She put the bottle of sweets and the ginger beer on the table, and looked to see if the plastic mugs on the shelf were clean. What fun it was to be welcoming the Secret Seven members once more!

A knock came on the door and Peter spoke at once. 'Password, please.'

'Scamper,' said the voice, in a low tone. And then other footsteps came and low voices spoke the password, 'Scamper! Scamper! Scamper! Scamper!'

Scamper the spaniel was delighted to hear his name so often. He began to bark loudly, and leapt excitedly up at everyone as they came in.

'Sit, Scamper! I shan't use your name for a password again if you get so excited,' said Peter. 'Anyone would think *you* were the head of this meeting, not me! Sit!'

Scamper sat, his tail wagging beneath him. Oh, how good to see all the Seven again – Colin – Pam – Barbara – George – and Jack – and Peter and Janet, of course.

Jack had come in alone, leaving his friend Bob outside as he had been told. They all sat down, and Peter sat on the stool at the head of the little table.

'Welcome!' he said. 'I'm glad you all remembered the password, and said it quietly. Now, Jack – will you please tell us exactly why you have called this meeting? But first call in Bob – he'll have plenty to tell us!'

Two

Bob Smith's story

THE Secret Seven meeting was soon under way. Jack stood up to tell everyone why he had wanted it called that afternoon. He looked worried, and spoke earnestly.

'Thanks awfully, Peter, for calling a meeting so quickly. You see, it's on account of something Bob told me. I saw him looking pretty worried yesterday and I asked him what was the matter and he told me about Old Man Tolly.'

'Old Man Tolly? The old fellow who lives in that tumbledown house on the top of the hill?' asked Peter, in surprise. 'What's the matter with him? *You* tell us all about it, Bob!'

'Well – he lives all alone except for an old horse and his dog,' said Bob. 'You've often seen that nice old horse – brown and white, with a lovely mane. Tolly's cottage has two rooms, and he lives in one, and Brownie the horse lives in the other.'

'Goodness – how odd!' said Pam.

'Not really,' said Bob. 'He loves that old horse. When old Tolly worked for the farmer on the hill beyond, he and the horse were together all the time. The horse was strong then, and could pull carts and wagons and goodness knows what. Then one day it pulled a heavy cart-load of stones down that big hill – and the weight made the cart run too quickly for the old horse, and it ran into his back legs and lamed them.

So he wasn't any use for heavy work any more.'

'What happened then?' asked Peter.

'Well – the farmer blamed Tolly for the accident,' said Bob, 'and he said the horse was only fit to be shot, *he* wasn't going to buy fodder for him, if he couldn't work for his keep.'

'Oh! How DREADFUL!' said Pam and Janet together, tears coming suddenly into their eyes. 'Poor old horse!'

'Well, Tolly was heart-broken,' said Bob. 'He was sure that the horse-doctor – that vet man called Whistler – could make the horse's legs right again, and he called him in.'

'Good for him!' said Peter, and the others nodded.

'Well, it might have been good for the vet, but it

wasn't very good for old Tolly,' said Bob. 'The farmer wouldn't pay the vet's fees, though the horse was his, and told him to send the bills to *Tolly* – and they came to over ten pounds!'

'Goodness!' said Peter, startled. 'What a lot of money! Surely Tolly couldn't pay all that?'

'Of course he couldn't,' said Bob. 'Apart from his pension, his wages are so low – he's old, you see, and can only potter about, and now he's really ill with worry. I was up there yesterday – my mother sent me up with some eggs – he used to work for us once, and we're fond of him . . . And he told me all about it then. He showed me the vet's bills too. Whew! I do think the vet might have kept his fees low.'

'My father won't use that new vet,' said Peter. 'He says he's too young and too hard. He hasn't learnt to love animals properly yet. He wouldn't even come to one of our cows one night when it got caught in a fallen tree. Poor thing, the tree had fallen on top of it in a high wind, and it was scared stiff, and one of its horns was broken.'

'Will he have old Tolly sent to prison if he can't pay?' asked Pam, in a frightened voice.

There was a shocked silence as the children thought of poor old Tolly all alone in prison, without the dog he loved, and without the horse whose friend he was.

'Have you come to us for advice?' asked Peter, at last. 'Is there something you want us to do?'

'Well – I simply don't know what *I* can do to help, and I thought you Secret Seven might have some ideas,' said Bob, looking round at them all, his face very worried indeed. 'How can old Tolly pay that bill? Where can he put the old horse now, so that the farmer won't take him away? I'm no good at solving puzzles like these – but I thought you Secret Seven could help somehow.'

There was a little silence, and then Janet spoke up, her eyes bright. 'Well, to begin with, I'm willing to empty my money-box to help to pay the vet's fees. Then that farmer won't have to worry about those, the mean old thing!'

Everyone began to talk at once.

'Yes, that's the first thing to do – pay the bill!'

'No! *I* think the first thing to do is to find somewhere to keep the old horse safely. Don't let's have him left anywhere near that horrid farmer!' That was Pam speaking, very, very fiercely!

'Yes – Pam's right,' said Peter, knocking on the little table for silence. 'Pam's absolutely right. We *must* get the old horse out of that farmer's reach if possible.'

'Well, that would be easy – if we knew anywhere he could live,' said George. 'He's a big horse – I know him. He would need a decent stable, not a tiny shed.'

'Peter – wouldn't Dad let us have a place in one of our stables?' said Janet. 'Just for the time being, anyway. Dad wouldn't charge a penny, I know!'

'That's a good idea of yours, Janet,' said Peter. 'But remember, if we take that old horse away and stable him somewhere here, that horrid farmer may come after us, and charge us with stealing the horse!'

'Oh my goodness!' said Pam, scared. 'What can we do then? We've simply *got* to do something!'

'Well – we could find out how much the farmer wants for the old horse, and see if we can possibly earn enough money ourselves to pay for him,' said George. 'We've all got money-boxes. And if we hadn't enough, we could jolly well earn some more. What's the use of the Secret Seven if they can't tackle a thing like this?'

Bob flushed red with excitement. He stood up and spoke earnestly to the meeting. 'I KNEW the Secret Seven would do something. I KNEW they would. I think you're fine. Well – I really can't TELL you what I think!'

'That's all right, Bob,' said Peter, kindly. 'We are all glad you came to us about this. We'll do SOMETHING, you may be sure – with your help too, of course. You can't be a member of the Secret Seven, but you can certainly be a helper with us, in whatever we do about this problem.'

Peter then addressed the meeting. 'I shall ask my father to let us have a stall in one of the old stables. Bob, will you please find out from Mr Tolly exactly how much the vet's bills are – there may be more than one – and if possible *get* the bills – and we could ask the vet if he would be generous enough to take some of the fees off, so that there won't be so much to pay.'

'Well – whatever the bills come to, even if the vet reduces them, old *Tolly* can't pay,' said Bob. 'He's only got his pension – his work is just a few jobs here and there for the odd pound.'

'We want someone to clear up our orchard,' said George. 'I'll ask Dad to get old Tolly, and pay him.'

Ideas came thick and fast, and everyone was sorry

when a knock came at the door, and Peter's mother put in her head. 'I'm afraid the meeting must soon stop. It's getting quite late!'

'Right, Mother,' said Peter, and waited till his mother had gone. 'Now listen, everyone. This needs a lot of thinking about – a lot of considering. I am now going to close the meeting, and everyone is to go home, and think HARD this evening to get some kind of good idea about this problem. Come back here tomorrow morning at ten – you too, Bob – and we will sort out all our ideas and decide exactly what the Secret Seven can do to help – decide the BEST way to help. Tonight I shall ask my father about a shed or a place in our stable. That's the most important thing at present.'

'Oh, thank you, Peter,' said Bob, his face red with delight. 'I shan't worry tonight. I know you'll all think of something super by tomorrow. I wish I had your brains.'

'You've got something better, Bob,' said Pam, unexpectedly. 'You've got a VERY kind heart!'

And then out came the new buns and the fizzy ginger beer. Out came the boiled sweets and some chocolate and biscuits brought by Jack and Pam. What a feast!

When the little feast was over, the meeting broke up, and everyone went their way. They certainly had something to think about that night – something very difficult – something that had to be dealt with at once.

Good old Secret Seven! Think hard, and see what *you* can do!

Three

Plenty of ideas

At exactly ten o'clock the next morning there came a number of raps on the Secret Seven shed-door. The password, which was still 'Scamper', was whispered through the door and Scamper, who was inside with Peter and Janet, cocked his ears with pleasure every time he heard his name. He gave little whimpers of delight as the Seven filed in and took their places.

Last of all came Bob, out of breath with running. 'Had to do a job for my father,' he panted. 'Hope I'm not late.'

'We shouldn't have started without you,' said Peter. 'It's important that everyone should be here. Now, the meeting will begin. Stop chattering, please, Pam and Barbara.'

The two girls stopped at once, and faced Peter. This would be a worth-while and exciting meeting, and they didn't want to miss a word!

'The meeting has now begun,' said Peter. 'Please address any remarks to me, because if we all start chattering to one another, we shan't get anywhere. First of all, I must tell you that Janet and I have asked our father about a place in one of our stables for Mr Tolly's horse.'

'He said yes,' began Janet, eagerly, and stopped as Peter spoke to her sternly.

'Janet! *I* was speaking!' said Peter. 'Please let me finish.'

'Sorry,' said Janet, going red.

'I'm very pleased to say that my father was sorry for Mr Tolly, and said that the farmer who owns the land on the hill was very hard-hearted,' said Peter, and everyone nodded in agreement.

'He said he would willingly give us a place in our biggest stable for Mr Tolly's horse – and he wouldn't charge him anything. BUT – he said he thought that Janet and I might like to keep the stable clean ourselves, so that the stable man wouldn't have to do any more work than usual.'

'I'll take my turn at that!' said George. 'No reason why you and Janet should have to muck it out all the time. I'd be pleased to come every Saturday.'

'Look – we'll *all* take turns,' said Colin. 'All of us. Why not? We've taken this thing on together, and we'll jolly well all share in everything. I'll come each Monday after tea.'

'And I'll come whenever I can,' said Bob. 'I must take my share. I'd like to – if the Secret Seven don't mind me butting in.'

'I think we'd better make you a temporary member,' said Peter, and the others nodded at once in agreement. Peter solemnly knocked on the table.

'I propose that we make Bob Smith a temporary member, until the matter he has brought to us is well and truly settled,' he said, in a very grown-up voice. 'Does the meeting agree to this proposal?'

Everyone agreed very loudly indeed. 'And now,'

said Peter, 'I'd like to hear whether Bob has found out exactly what amount the vet's bill is.'

Everyone looked so solemnly at Bob that he felt he must stand up. He looked round at the others, feeling just a little wobbly on his legs. 'Er – thank you very much for saying that I can be a temper – tempory – well whatever it is – member. It's jolly kind of you. Yes, I did go and find out about the vet's bill. I went to Mr Whistler and I just asked him straight out how much old Mr Tolly owed him.'

'What did he say?' asked Peter.

'Well – he looked a bit startled, and asked me why I wanted to know,' said Bob. 'And I told him we were sorry for Mr Tolly, because he was afraid the horse would be shot if the bills weren't paid – and that we would do our best to get at least *some* of the money pretty soon, if he would wait.'

Bob paused for breath and everyone looked anxiously at him. What had the vet said?

'Well, the vet was jolly decent. He said that he hadn't understood that Mr Tolly would have to pay – and he said he would reduce the bill by half – and that I was to tell Mr Tolly he wasn't to worry, and that he'd still go on coming to see the horse and how it was getting on – and not charge him a penny more!'

'That was marvellous of him!' said Janet, her face one big smile. 'Did you tell him *we* would pay the bill ourselves, if he'd let us have time to earn the money?'

'Yes, I did, and he looked so astonished that I was sure he didn't believe me. He asked me what on earth we thought we could do to earn so much money. Even if he halved his bill, there would still be nearly eight pounds to pay. He said that Brownie's legs had needed daily attention for some time, and that was why his fees had mounted up. Actually they came to fifteen pounds fifty pence – and half that would be seven pounds seventy-five pence!'

'What did you say?' asked Peter.

'I just said that we'd talk it all over at our next Secret Seven meeting, and I'd let him know. I didn't like to make big promises on my own,' said Bob. 'But I did ask him if there was anything *he* wanted done, which one of *us* might be able to do.'

'*Was* there anything?' asked Colin, eagerly.

'Yes. He said his delivery boy – you know, Fred, who delivers any medicines for animals that the vet has seen during the day – well, he said Fred wanted two weeks' holiday to go and stay with his grandfather, and if any of us would like to do his rounds each evening, he'd pay him the same as he pays Fred.'

'How much is that?' demanded three or four voices at once.

'He pays him fifteen pence a night,' said Bob. 'So I said *I'd* take Fred's place while he was away. You see, if I earn fifteen pence a night for a whole fortnight – let's see, that's fourteen evenings at fifteen pence a time – er – er – that would be . . .'

'You're no good at figures, Bob!' said Jack. 'You would earn exactly two pounds ten pence – and let me tell you, that's a lot of money! It would probably pay over a quarter of the vet's bill – golly, this *is* a bit of luck, your getting the errand boy's job for a fortnight.

If you get tired of it, one or other of us will take over for you.'

'I shan't get tired of it,' said Bob. 'The only thing is, I have to have one evening off a week to go to choir practice, so one of you can take over then.'

'Right. I'll do that evening for you this week,' said Peter. 'My word – fancy being able to knock off over a quarter of the vet's bill like this! Good for you, Bob. You did well.'

Bob sat down, his face flushed with pride. He decided to be the best errand boy that the vet had ever had. He decided to ask him if he could clean out the kennels in which the vet kept dogs when they were boarded out with him. That would be more money earned, perhaps. And would the vet like him to feed the cats each morning – or . . . Bob's mind ran on and on, and when he finally came to the end of his thoughts about the vet's jobs, he felt almost like a vet himself!

Yes – it WAS fun to be one of the Secret Seven – or was it the Secret Eight now? Bob made up his mind to be the best member they had ever had. His heart swelled with pride. A member of the Secret Seven – and the vet's errand-boy too – he really was getting on in the world!

Four

Mr Tolly – Brownie – and Codger

In bed that night Peter thought about the successful
meeting the Secret Seven had had that day. He and
Janet were to clean out the stables in return for shelter
for Mr Tolly's horse. The others would do their share
of stable-cleaning too. Bob was to be an errand-boy –
and they could take turns with him, if he wished. There
must also be quite a bit of money in the money-boxes
belonging to the Secret Seven. That would help to pay
for fodder for Mr Tolly's horse. He would need something more than grass to eat . . .

Peter's thoughts grew muddled, and he found himself drifting off to sleep. He was happy. His worries
about Mr Tolly and his horse began to fade, and his
eyes closed in sleep. His last thoughts were of money-
boxes – he must tell the members to open – their – to
open their – money-boxes. Yes, their money-boxes!
And then, with his thoughts getting all twisted up, he
slid into dreams – queer dreams in which Mr Tolly,
dressed as a little horse, ran about delivering medicine
bottles to all the cows in his father's field!

Next morning Peter and Janet set off with Scamper
to find Mr Tolly in his little tumbledown cottage on the
side of the hill. He must be told the good news – that
the Secret Seven were going to earn money to pay Mr
Whistler's bills. Then he wouldn't worry any more

about having to sell his brown and white horse.

There was the little cottage, whitewashed, leaning against the hill. Down in the valley below were flocks of sheep, every nose touching the grass in the meadow as they fed. Playing round them was Codger, a nice but ugly little mongrel dog, who thought his master was the finest man he had ever seen!

'Mr Tolly isn't with the sheep,' said Janet, looking down the hill. 'He must still be in his cottage. Let's go and see.'

As soon as the little mongrel dog saw the children going towards his master's cottage, he came tearing up the hill at top speed, barking fiercely. Who was this, DARING to go to his master's house? He barked round their ankles, and Janet was a little scared.

'Don't take any notice of his barking,' said Peter. 'He's only behaving like a good little watchdog. Come on, little dog – take us to your master!'

Tolly wasn't in his cottage. The children knocked and knocked, and finally tried the door. It opened. They peeped inside. The cottage was trim and neat and clean. Old Tolly couldn't keep it like that himself, surely! They went round to the back, where there was a small garden with a vegetable plot, and a washing-line. Taking down a sheet was a thin little women.

'Hallo!' said Peter, surprised to see a woman there. 'Is Mr Tolly in?'

'No, he's gone to do his shopping,' said the little woman. 'Look, isn't that him coming up the hill? Run and take that heavy bag from him. I've just finished his washing.'

The two children went to meet Tolly, and he was very glad to give them his bag of shopping. His dog raced to meet him in delight, barking loudly. His beloved master was back again! Scamper, who was with the children, jumped up eagerly at the old man, too, for he knew him well. Tolly laughed and sat down on an old wooden seat he had made years ago.

'That hill!' he said. 'It gets steeper and steeper, I do declare! I'll get my breath in a minute. So you've made friends with Codger, have you? Fourteen years old, he is, and as good as any five-year-old. Down, Codger, you'll be tearing the young lady's jumper!'

'Oh, I don't mind him jumping at me,' said Janet. 'I think he's a fine little dog. He's got such a nice face too. I like dogs with nice faces. Some have rather fierce ones.'

'Aye, he's a good, kind little dog,' said Tolly. 'When I broke my leg two years since, and laid out there in the rain, at the bottom of the hill, Codger stayed with me all night long. Wet and cold he was, and miserable, but he warmed me all he could, and when morning came, he left me and went to the farmer's place, and pulled at his coat to make him come to me. Aye, he's a good little fellow. My old horse is a good 'un too. I'm a lucky man I am – I've got the two best friends a man can have – a horse and a dog. Come and see the old horse.'

They went to the old, draughty, tumbledown cottage. A brown and white horse put his great head out over a half-door, and nuzzled Tolly and the children. He tried to nuzzle Codger too, but he couldn't reach far enough down over the door. Codger leapt up and

licked him on the nose. Tolly undid the door catch and
the great horse lumbered out at once, keeping close to
Tolly.

The old man fondled both the dog and the horse,
talking to them gently. He looked tired and ill. The
little woman in the house came out with a cup of tea for
him.

'Here, old man, you come and sit down after that
long walk up the hill,' she said. 'You leave your horse
be, he's all right. You're for ever a-mothering of him,
and bless me if he doesn't mother you too – or try to.
Look at him nuzzling about you! Or maybe you've
biscuits in your pockets?'

'Yes, yes, I have – and old Brownie knows it,' said
old Tolly.

'You'll have to look after him well!' said the little
woman, jokingly. 'There's horse-thieves about this district, so I've heard. One of these nights they'll come
and steal your old horse away!'

The old man sat down suddenly on a near-by seat.
He looked upset. 'HORSE-thieves!' he said. 'They'd like
my brownie, so they would. He's got good blood in
him, Brownie has. The prizes he won when he was
younger! I've got them all in the cottage. You must see
them, youngsters, you must see them. Horse-thieves
you say, Mam, horse-thieves! Where can I put my
Brownie?'

'If you think there *is* any danger of Brownie being
stolen, bring him down to our stable,' said Peter. 'We
had already decided it would be a good place for him
to live, if you'd like him to. He can't go back to that

horrid farmer. And you could bring your little dog Codger too – see how he has made friends with Scamper! Goodness, he can run as fast as our spaniel – faster! Do come down to stay at the farm, and bring the horse and dog. You can have the shepherd's old hut. He's not using it now the lambing season's over.'

'Yes now, Mr Tolly, you do that,' said the little woman, who had been listening all the time. 'You take your horse down to Peter's stables, and Codger as well. If you can have the shepherd's hut, you'll be right grand in it! Go on now – I'll get my sister Agnes to keep an eye on you and the cottage – she'll do your shopping for you too. You go this very minute, with the children. I know their mother, I've worked for her at spring-cleaning time. She'll maybe give you an easy job or two to do. And while you're gone I'll give your old cottage a right good turn-out!'

The old man didn't quite know what to say. Peter took his arm. 'You come with us. You *couldn't* let Brownie be stolen. He'll be safe in our stable. Come along, come along!'

Before old Tolly quite knew what was happening he found himself being led down the hill to the valley below, where the farm lay, peaceful and lovely. Brownie and Codger followed behind. Tolly was quite bemused and certainly more than a little scared by the mention of horse-stealing. His long memory stretched through the years, bringing back vivid pictures of his sorrow when horse-stealers had taken six of his most-prized shire-horses.

'Aye,' he suddenly said, out loud. 'Aye! I reckon old

Brownie would be safe down in your father's stables, youngster – and I'll be sleeping alongside of him. Mebbe your Dad has got a few jobs I can still do. I don't like working for Mester Dinneford now – he's hard, he is, and he don't understand that animals have got to be loved as well as fed. He don't love even a lamb – no, nor even his dog. And he was going to shoot old Brownie that's worked for him for years – just because he hurt his back legs working for him.'

'Don't worry any more,' said Peter and Janet together. But the old fellow went on worrying. 'You see – old Brownie's really Mester Dinneford's, not mine – but I've cared for him all the years, and he's like a brother to me now. It nigh broke my heart when that heavy-loaded cart ran on to his poor old back legs!'

Janet was upset to see a large tear run slowly down

old Tolly's rough cheek. She slipped her arm through his. 'Don't you worry any more,' she said. 'You shall come and live in our shepherd's old hut, and when Brownie is in our stable, quite safe, you'll feel happy.'

'The vet can come and see his legs and make sure that they get quite better,' said Peter, saying everything that he could possibly think of, to comfort the old fellow. But this didn't bring any comfort at all! Tolly stopped as if he had been shot, and pulled his arm away from Peter. He faced him, looking very scared.

'The vet – Mr Whistler?' he said. 'I'll have to go to prison if his bill isn't paid. That's what Farmer Dinneford told me! Go to prison, and leave my dog and Brownie behind! Mester Dinneford wouldn't bother to feed them – they'd be dead when I came out. No, no, young sir, you be very kind, I know, but I can't have that Mr Whistler any more. Mester Dinneford, he says I'M to pay those bills, because he reckons it was my fault that old Brownie got so badly hurt. He knows I think of Brownie as my own – I've looked after him so many years now, and we've worked together for the master, and . . .'

He broke off and bent down to pat Codger, who was very worried because his master sounded so angry and so sad. He licked old Tolly's hand gently.

'How much money would Farmer Dinneford ask for Brownie?' said Peter.

'Old Brownie wouldn't fetch much now, young sir,' said Tolly. 'He's old, and now that his back legs are weak-like, because of that heavy cart running into them, he's not all that good for farm-work. But he still

417

costs as much in fodder, and those vet-bills are a real worry. I'm right down afraid that Mester Dinneford will think he's not worth his keep any more, and – and will have him shot.'

'Don't you worry,' said Peter, feeling quite desperate. 'We'll see that he's not shot. Er – Janet and I are thinking of buying him ourselves – and then he'd be quite safe, wouldn't he?'

Janet stared at Peter in the greatest surprise. *Buy old Brownie?* Where would they get the money from? What would their father say? Would Farmer Dinneford sell him? Yes, probably – but he would put a good price on the old horse if he thought that somebody else wanted him! She tugged at Peter's arm.

But he shook off her hand impatiently. 'Well, Tolly, what price do you think Farmer Dinneford would want?'

Tolly had been so surprised when he heard Peter say that he and Janet were thinking of buying Brownie that he just couldn't say a word. He gaped at Peter, opening and shutting his mouth like a fish.

'Well – what price *would* Brownie be?' asked Peter again. 'Ten pounds, do you think?'

'Oh more than that, youngster, more than that,' said Tolly, finding his voice. 'Why, you and the little Missy couldn't possibly buy a horse. What pocket-money do you get – twenty pence a week?'

'We've saved up quite a bit,' said Peter. 'But we couldn't pay more than ten pounds between us.'

Tolly shook his head. 'Mester Dinneford would say twenty pounds, mebbe more,' he said. 'Though I'd say meself that's too high a price for an old horse that's got poor hind legs. Them legs might go weak any day, and then Brownie would be no good at anything except cropping the grass.'

Peter gave a heavy sigh. What a pity he wasn't grown up. He could then do as his father did – go to the bank and take out quite large sums of money. He could buy Brownie easily then!

'Er – my friends and I are going to help to pay the vet's bill – Mr Whistler's account,' said Peter. 'I thought I'd tell you now, to save you worrying. We haven't got the money yet, but we're earning some. One of my friends is working for the vet at night – taking round medicines. He reckons he'll earn two pounds ten pence in two weeks.'

'And Dad says that if we muck out the stable and keep it decent when Brownie comes, he'll provide the old horse with free fodder,' said Janet. 'And I bet the others are thinking of some more ideas too. So don't you worry, Mr Tolly. We'll be sure to get enough money for the vet – and Brownie will be safe from harm down in our stable – he'll be happy with the other horses. They're nice ones – they don't kick or anything like that. I'm sure they'd love Brownie.'

'Oh Missy, what's all this you're saying?' said old Tolly, staring at the two children in surprise. 'I've heard your Dad is a good kind man, and it's certain that he's got children like himself! All right, Brownie and me, we'll leave Mester Dinneford. I'll leave Brownie with you, and come to sleep in the stables at night – and work out a week's notice with Mester Dinneford. He'd be after me if I left at a moment's notice. And don't you say a word to anyone about my Brownie being with you – in case the farmer hears of it and comes after him. Not a word!'

'We certainly won't!' said Janet. 'Look, here we are. Let's go into the stable. We've already chosen a stall for Brownie, next to a nice kind horse – and there's plenty of good fresh hay for him!'

They all went into the stables, Codger wagging his tail fast. This was quite an adventure! Brownie gave a little whinny, as he smelt the horsy-smell, and tapped on the floor with his foot as if to say, 'Very nice. Very nice indeed!'

There were no other horses in the stables. They were all out working, or feeding in the fields. Brownie began to nibble at the fodder in his stall.

'Look at that now. He's at home already,' said Peter. 'Good old horse. You're safe here, Brownie. Come down tonight and sleep in the stables with him, Mr Tolly. You'll *both* be safe – and happy – and warm. You come down here, see?'

Five

The police vet calls

AFTER tea time that same day Tolly arrived at the farm to sleep in the stables with Brownie. He found the children's father waiting to see him.

'Ah, Tolly – I see you've put your horse – or is it Mr Dinneford's horse? – safely in our stable,' he said. 'Well, I'm glad to see it there, as, according to the children, there's a chance of it being shot because of the accident it had. But – er – what does Mr Dinneford, your master, say about this arrangement? I hope you told him. I've examined the horse's hind legs myself, and they're not right yet, by any means. I doubt if he'll be any good for farm-work now. Nice horse too – good strong animal.'

'Yes, sir,' said Tolly, anxiously. 'The vet said his legs *would* get better, he thought – but slowly, sir. And I expect you know that Mester Dinneford, he's impatient-like, and he won't keep any animal that can't do much, but eats its head off all the time, and costs money in fodder, and . . .'

'Yes, yes. I know your master's reputation,' said Peter's father. 'Well, I'm willing to let you and the horse sleep in my stable at night, in order that Brownie shan't be shot. If you've given notice to your master, I'll take you on myself, as I'm short of a man. You'd do general work – horses – sheep – field-work, and so on. What about it?'

'Well, sir, I'm very, very grateful indeed. I've given in my notice, sir, and Mester Dinneford, he was right down angry with me, and said I must go at once. And, sir, he said he was going to shoot Brownie tonight, as I wouldn't be there to see to him and his bad legs. They have to be rubbed at night, sir, with this liniment stuff that the vet gave me. The master, he said the vet was making a fuss, but this stuff is good, sir. It's helping Brownie's legs, I know it is.'

'Right. Keep it then, because you'll be in charge of Brownie, with the two children as your helpes,' said Peter's father. 'And don't worry about the horse – he'll be safe here. In any case I shall get in touch with the police in case of any trouble.'

'Yes, sir,' said Tolly and touched his cap. Well! he thought, this is the kind of man I want to work for. Knows his own mind – kind – sensible – forthright. And I've got old Brownie too. What'll happen if Mester Dinneford comes after him, though?

But Peter's father had thought about that. He had telephoned the police and had told them about his engagement of Tolly, and the fact that the man had brought the horse to him.

'Dinneford was going to shoot it – or so he says,' said Peter's father to the police sergeant who answered the telephone. 'I'm willing to buy it off him at a reasonable price to save its being shot. The horse's hind legs are no good at the moment, so he's a bit of an old crock – but they may mend. Shall I get the vet in to say what he's

worth at the moment – in case Dinneford makes a fuss, and puts an enormous price on the horse?'

'No, sir – don't get Mr Whistler,' said the police sergeant. 'Better get our own police vet – he'll be here soon to look over the police horses we have for our two mounted police – the ones that go round the markets when there are great crowds about. Wonderful what a horse can do, when crowds gather, and won't clear away. People scatter like sheep when the police horses gallop up! I'll ask our vet to go down to your place tonight, sir. Thank you. Good evening, sir!'

So that night the police vet came along, smart and spruce, and very quick. He examined old Brownie from head to tail, from shoulders to hooves, looked into his mouth and even inside his ears! Tolly stood near by, looking very anxious. He didn't know *what* to think!

If he says the horse is fine, strong as can be, healthy and able to work hard, it'll mean he's worth a lot of money, and I shan't be able to pay the price for him, he thought. And if they think he's a poor old horse, because of his accident, I'll not dare to work him, in case of harming him. I don't know WHAT to wish for!

The police vet went to talk to Peter's father when he had finished.

'Well, sir,' he said, 'he's a good horse, as good as ever he was. But he does need gentle handling, sir. He's a bit nervy. That may be because of the accident he had, of course. If he could be handled now by someone he knows and trusts, he'll soon be all right – but don't let any stranger handle him, sir – he'll get more nervy, and not be a bit of use to anyone in a few months' time.

Gently does it, sir, with that horse. I'd take him off your hands myself, if I could. He's a beauty!'

'Thanks very much indeed, Sergeant,' said Peter's father, pleased. 'You've said more or less what I myself thought. What would he be worth now, if anyone bought him?'

'Well, sir, not much if you sell him to a stranger, or to a bad handler,' said the vet. 'He seems happy enough here. Why don't you keep him? You wouldn't get more than ten or fifteen pounds for him now, with those damaged back legs. But a patient owner, who wouldn't work the horse at all for say, six months, would find he had a first-class horse at the end of that time, strong, willing, and as good as ever!'

'Fine, fine!' said Peter's father, and the two children, who were listening, squeezed each other's arms in delight. Now Brownie would be bought – and kept. And Tolly would come to them, and have a good job, and be with the horse he loved!

How they hoped that Mr Dinneford wouldn't want Brownie any more! Anyway, he'd be safe with them for some time, recovering slowly in their stables!

Six

Brownie gets a new home

WHEN the police vet had gone, Peter's father and mother, Mr Tolly and the two children and Scamper went into the summer-house for a good long talk.

'We have to decide straight away what we can do about Brownie,' said Mr Tolly, anxiously. 'He can't go back to Mester Dinneford, sir, to the farm. He'd be worked and worked there, or shot, maybe, and he's not as strong as he was. Have you examined his hind legs, sir? What did *you* think of them?'

'Well, it's a toss-up, Tolly,' said Peter's father. 'With careful, friendly handling Brownie might be as good as ever in six months' time – but his hind legs are definitely not strong enough for hard work yet. But who's going to keep a horse for six months or maybe longer and not work him – and possibly find at the end of that time he's no good at all? It would be money down the drain for anyone who bought him then.'

'Sir – would you tell Mester Dinneford that?' asked Tolly, anxiously. 'If he'd sell Brownie now, while he would go cheap, I'd buy him. I wouldn't work him at all for six months, and I'd be glad to buy his fodder and see to him. I shall soon be leaving the farm up on the hill there – I can't work for Mester Dinneford any longer, and anyway, I've given in my notice. I could go somewhere with Brownie, and get a job for myself, and see that the old horse was quiet and happy till his legs were quite mended.'

'You know you can stay here, Tolly,' said Peter's father. 'You're an old man now, you want a quiet job, with not too much heavy work. If you like to come to me and see to my horses for me, as I said, you'd be welcome. Sleep in the stables, or in the shepherd's old hut, or out on the hills, wherever you please.'

'Thank you kindly, sir, you're a real gentleman,' said Tolly, warmly. He turned to Peter. 'Yes – you're lucky, you are – that's a *real* gentleman your father is, and just see that you grow up like him, young sir. You won't go far wrong, then!'

Peter grinned, delighted at this praise of his father. 'Are you going to buy Brownie from my father?' he said. 'That's if Mr Dinneford will sell him, of course – and I bet he will if he thinks he can't work Brownie for ages.'

'Young sir, I haven't even five pounds to my name!' said Tolly. 'Else I'd buy him this very minute. What with having to pay out for my rent and fire and light and clothes and food, and with having to help an old invalid sister of mine, I don't have as much money to spare as you have! But I'm going to ask your Dad if he'll keep back so much of my wages each week, so that when I've about ten pounds saved, I can buy Brownie for my very own. That's if Mester Dinneford will sell the horse to your father, of course!'

'Mr Tolly, would you let us share Brownie with you, if we pay *half* the ten pounds for him?' asked Janet. 'If he's coming to live here with us, I'd so like to think we could share him.'

'You can share him all you like, when he's mine,' said Tolly. 'You can consider him half yours and half mine. He'd like that. He likes children. You don't need to pay me.'

'Oh but we must,' said Peter. 'We shouldn't feel as if he really *was* half ours, if we hadn't paid something for him. We'll buy the half with the bad legs, if you like, so that you can have the best half.'

'Well, whatever will you say next?' said Tolly, astonished. 'Now look – you save up and buy half of him if you badly want to. I know how you feel. I feel like that myself. I shan't be happy till I've paid over that ten pounds to your father and then can look at old Brownie and say to myself, "You beauty, you're mine. I've worked for you, and cared for you, and paid for you – and now you're mine to look after for the rest of *your* life!" There's something about horses that just *gets* me. And old Brownie – well, he's – he's . . .'

'The best horse in the world!' finished Peter, with a laugh. 'I feel rather like that about Scamper, our dog. You know – best dog in all the world! Are you, Scamper? Cook says you're just a scrounger with muddy feet and an inquisitive nose. But *I* think you're the Best Dog in the World!'

'Woof!' said Scamper, wagging his tail very fast indeed. 'Woof!' He ran to Peter and licked first one of his hands and then the other. Peter patted him lovingly. 'Old fuss-pot! You do love a bit of petting, don't you? Good lad Scamper! Good dog, then!'

Peter's father was standing by, very much amused by all this. 'Well – when we've all finished saying nice things to each other, I think we'd better go in,' he said. 'It will soon be supper-time. Hallo – who's this?'

There was a clattering of hooves, and a pony-cart drew up outside the front gate. 'WHOA!' said an enormous voice.

'It's Mr Dinneford!' said Janet, in a fright. 'Oh Daddy, Daddy – DON'T let him take Brownie away, will you?'

'Of course not. Go indoors,' said her father. 'Both of you. Look out of the window if you like, but no listening. You stay here, Tolly.'

The children fled indoors and pulled a curtain so that they might look out and see what happened. Oh dear – how dreadful if Brownie was taken away!

They could hear loud voices, but couldn't understand a word. The three men were very angry.

'Tolly! What do you mean by stealing my horse?' shouted Mr Dinneford.

'You said you were going to shoot him, so he was as good as dead, wasn't he?' shouted back Tolly. 'I'm not going to let a good horse like that be shot, even if he *has* got useless hind legs.'

'Useless! You're about right there!' yelled Mr Dinneford. 'Why should I keep a useless horse, eating his head off in my stables? He's *my* horse, isn't he? Can't I do what I like with my own horses?'

'Within reason, Dinneford, within reason,' said Peter's father. 'But *you* need horses that are strong enough to pull very heavy loads – and that horse will

never pull loads again. He will be quite useless to you. Why don't you sell him for what you can get?'

'How do you know he's useless?' yelled Mr Dinneford, angrier than ever.

'Well – we had the police vet here just a little while ago,' said Mr Tolly. 'And I'm afraid he didn't give a very good report.'

'What did he say?' asked Mr Dinneford, rather taken aback to hear that the police vet had been along. He wondered if Mr Tolly had told the police that he, Mr Dinneford, had proposed to shoot the horse.

'He said that the horse was nervy, sir, because of his accident,' said Mr Tolly, 'and wouldn't be a bit of use to anyone for some time. He said you wouldn't get more than fifteen pounds for him now.'

'Fifteen pounds! And I paid thirty!' shouted the exasperated Mr Dinneford. 'And who'd give me fifteen pounds for him like he is now, tell me that!'

'Well – maybe he'll be better in a few months' time,' said Mr Tolly, 'and then . . .'

'Oh, don't tell me fairy stories about that horse! Those hind legs will *never* get better – they'll get worse! I shan't even be able to get ten pounds for him, let alone fifteen, you know that!'

'I'll give you ten,' said Mr Tolly, unexpectedly. 'And that's because I'm fond of him and don't want to see him shot.'

'Well, you're a nincompoop if you think that horse is worth even *ten* pounds!' raged Mr Dinneford. 'I don't believe the police said the horse was worth a penny! He should be shot!'

'Right. If you don't want to sell him, take him away and go,' said Peter's father, in a stern voice.

Mr Dinneford swung round. 'Do *you* want to give me ten pounds for him?' he said. 'Are you a fat-head too, like Tolly here?'

'I may be,' said Peter's father, 'but it's worth ten pounds to be rid of you. Either go and take the horse with you – or leave it here and take this ten pounds. But make up your mind!'

'All right. I'll take the money,' said Mr Dinneford, a little ashamed of himself as he saw Peter's father's disgusted face. 'Good riddance to a nuisance of a horse, I say. Thanks for the money, sir. Good evening.'

He pocketed the money and away he went striding off, leaving the horse behind. It had been scared of the angry voices, and had gone to Tolly for comfort. 'Now, now!' he said, stroking the soft nose. 'He's gone. You won't hear his loud voice again. You don't belong to him any more.' And he led the horse to Peter's father.

'Well, Tolly – the horse is *yours*,' said Peter's father. 'That is – if you want him. I'll deduct a pound a week from your wages till the money is paid off. That be all right?'

'Yes, sir. Thank you very much, sir,' said Tolly, his face one big smile. He put his arm round the horse's neck. 'Well, my beauty! You belong to *me* now – or you will in a few weeks' time – say five weeks. Could you, sir, deduct *two* pounds a week from my wages for five weeks? That will clear the debt. Ha – ten pounds of very, very good horse! You wait till a few months have gone by, my beauty, and you'll be as good as ever you were! You'll be worth your weight in gold!'

'Very well, Tolly,' said Peter's father, smiling at the old man's joy. 'You'll be less two pounds a week till the debt is paid off – and then Brownie will be yours for keeps. And a fine horse he is too, except for those weak back legs. But they'll improve. He'll be a fine horse again before very long – and you deserve to have him, Tolly. Take him off now and bed him down in the stables. He'll be happy to have you fussing round him again, I've no doubt!'

Seven

Tolly and Brownie

As soon as the children saw that Mr Dinneford had gone off and that Tolly was leading the horse to the stables, they raced out of the house to him.

'Tolly! What happened? Is he yours? You said you hadn't enough money to buy him. Oh, isn't he a darling?'

Brownie nuzzled both children gently. He liked them very much.

'He's mine all right,' said Tolly, proudly, as he backed the horse into his new quarters. 'There you are, my beauty. You stay there awhile till we find some supper for you and some water. Ha – someone's put plenty of good straw bedding down for you. You'll be well-off here, old horse.'

'Have you really bought him, Tolly? Was Mr Dinneford very angry? We heard him shouting,' said Janet.

'Yes. I've bought him – though he won't be rightly mine for five weeks,' said Tolly, rubbing the horse's long nose lovingly. 'Your Dad's going to take two pounds a week off my wages till Brownie's paid for – ten pounds your father gave for him – but *I* wouldn't sell him if you offered me five hundred!'

'Don't forget that you promised us we could have half of him for our own,' said Janet. 'We shall give you our share of the price as soon as we can. We've got some money in our money-boxes, and Granny is coming next week – she always gives us about fifty pence each.'

'Now don't you worry about the money,' said Tolly. 'You don't *need* to pay me a penny for your share of him. I'll willingly share him with you. It isn't often children love horses like you two. You deserve half of my Brownie!'

Brownie was very pleased with his new stable. He threw back his head and sent a loud, delighted whinny through the whole place. The two other horses who were there were startled, and said 'hrrrrumphs' in surprise.

'He'll be pleased when he goes out into the fields,' said Peter. 'I bet he'll gallop all over the place, and make friends with any animal there, horse, sheep, or dog!'

'Your Dad's been a right good sort over Brownie and Codger,' said Tolly. 'Well, I must go back to Mester Dinneford's and get all my things. Stay quiet now, Brownie. I'll be back to sleep with you tonight. Can't have anyone stealing you!'

He said good-bye to the children and went back up the hill to Mr Dinneford's farm. Now – if that Mester Dinneford started on at him about old Brownie, he'd tell him a few truths and see what he made of those!

But Mr Dinneford didn't come near Tolly. He was now wishing that he hadn't told him to go! Tolly was a fine, trustable worker. Whatever would he do without him?

I'll clear up everything, and leave it all shipshape! thought Tolly. I'll miss all the horses – but there, my new master will have plenty of them for me to care for!

That night Tolly went to see that Brownie was safe and happy in his new stable. In the afternoon the old horse had been out in the fields, getting to know one or two of the other horses who were grazing there. Then he had brought mangolds to the yard in a cart – a very light cart indeed, which did not strain his back legs at all.

Tolly watched him, very pleased. 'Those back legs of yours are better even than last week!' he told Brownie. 'Now you be careful of them, see – and lie down in your stable as much as you can. Don't stand all the time – even if you *do* want to talk to the horses next to you!'

Brownie had given a happy little whinny, as if he had understood every word. He sensed that his master was happy, for some reason, and so he was happy too. He wondered why he was in such a strange place, but as long as he could hear Tolly whistling somewhere not too far off, he was content.

And now here was Tolly settling down on an old mattress in the empty stall next to Brownie. The old horse was delighted. He couldn't *see* Tolly there, but he could smell his familiar smell, and he was comforted to feel that Tolly was nearby, as he stood in his stall in the strange stable.

'Now I'm here, near you, old horse,' said Tolly in a low voice. 'Sleep well. Lie down in your straw. I'm here, close to you. Nice and warm, isn't it? Good night, Brownie. You don't need to be afraid of horse-thieves while *I'm* close beside you! And old Codger is here too, in the straw. Say good night, Codger!' And Codger gave a small bark as if to say 'Good night! Sleep well!'

Codger was the first one out and about the next morning. He scrabbled out of the straw in the stall he had slept in, and went to lick his master's face.

'Don't,' said Tolly, sleepily. 'How many times have I told . . .' And off he went to sleep again before he could finish his sentence!

Codger looked up at the half-door that shut him and his master into the stall. Yes – he could just about jump it. He crouched – leapt as high as he could – and just failed to get over the half-door. Instead he fell back heavily on to Tolly who awoke with a jump and a shout.

'HEY! WHO'S THIS? THIEVES, THIEVES!'

'Wuff!' said Codger, in a small, scared voice. Oh dear – what had he done? Awakened his master, and made him think there were thieves about!

'You silly little idiot, Codger!' said Tolly, crossly. 'What did you jump on me for? It isn't time to get up. Now you've woken up the horses. Hark at them hrrrrmphing! I'll have to get out of this stall and quieten them!'

So up he got and went from stall to stall, patting and stroking, trying to quieten the frightened horses. 'Anyone would think horse-thieves were about!' he grumbled, as the horses stamped and shuffled uneasily. 'Now just you lie quiet, Codger, and don't move so much as a whisper. I want to go to sleep!'

Eight

Next morning

WHEN Peter and Janet woke up the next morning they each remembered about Tolly, and how he had bought old Brownie. Jane lay and thought about it for a little while, and then she slipped out of her room, and ran to wake Peter.

He was so sound asleep that it was hard to wake him. She shook him and pummelled him, but he just gave little grunts and turned away.

'Peter! You *know* you're not as deeply asleep as all that!' said Janet, crossly. 'All right. I've a pin here and I'll just see if *that* will wake you.'

Peter sat up immediately! He was cross and frowning. 'What's the matter? Don't you dare to stick that pin into me, you horrible girl. It must be awfully early in the morning. What's the matter?'

'It *isn't* early. It's only ten minutes to breakfast time,' said Janet. 'Do get up. I want to be down early to breakfast, and to talk to you about calling a meeting of the Secret Seven. We MUST let the others know about Tolly and Brownie and Codger. We've done everything on our own so far, and we oughtn't to do any more without at least *tell*ing them!'

'All right. Call a meeting then. I'm going to sleep again,' said Peter, snuggling down under the bedclothes once more.

'You really are a stupid, silly sleepyhead!' said

Janet, crossly. She got off the bed. 'All right, I'll take you at your word. Go to sleep all the morning if you want to. *I'm* going to call a Secret Seven meeting myself, see. I'll go round IMMEDIATELY after breakfast and warn everyone. I'll tell them you're not feeling too good, and that I'll take the meeting, and be its head, instead of you.'

'You will NOT!' said Peter, fiercely. He flung off the bed-clothes so violently that they fell all over Janet and she was nearly smothered. 'Go away, you horrid girl. I'll turn you out of the Secret Seven if you go on like this!'

Janet gave a chuckle and went off to her own room. Ah now – *now* they would be sure to have a Secret Seven meeting. How she loved them! There was quite a lot to report too. 'I'll take some of the chocolates that Auntie gave me last time she was here. And I'll ask Cook for some of the ginger cake she made two days ago. It was an enormous one – there must surely be lots left! There's such heaps to talk about we'll *need* something to eat. We'll talk about Tolly – and Brownie – and how Daddy bought Brownie for ten pounds, and that half Brownie is ours – and Tolly is sleeping in the stable with Brownie and our other horses . . .'

There was still quite a while before breakfast and Janet scribbled as many Secret Seven notices as she could.

'IMPORTANT: *A Secret Seven Meeting will be held in our shed at ten o'clock sharp, to report further proceedings on the complaint that Bob*

Smith made at our last meeting. Please come, as plenty has happened. Bring sweets or chocolates or ginger beer if possible.

Janet. Secret Seven Club.'

Peter was cross with her at breakfast, so she didn't say a word about the meeting. Soon Peter spoke to her commandingly. 'After breakfast we'll go and write those notes to the others. Buck up. There's not much time if we want to hold it at ten.'

'My *dear* boy – *I* wrote all the notes while you were half-awake!' said Janet. 'I was afraid you might not wake up even for breakfast!'

'Don't be a fat-head,' said Peter. 'How *dare* you write notes to the Secret Seven members without even asking *me* what you're to put.'

'Well – it wasn't much *good* asking you,' said Janet. 'You were so sound asleep. I just hadn't the heart to wake you properly, you looked so very peaceful. Still – I can tear the notes up if you like. Perhaps you *had* better write them, and dictate every single one to yourself.'

'No – no, don't tear them up!' said Peter, as Janet took up the little pile of notes. He was alarmed at such an idea. *He* didn't want to have to begin writing out the whole lot again himself!

'Well – will you take them round to the others then?' said Janet. 'I'll get the shed ready.'

'All right. I'll go immediately,' said Peter. 'I *would* like to go and see how Tolly and Brownie and Codger are first, though. I dreamed about Brownie all night!'

'What did you dream?' asked Janet, with interest.

Peter sometimes had very, very interesting and exciting dreams.

'I dreamt he ran away with Codger because thieves came,' said Peter. 'And please don't remind me of it because I shall be scared of it coming true.'

'Baby!' said Janet. 'Buck up with our breakfast. I'll go and make the beds.'

Peter gobbled the rest of his breakfast, snatched up the notes Janet had written and tore off to deliver them. He saw nobody at all as he pushed them through each letter-box and rang the bell before trotting off again down the front path. He was home in record time, and went to find old Tolly. Janet rushed after him.

Tolly was helping to milk the cows, and looked very happy. The other men had made him welcome, and

had admired Brownie so much that Tolly nearly burst with pride.

'How's Brownie?' asked Janet, smiling as the old man placed a bucket under another cow, to milk it.

'Brownie's fine!' said Tolly, as the good rich milk squirted into the pail. 'Fine! He likes being with so many other horses. He's perked up a lot, Miss Janet. You go and say good morning to him. He'll be pleased to see you. He'll be giving you gallops on his back over the fields and hills before you know where you are!'

Janet went to see the old horse. His head was over the stall-door, and she opened it and slipped in beside him.

'Brownie! Did you have a good night? Are you happy here? You weren't frightened, were you, the first night in a strange place?'

'Hrrrrrumph!' said Brownie, and pushed the girl gently with his nose. She rubbed her hand up and down it.

'I like you, Brownie. I like you. Your legs will soon be QUITE all right, won't they? I'm sure they will!'

The other horses now had their noses over *their* doors, waiting for Janet to come by. They all knew her, of course, and loved her. She was always gentle and loving to them.

A bell rang out from somewhere. 'That's the bell to say I'm wanted indoors!' she told the horse. 'I must fly. Did Tolly sleep with you last night? I've just been to say good morning to him.'

And away she went, her hair flying in the wind just like a horse's mane!

Nine

Another meeting

THE two children soon gathered up the things they wanted to take to the meeting-shed. Cookie had been very nice and had given them half the gingerbread cake. 'It wants eating up,' she said. 'It's getting a wee bit stale, but you won't mind that, *I* know. And here's an apple for each one of you. Gardener brought them in – he says they're only windfalls, but they'll be sweet.'

'Oh, thank you!' said Janet, pleased. 'I usually buy

some sweets or something for the meetings, but I haven't enough time now – not till I find my purse anyway – and goodness knows where that's gone! Buck up, Peter. I'm just going down to the shed. The others will be here in half a tick.'

'I'm just going to make a few notes,' said Peter. 'I think we ought to find out if anyone has got money in to help to pay the vet's bill. We ought to begin to pay some of it off. We promised we would.'

'Well, I've got five pence,' said Janet. 'I didn't earn it, though. I found it on our gravel path this morning. I only hope I can remember where I put it!'

'Lucky thing!' said Peter. 'I'm taking a collection this morning at the meeting, so you *could* put it in that. Every little helps.'

'I was going to, of course,' said Janet. 'And I've opened my money-box too. Mother said I could take half of what I had there, to help to pay the vet's fees, if I really wanted to. I said that I'd do anything to help poor old Tolly.'

'So would I,' said Peter. 'I'll get *my* money-box too. I wish I hadn't spent so much on bull's-eyes lately. But I've had several good books to read – and a bull's-eye is just right for a good book. It lasts and lasts!'

At five minutes to ten they were down at the shed. Clean writing-paper was there, a pencil and a pen and a rubber. Even a ruler, though Janet felt sure that Peter wouldn't want *that*! Their money-boxes were there too, each with their keys in them for unlocking.

'Gingerbread cake!' said Janet, putting a plate on the table. 'A bit stale, but what does that matter? And an apple each. These two are a bit bad, Peter, *we'd* better have those and give the good ones to the others.'

'Right,' said Peter. 'Oh, you've brought some of your chocs too. Good! Shut the door, quick. I can hear someone coming. It might be Susie, that tiresome sister of Jack's, and we're not having her in!'

Knock-knock.

'Password!' shouted Peter and Janet together. A plaintive voice came from outside. 'Peter – Janet – is it *still* "Scamper" because if there's a new password, I've forgotten it.'

'Enter!' called Peter, and in came Pam, with Barbara close behind her. 'Hallo!' said Pam. 'I *thought* we hadn't changed the password. Hallo, Scamper! How do you like being a password?'

Scamper licked her bare legs, and sat down by Janet. He liked these meetings. There were always titbits of some sort!

One by one the others came, and soon the meeting was complete. Bob was there too, looking very thrilled. 'Any news of old Mr Tolly?' asked Colin. 'I don't seem to have seen *any* of you at all. I've had to do a lot of swotting.'

'Now,' said Peter, 'I will declare the meeting open, and ask the members if they have anything to say. You will remember what we talked about at the last meeting, and how we were all going to try and help Mr Tolly in some way.'

'Let's tell *them* what's happened since the last meeting,' interrupted Janet.

'Yes, yes – do tell us,' said Pam, Jack, and George all together, while Colin, Barbara, and Bob nodded their heads. 'We're just bursting to know!'

'Well actually, quite a *lot* has happened,' said Peter. 'Old Mr Tolly brought his horse Brownie here to us yesterday, and it's in our stable now. That horrid Mr Dinneford was very, very angry with Tolly. He said that Tolly had ruined the horse's back legs, and . . .'

'Oh – is the horse *here*?' said Pam, in excitement, and Peter frowned.

'Don't interrupt when I'm speaking,' he said. 'I'm the head of the Secret Seven, aren't I?'

'Ooooh, sorry, Peter,' said Pam, going very red. 'It's just that I so badly wanted . . .'

'Be quiet! Sh!' said everyone, and Pam sank back into her chair, half sulky.

'Where was I now?' said Peter. 'Oh yes – when the police vet came, he said that the horse's legs were quite badly damaged and that he was in a very nervy state – but that with gentle handling and kindness, he might be quite all right again in a few months' time. He said his legs were to be rubbed with some kind of stuff – Janet knows more about that than I do – she's done a little of the rubbing because she has gentle hands. And that's about all.'

'Oh *no*, Peter – you've forgotten the most important part – about *buying* the horse!' said Janet. 'That's what we want the *money* for!'

'Why – do you want the horse to belong to *every-body* in the Secret Seven Club, instead of just us and Tolly?' said Peter. 'That's silly.'

'No, it isn't silly!' said Barbara, who was fond of horses. 'I'd just LOVE to think I owned part of a horse. I once owned half a dog. I and my cousin, who lived next door, shared it between us – we each put down half the money. I really do think that the dog *liked* being shared. I'm sure Brownie would. Think of having *seven* people spoiling him instead of just one. What a wonderful time he'd have! Fancy the Secret Seven owning half a horse! I bet no other club in the world does that!'

'Where *is* this horse?' asked Colin. 'I didn't see him when I came past the stables. They seemed empty to me!'

'Somebody must have stolen him then!' cried Janet, jumping up. 'Or left the door open. Peter, did you?'

'No! I haven't been *near* the stables!' said Peter, jumping up too. 'Oh – Oh, I say – just look!'

And, as they all turned towards the open window of the shed, they saw a very, very pleasant sight. Brownie was putting his long nose inside! He had somehow got out of his stall, and had heard the sound of voices, and come to investigate! What a lovely thing he looked, staring shyly in at the window. 'Hhrumph!' he said, in a mild, inquiring voice.

'He wants a piece of gingerbread!' said Pam, and would have given him the whole lot if Peter hadn't snatched the plate from her!

'The meeting is put off for half an hour,' said Peter, desperately. 'We really *can't* have Brownie at a meeting. STOP barking, Scamper. Oh goodness – there they go together, tearing over the lawn. *Look* at those hoofmarks! Now we're in for trouble!'

It took some time to capture the excited Brownie. *He* thought that it was a wonderful game of 'Dodge About' and 'Don't be Caught' and he darted here and there, over flower beds and vegetable beds and lawns to his heart's content. The gardener and Tolly caught him at last, and led him firmly back to his stable.

'I'm ashamed of you, Brownie!' said the panting Tolly. 'Right – Down – Ashamed – Of You! I'll be working all day long on the beds you've trampled!'

'We'll help!' said the children, and they did. Tolly was very thankful to see the garden more or less itself again before Peter's father came out!

'We were in the middle of a Secret Seven meeting,' said Peter to Tolly. 'I suppose you couldn't come to it now, could you? – we're going to hold the rest of it immediately – in the shed – and we'd like you to tell us a few things.'

'Right,' said Tolly. 'I've got about a quarter of an hour to spare. What meeting is this?'

'We were going to discuss money,' said Peter, leading everyone back into the shed. 'You see, we have promised to pay the vet's fees for Brownie – and we've got some money towards them this morning – and we also want to discuss the *buying* of Brownie.'

They were now all sitting round the shed, looking eagerly at the surprised Tolly. He gazed at the various money-boxes on the table, and at one or two envelopes and purses.

'That's what we've got already towards the vet's fees,' said Pam. 'That's my purse. I weeded my

Granny's garden for a day and a half, and she gave me fifty pence! So *that's* to go towards the vet's fees.'

'And I took care of our neighbour's dog for two whole days while he was away,' said Jack. 'Awfully nice dog too, it was. *I* didn't take it walks. It took *me* walks! And guess what old Mr Kay gave me for that. He gave me twenty-five pence at first – and then when he heard what I was going to do with it – help with the vet's fees, of course – he trebled the money and gave me *seventy-five* pence!'

'Good *gracious!*' said everyone.

'I'm afraid I wasn't so lucky,' said Colin. '*I* took *two* dogs for walks, but one jumped into a very dirty part of the river, and it came out absolutely *covered* with mud. So I'm afraid I only got fifteen pence – *and* I had to give the dog a bath too!'

'Bad luck,' said Peter. 'What about you, Barbara?'

'I brought my money-box. I think it has about ninety pence in it,' said Barbara. 'I had to buy rather a lot of birthday presents – three lots in three weeks – and the last one was two days ago. I'm sure there's only ninety pence in it now.'

'Bad luck. Never mind, you can always save up a bit more later on', said Peter. 'We shan't be able to pay much of the vet's bill *this* time. George, what about you?'

'Ha!' said George. 'I've got some NEWS. Some weeks ago I went in for a competition for an essay about clubs – the first prize was ten pounds and . . .'

'You surely didn't win THAT!' shouted Peter, standing up in excitement.

'No, no, I didn't win the first prize of ten pounds –
but I *did* win the second prize – and that was *five
pounds!*' said George, his face glowing. 'I heard this
morning. I haven't got the money yet, but Dad says it
will come all right. He gave me the five pounds in
advance, so that I could give the whole of it to the vet
for his fees for Brownie. I shall give the money back to
Dad when my prize money arrives.'

There was a silence. *What* a wonderful thing to do!
What a gift! Good old George! Now he was being
hugged by Janet, and patted on the back by the others!

'Did your parents *say* you could give it towards the
vet's fees?' asked Peter.

'Yes. I told them, of course. They were frightfully
bucked,' said George. 'In fact, Dad nearly gave me
another five-pound note to match this one. Mother just
stopped him in time!'

The gifts from the others didn't seem very exciting,
after hearing about George's magnificent prize of five
pounds! Peter put in his money-box savings, which
amounted to seventy-five pence and Janet put in hers
which came to forty pence altogether. Bob shyly put in
forty-five pence. 'Mostly for errands,' he said.

'How much does it all amount to?' asked Pam,
eagerly. 'It looks an awful lot of money now it's out on
the table. Enough to pay a dozen vets!'

Peter solemnly and slowly counted the collection of
money on the table, including, of course, the exciting,
crisp five-pound note!

'We have here the large sum of eight pounds ninety
pence,' he said. 'There!'

Jack lost control of himself in his excitement, and jumped up, cheering so loudly that Scamper fled out of the shed with his tail well down!

'HIP HURRAY! HIP, HIP HIP, HURRAY!' And, of course, everyone joined in, including Tolly, who was almost as excited as the children.

'We've got enough for the vet's fees!' cried Peter, in delight. 'Oh, George – you *are* a brick to put in that five pounds! We'll never, never, forget that. NEVER! What a happy ending to a WONDERFUL meeting! HURRAY!'

Ten

Off to see the vet

TOLLY hadn't said a single word. He had sat open-mouthed, listening to the excited children in the greatest wonder. He kept staring at the five-pound note on the table as if it was the first time he had ever seen one. Then he looked from one to other of the children with admiration and gratitude.

'I think we'd better explain things to Tolly,' said Peter, at last. 'We're all getting too excited – and Tolly must be wondering what all that money is doing on the table! Even Scamper's excited! SIT, SCAMPER. Will you please SIT?'

'Well, young sir – I can't say that I'm used to seeing five-pound notes lying about,' said Tolly, with a wide grin. 'That looks as if it's just come straight from the Mint, it's so clean and new.'

'Anyway,' said George, proudly, 'it's for paying the vet's fees for Brownie. Or it *could* go towards buying him.'

'What's all this about buying him?' asked Tolly. 'I'm having two pounds a week docked off my wages for five weeks – and then he'll be mine. I said Master Peter and Miss Janet here could share him, seeing that they live here, like, and can look after him sometimes. But he's *my* horse – *I'm* paying for him!'

'We thought that if you'd let us pay *part* of the money, we'd *really* feel he was partly ours. Which half of him shall we have?' Janet looked seriously at Tolly, and he laughed as he looked back at her.

'Now don't talk ridiculous, Miss,' he said. 'You can't buy a horse in two halves. We'll each share the whole of him, and I'll be pleased to think you've a share of his love. I never did see such a loving horse before. Why, I believe he'd work his heart out for his owners!'

'Well, Tolly, listen,' said Peter. 'We shan't feel as if we're *really* sharing him if we don't pay part for him – all the club members think the same. We'd all like to feel that we've shares in such a lovely horse. But we know he's *really* yours! Just let's share him a *bit*!'

'Right,' said Tolly, understanding at last. Of course! None of these children actually had a horse of his or her own – and they longed to have even a small share in one. Tolly understood that. Yes, he understood that. He nodded his head and gave the children a wide grin.

'All right, Master Peter. That's settled then. Pay me five pence down, and you can reckon on your bit of him! And if you've any money left over, as I know you will have, then pay off a bit of the vet's fees – that would be right kind of you! I'll be a bit short for some weeks, paying over to the master for Brownie – and I can't manage the vet's fees too.'

'I tell you what!' said George. 'Let's pay half the vet's fees, and then just hand over what's left to Tolly, to tide him over a bit. *We* don't want the money. The Secret Seven don't owe anything to anyone – and we can always earn a bit more if we want to by doing odd jobs for our parents. And there will be birthdays coming along soon.'

'I wonder when *Brownie's* birthday is,' said Pam. 'If we have any money left over we could buy him a whole bag of carrots. When's his birthday, do you know, Tolly?'

'That's in about ten days' time,' said Tolly, screwing up his eyes as he tried to remember. 'I've got it written down somewhere, Missy. A bit of a thing he was – all legs and head – a bonny wee horse, though. Now look at him – as fine a horse as ever I did see!'

'I think we might as well go and visit the vet today,' said Janet. 'We'd just have time to catch him before he goes out on his rounds. Shall we go?'

'Yes,' said Peter. 'We'll have time to go to his place, talk to him, and get back to finish our meeting. We'd better take the money with us. I do hope to goodness we've got enough. Come on, Scamper!'

They said good-bye to Tolly, and set off to the vet's house with Scamper trotting beside them. They were lucky. He was *just* going out after having seen his surgery patients, and was on his own fine horse.

'Hallo, Mr Whistler,' said Peter, raising his cap. 'Can we speak to you just for a minute? You don't need to dismount, sir. My, isn't he a fine horse?'

'Yes. He's a grand fellow,' said the vet, patting the horse on his neck. 'His name's Lord Lofty – suits him, doesn't it?'

'Yes!' agreed the children, also patting the great horse. And Pam added, 'He *is* lordly – look at the way

he holds his head aloft, and see how proudly he paws the ground. I'll bring you some sugar lumps next time I come, Lord Lofty, and kneel and present them to you on a silver plate!'

That made them all laugh. 'Well!' said the vet. 'Now what can I do for you? I'm just off on my rounds, and can only stop for a moment.'

'It's just that we've saved up the money to pay your bill for the horse called Brownie,' explained Peter. 'You know it, sir – Mr Dinneford had it – a lovely brown horse with a beautiful head. Mr Dinneford sold it to my father, and now my father has sold it to Tolly, who's left Mr Dinneford, and is now working for my father. Rather a long explanation, I'm afraid, sir.'

'Yes, yes. I know the horse well – he pulled a heavy cart downhill, and the cart pushed into his hind legs in some way, and injured them,' said the vet. 'I was angry with Dinneford over that – he always overworks his horses – uses two when he ought to use four! That horse suffered a lot – how are his legs now?'

'Well, sir, *we* think they are a lot better, now that Tolly's with us and looking after Brownie,' said Peter. 'And Tolly told us that you were a great help with old Brownie, and did a lot for him and his poor hurt legs. And, sir, we've come to pay the bill. You kindly said you would halve the fees, which is very good of you. So if you could tell us EXACTLY how much the bill is now, we thought we'd pay it, and then Tolly wouldn't worry about it any more. We've got enough money, sir. We've all saved up – and George here, he won five pounds in an essay competition.'

'And he gave it towards your fees, sir, and towards buying a share in Brownie. We're *all* going to share in Brownie,' said Colin, his face beaming. 'So he'll be jolly well looked after, sir.'

'Well, I'm blessed! So *that's* what you've come for!' said the vet, smiling. 'Let's see now – my bill was pretty high – and I said I'd halve it – now look, I suppose you wouldn't like *me* to have a share in that horse, would you? I'm fond of him too, you know – and if I had a share in him, I could come and look after him for nothing if anything went wrong, couldn't I?'

There was a silence, as the children worked out what this meant. '*Er* – well, sir,' said Peter. 'Of *course* you could have a share in him too. You must be fond of him, seeing you've done such a lot for his poor old back legs. Yes, I'm sure Tolly would like you to have a share in him. But about your bill, sir – if you could tell us what the half-payment is, we . . .'

'Good gracious – as if I should charge anything for looking after a horse in which *I* own a share! said the vet, looking quite upset.

'But you *didn't* have a share when you attended him, sir,' said Colin.

'Quite right. But I didn't know then that I was going to be lucky enough to be *allowed* a share in him, did I?' said the vet. 'No, no – you must let me have my way in this. Give me a share in the horse, and there'll be NO fees to pay for my attending Brownie when his legs were so bad. I wouldn't HEAR of it. Well, I must go. Good-bye – and pat Brownie for me, will you, and tell him that he's partly mine now, bless him!'

And with that the vet galloped off at top speed on Lord Lofty.

'WELL!' said Peter, jubilantly. 'That's that. What a wonderful thing to happen! Good old vet – he's a sport! And to think that if Brownie gets anything wrong with him, he'll get free treatment. No big bills for Tolly to worry about. Why, Pam – what's the matter? What on *earth* are you crying for?'

'It's only just because I'm so happy, all of a sudden,' wept Pam. 'I don't know *why* I'm crying. I just can't help it. I'm so surprised and happy. Don't look so worried, Scamper. I tell you I'm very *happy*!'

All right, Pam. Everyone understands! Quite a lot of people would do the same, if they came across such unexpected kindness!

Eleven

Everybody's pleased

THE children all went back to Peter's house as fast as ever they could. They could hardly believe their good luck! How kind of the vet! But how like him!

'I hope I'll be as generous as that when I grow up,' said George, solemnly. He had been very impressed with the vet's simple, heartfelt kindness. So money didn't count with some people, then? That was wonderful. Kindness mattered much more to the vet than even *pounds* of money. George never forgot that morning – and one day he was to grow up, and do the same kind of things – all because he talked to the vet about Brownie!

Tolly couldn't believe their good luck either, when they burst in on him as he sat having his mid-morning snack, in the little old shed near the stables.

They slapped all the money down on the bench beside him – the five-pound note and the rest.

'The vet wouldn't take a penny!' said George. 'Not a penny. He said that all he wanted was a share in Brownie, he likes him so much and he'll come to see his legs for nothing! It's *true* Tolly!'

'You're having me on!' said Tolly, disbelievingly. 'That's what you're doing. Pulling my leg. Go on with you. You haven't been to the vet's! Have they, Scamper?'

It took some time to persuade Tolly that what they

were telling him was the truth. Then he stood up, looking amazed. 'You mean to say that the vet didn't take a
penny of your money?' he said. 'Not a penny? He's a
gentleman, he is. A right-down, slap-up, true gentleman! And I'm going to take up to him all the eggs that
my hen Sukey lays, every single one of them. He likes
new-laid eggs – he told me he did. And he shall have
Sukey's, if I go without eggs for the rest of my
life.'

The children were amused by Tolly's outburst, and
very pleased. Now the vet would have new-laid eggs
every breakfast-time – and he certainly deserved them,
everyone agreed on that.

'Funny how one kind deed leads to another, isn't it?'
said Janet. 'Dear me – things have been very exciting
lately. A bit *too* exciting. I feel quite out of breath. Oh
well – I expect they'll quieten down now – but I must
say I've enjoyed the last few days!'

Janet was wrong! They *didn't* quieten down! Instead they became very exciting indeed.

Peter went to tell his father what the vet had said,
and Janet went with him. He listened without saying a
word. Then when Peter came to the end of the story, he
nodded his head.

'So he wouldn't take your money!' he said. 'Well,
what are you going to do with it? It amounts to quite a
bit.'

'We'd like to give it to you to pay for Brownie, so
that Tolly can have him really and truly. He does so
love him. Daddy – and after all, *he'll* be the one that
has to look after him – we'll soon be back at school –

and you're always busy. He'll be safe with Tolly and the other horses, won't he?'

'He'll be safe all right,' said Daddy. He gave them each a hug. 'Very well. I'll take the money, and it shall all be spent on Brownie – on his food, his stabling, and everything. And maybe there'll be enough to spend on a good saddle, so that you can ride him. He'd like that.'

'Oooh – so would *we*! said Janet, at once, her eyes bright. '*I* know, Daddy – let him be *your* horse and Tolly's when we're at school – and *our* horse when we're on holiday. That's fair enough, isn't it?'

'More than fair!' said Daddy. 'Now you go and tell Mother all about this – I've some work to do out in the fields. I'll have a word with Tolly and tell him the arrangement we've made.'

'Well – that's fine!' said Peter, to Janet, as they went to tell their mother. 'I'll try to give Mother three pence a week for a supply of sugar lumps for Brownie. He gets some from Tolly too, so he'll be well off. Isn't he a nice horse, Janet – and to think we can ride him every day!'

Tolly was as pleased as anyone else about the new arrangement. 'Do Brownie good to have someone to ride him every day,' he said. 'He'll get fat if he doesn't get plenty of exercise. His kind of horse runs to fat very quickly. You can jump him, too, you know. He's a good jumper. You should have seen him leaping over the stream yesterday when a dog came barking round his ankles. I vow the dog thought he had wings! Anyway, he took to his heels and fled, and old Brownie, he stood grinning there on the other side of the stream, showing all his beautiful white teeth. I guess that dog thought he was going to be eaten up, when he caught sight of those teeth!'

The children laughed. Old Tolly knew how to tell a story all right! They followed him into the stables and sat down in the sweetly-smelling hay.

'Tell us a story, Tolly,' said Janet. 'You know such a lot of tales about the animals you've worked with.'

'No, no – I'm busy now,' said Tolly. 'These stables have got to be mucked out. Look, you take that fork there, Master Peter, and give me a bit of help. You go and talk to old Brownie, Miss Janet. He's along there,

and maybe he'd like an apple out of the loft. And maybe you would, too!'

Soon Janet was sitting in Brownie's part of the stable, each of them munching apples. The horse gave a gentle little whinny, and nosed at Janet lovingly. The girl put her arms round his neck and smelt his nice clean horse-smell.

'I do like you, Brownie,' she whispered in his pricked ear. 'You won't get stolen, will you? I couldn't bear it. I'll look out of the window tonight to make sure there are no thieves about. It will be a clear, moonlight night, and I can see your stables from my bedroom. So don't feel afraid – I shall be looking out to see you're in no danger – or the other horses either. I'll send Scamper out to you if I see any thieves!'

Twelve

In the middle of the night

EVERYONE went to bed early that night. Peter's father was tired for he had been helping with the farm-work, as one of the men was on holiday. Mother was always sleepy at night, and glad to go early. Only the children wanted to stay up to finish their books, but they were sent off to bed in spite of their complaints.

'And you're not to read in bed for hours and hours, see?' said Mother. 'You're to put out your lights in good time. Be good children, now.'

So off they went, grumbling. Their bedrooms were next to each other, so they could call to one another easily. They settled down with their books. Janet had a very, very exciting one, about smugglers' caves, and she read on and on, quite forgetting the time.

'You'll get a jolly good scolding in the morning when you own up to the time you put out your light!' called Peter, putting his out. 'Good night, bookworm.'

Janet's book was certainly very exciting. She forgot all about the time. In fact, she forgot that she was in bed, she was so sure she was in the smugglers' caves with four children and their dog Timmy.

The clock downstairs struck very solemnly indeed. It was the big grandfather clock, and he had a deep, grave note. Janet listened, and counted. Good graci- ous — ELEVEN o'clock! Whatever would Mother say when she had to own up in the morning that she had heard old Grandfather strike eleven? Guiltily she put her book on the floor, put out her light, and drew back the curtain. At once the room was absolutely flooded in bright silver moonlight!

'How beautiful!' whispered Janet. 'Oh, how BEAU-TIFUL! Just like extra lovely daylight with a sort of silver sheen.' She stood and looked out for a while, and then made up her mind.

I must go out in it, I must, I must! she thought. It's a fairy sort of night. I'll put on my dressing-gown and go and dance in the moonlight. I shan't tell anyone though – they'd think I was mad!

She pulled on her dressing-gown, called Scamper in a whisper from Peter's bedroom, and set off down the stairs. It all seemed very exciting, and not a bit frightening. The moonlight was so very, *very* bright!

She went out of the back door, and stood in the yard gazing up at the moon sailing along in the sky. It looked very big indeed.

I *can't* go back to bed when the moon is shining so beautifully! thought Janet. I know! I'll go and see if Brownie is awake! I'll whisper in his ear and tell him I've come to see him, because the moonlight is so bright. He'll be so pleased to see me.

She was afraid to walk round the yard in the moonlight just in *case* her mother or father happened to be awake and standing at the window to look at the moon. So she went quietly all round the yard in the shadows, Scamper close beside her.

And then Scamper suddenly gave a growl and stopped. He pulled at Janet's night-dress and gave another little growl. She stopped absolutely still in the dark shadow of a tree, and listened. What was Scamper growling at? A rat? A mouse running into its hole? She could hear no sound at all, and see no mouse or rat. So on she went again, still keeping in the shadows.

And then she heard a noise. It sounded like an exclamation – somewhere in the stables. Who could be there? Well, Tolly, of course. He always bedded down in straw or hay in the stables, his old mattress beneath him. He couldn't bear to leave his beloved horses!

Janet's heart began to beat very loudly indeed, and very fast. She put her hand on Scamper's collar, and whispered in his ear. 'Don't bark or growl. Keep close to me. I'll find out what's going on. I'll peep in at one of the stable windows. Now be quiet, Scamper, be quiet!'

Together they kept in the shadows and came to the big stables. The horses were restless, and were stamping their feet and moving about. One gave a little whinny.

And then a great noise sprang up! At least, it seemed a great noise to Janet, crouching in the shadows! There were shouts – yes, shouts in Tolly's voice. There were excited whinnies. There was the sound of men's feet. Then Tolly's voice came, 'HELP! HELP!'

Janet could now see into one of the stable windows. She looked down into the stables, and saw a fight going on. There were three men there, one holding Brownie, one holding another horse, and the third fighting poor Tolly! Crack! Bang! Biff! What a fight. Janet was terrified and couldn't help giving a scream. Tolly

heard her, but the others didn't. He called out to the frightened girl peeping down at the fight from the window just above him. 'Get help quickly! Save the horses!'

'No good calling for help, old man!' said one of the thieves, roughly. 'There's no one near these stables!'

Janet, really frightened, raced back to the house in her dressing-gown and slippers. 'DADDY! MUMMY! Quick, the horse-thieves are there! Tolly's fighting them! Daddy, DADDY!'

Her father and mother awoke at once, and her father raced downstairs in his pyjamas. When Janet ran into the house, her mother was already telephoning the police!

She sobbed out about Tolly being attacked, and her mother comforted her. 'The police will be here in a minute,' she said. 'You go into the drive and wait for them, and take them to the stables. I must go and see if I can help your father!' And, taking a large kitchen poker with her, she fled outside in her dressing-gown. How brave! thought Janet, proudly, waiting in the drive. Oh dear – why doesn't Peter wake up!

Just then the police drove up in their car. 'Hey, Miss – where's the fuss? Quick, tell us!' called a voice, and a big, strong policeman ran up to her.

'I'll take you,' cried Janet. 'Someone's stealing our horses. I saw them. Daddy's gone to stop them and Mother's gone too.'

What with shouts and yells, and whinnies and barks, a tremendous noise was coming from the stables! Janet began to tremble, but she bravely trailed behind the

police in her old dressing-gown! Were her mother and
father all right? What had happened to Tolly? Were
the horses hurt – or Scamper?

She didn't want to go to the stables to see what was
happening, but she had to. Good gracious, what a turmoil!

There was Daddy firmly on top of one horse-thief.
And there was Tolly on top of another, hitting him well
and truly. And dear me, there was a third one, down on
his knees in front of Mother, begging her to let him go!

Codger and Scamper were having a simply
wonderful time. They kept darting at the men and
snapping at them, and the men were scared stiff. All
the horses were upset and excited, scuffling and stamping and whinnying in their stalls. Janet felt as if she
simply must sit down. Everything was *much* too exciting. So she sat on the cold stone wall outside the stables
and waited for the fight to die down. Good gracious –
WHAT a thing to happen! Oh, poor Peter – he was in
bed, out of all this excitement. She really, really, must
fetch him!

Thirteen

What an excitement!

JANET decided to go and get Peter before all the excitement was over. He'd never, never forgive her if she didn't. So she flew upstairs at top speed, and shook him awake. 'Peter! Come quickly! We've got horse-thieves in the stable! Tolly fought them, and now the police are here and Daddy and Mother and everybody's fighting in the stables!'

'Don't be silly! You've just had a bad dream!' said Peter, astonished and cross. 'Go back to bed. Fancy waking me with a silly story like *that*!' And he turned over to go to sleep again. Janet shook him hard.

'Sit up, sit up!' she shouted. 'Then you can hear the row. You'll miss all the excitement. Anyway. I'm going to watch from the window!'

By this time Peter began to think there might be something in what Janet was shouting about. So he leapt out of bed and ran to the window with her. Good gracious! What a row – what shouts – what biffs and scuffles – what barks from Scamper and excited neighs from the horses!

'Come on!' said Peter, and without waiting to put on his dressing-gown or slippers he fled downstairs, out into the yard, and into the stable. Whew, *what* an excitement!

Most of the trouble was over now. But what a fight it had been! Tolly had gone for the thieves with a pitch-

fork, and made them dance in pain. They had tried to
let out the horses, but the brave beasts had stood their
ground, and Brownie had done quite a bit of snapping
and kicking. The men were terrified of him. He had got
one of them into a corner, and the man did not dare to
move, and was glad when a sturdy policeman came up
to handcuff him! 'Take that horse away from me,'
begged the man. 'He's just about broken my ankle
with a kick, and I wouldn't be surprised if he's bitten
my ear off.'

'I hope he *has*,' said the policeman, grimly, and
pushed the man roughly into the next stall, where two
other men had also been imprisoned. One had been
kicked on the arm, and was nursing the wounded limb,

his face angry and fierce. The third man had been knocked down when Tolly had flung himself on him, and had a badly cut head.

'Are the horses hurt?' Janet asked Tolly, who, breathless with the fight, was standing holding on to one of the thieves.

'No, Miss – not hurt at all,' panted Tolly. 'Old Brownie's enjoyed the shindy. My, my – the way he pranced about, and kicked out with those big hooves of his! I began to feel sorry for these horse-thieves! I was knocked down once, but old Brownie came up and almost snapped the man's arm off. Good old Brownie. He wasn't a bit afraid, Miss. He was clever too. He never so much as snapped at a policeman – only at the thieves!'

With a lot of shoving and pushing the horse-thieves were taken to the police cars. They were difficult to handle, and, to Peter's delight, he saw that every thief had a good stout policeman sitting down hard on him. There certainly would be no escape for *them*!

'Everything seems very quiet suddenly,' said Mother. 'My word, what an adventure! What a good thing you were awake, Janet, and heard the thieves.'

'Er – well, actually I was still reading,' confessed Janet. 'And the moonlight was so lovely I decided to go out in it with Scamper – and heard the noise in the stables. Are you hurt, Tolly? Fancy – you *thought* horse-thieves might be coming some night, and you were right. What a good thing you sleep with the horses!'

'I wouldn't sleep anywhere else if I knew horse-thieves were about!' said Tolly, brushing himself down.

The horses were restive and uneasy. 'I think, sir, if it's all right with you I'll take them all out for a quiet canter,' said Tolly. Then they'll probably settle down quietly for the rest of the night.'

'Right, Tolly. And thanks for all your help tonight,' said Peter's father. 'I'll see you get some reward for it. It's good to have a man like you on the job.'

'Tolly – what exactly happened?' asked Janet, excitedly.

'Well, Miss, I bedded down in the straw on my old mattress, in the stall next to old Brownie, see? And the horses, they went to sleep, seemingly, because I didn't hear much stamping or whinnying. And then, some time later on, old Brownie here he whinnied right in my ear – leaned over my stall and whinnied, he did. Quiet-like, as if he wanted to whisper.

'Well, I sat up, of course, and there he was looking down at me anxious-like. The moonlight was shining into the stable and it was as bright as day, Miss. Then I heard another noise – and that wasn't a noise made by any horse, Miss. It was a man sneezing, and trying to stop his sneeze. And I thought to myself, Oho, Here we go! Horse-thieves, or I'll eat my old cap!'

'What then?' asked Janet, breathlessly, her heart still beating fast.

'Well, then up I gets, pushes open the half-door, and stands up to see what was what. And I saw a man undoing the latch of Major's stall, up there, see. And old Major he began to carry on alarming. He snorted and whinnied and stamped till I thought he'd bring the stable down. How that man got him out of his stall, I don't know – but I do know that as soon as Major had room to kick out, he did – and that fellow went flying from one end of the stable to the other! Then I saw more chaps and I went mad. I picked up that there pitchfork and they struggled with me like madmen. They didn't want to get pricked by that sharp old fork. But there's one of them won't be able to sit down for a fortnight, that he won't!'

And old Tolly went off into a hoot of laughter that made all the horses turn round and look at him.

'Go on, Tolly. This is a tale worth telling,' said Peter's father, looking grim and amused at one and the same time.

'I don't rightly know what I did next,' said Tolly, scratching his head. 'I do know I saw one of them with my old Brownie again, and I caught hold of Brownie's head, swung him round and told him to kick the fellows out – send them flying. And old Brownie, he's always obedient, you know. My word, he sent two of them flying! One cracked his head on a door – and didn't he howl! "Shame on you," I said, "you'll wake up all the bobbies in the district" – and bless me, sir, at that very minute the police came and joined the fight. Like magic, it was!'

'Well, you've done a grand and a brave job tonight, Tolly,' said Peter's father. 'I hope you'll regard yourself as on my permanent staff now – head of the stables – and over any of the younger staff. I can do with a man like you here! Why that fellow Dinneford let you

go, I don't know! Well – see to the horses for a while
and quieten them and then bed down yourself. Good
night.'

And with that he put his arm round his wife's shoulders, motioned to the two excited children to go on in
front and shepherded everyone back inside the house,
including a most excited Scamper.

'How any of us are going to sleep tonight, I don't
know!' he said. 'Too exciting for words! Well – we'll
yarn about it in the morning – and now – good night,
Peter, good night, Janet. Sleep well!'

The children didn't want to go back to bed. They
wanted to stay and talk and talk about all that had
happened. They wanted to go and speak to each of the
horses, they wanted to talk to Tolly – in fact, they
wanted to do anything but go to bed.

But their father was determined. 'I said "Go back to
bed" and I meant it. You'll catch frightful colds staying out here with so little on, after being in warm beds –
and you're missing your night's sleep. If you don't go
back to bed straight away now I shall forbid you to go
near Tolly *or* the stables tomorrow, and that you won't
like at all!'

'All right, Daddy – we're going,' grinned Peter.
'Goodness, what a night! I've never had an adventure
like *this* before – in our very own home. What in the
world will the other members of the Secret Seven say
when we tell them tomorrow!'

'Off you go, for the last time!' said his father, giving
him a firm push. 'Go and think about it in bed.'

At last the two children were safely in bed, shouting

remarks to one another from their different rooms. Then suddenly Peter had no answer to his questions and knew that Janet was asleep!

Both children slept late when morning came, and didn't even hear the breakfast gong. Their mother let them lie in bed, remembering how late they had been the night before. But they were cross when they got up at last and found that quite a bit of the morning had gone. 'Oh, *Mother*! We wanted to go round and call the Secret Seven to another meeting!' grumbled Peter. 'They *must* know all that happened last night. It was so very, very exciting.'

'Will you please finish your breakfast and stop grumbling, Peter dear?' said his mother. 'You've the whole day to call a meeting. I shall clear away your breakfast in exactly ten minutes' time, so if you *want* a good breakfast you'd better get on with it.'

It was exciting to talk about the night before. Immediately breakfast was over they went to talk to Tolly. He was rubbing down one of the horses, whistling between his teeth. He grinned at the two children.

'Well – we had a night of it, didn't we?' he said. 'They nearly got my old Brownie! Ah, they didn't know how loudly he could hrrrrrrrumph! Woke me up at once, he did.'

'They didn't know that you slept in the stable with the horses, either, else they'd have been more careful,' said Janet. 'You're very fierce, aren't you, Tolly? I felt quite scared of you last night when I saw you with that hay fork.'

'I reckon *they* feel scared of me this morning too,'

said Tolly, wringing out his cloth in the horse-pail. 'I keep thinking of that chap that won't be able to sit down for a week – and the other one, *he* won't be able to walk for a fortnight!'

'A jolly good thing too!' said Peter.

'Well, it's what horse-thieves deserve!' said old Tolly. 'I remember the last time I had to do with a horse-thief. He came stealing past my cottage into the stables I was in at that time, and I saw his shadow on my blind. Well, me and Codger, we got up at once, and I took my old pail with me – and I told Codger to chase the man to the old pump – and my, when I got there too, I worked the pump and filled my pail, and over the fellow's head went the icy-cold water. He couldn't get away – Codger saw to that – and I threw five more pails of water over him. Laugh! I had to sit down on the old wall to get my breath, I'd such a stitch in my side.'

Tolly knew how to tell a story very well, and the children could have listened for ages. But Tolly had work to do.

'Wait a minute, Tolly, wait,' said Peter. 'We're going to spend some of that money on a birthday party for Brownie, and all of us – you too – are to come. We'll get some very special oats for Brownie, and a whole pound of sugar lumps and . . .'

'Now look here, Master Peter, nobody's going to give my Brownie a pound of sugar lumps!' said Tolly, in alarm. 'He'd be as fat as an old cow in no time – and his poor back legs would have even more weight to carry. He . . .'

'It's all right, Tolly. We shall give *you* the sugar lumps to dole out to him!' said Peter. 'Or you can dole them out to us to give him. We promise not to make him fat. He's exactly right as he is!'

No notes needed to be written to call the Secret Seven to a meeting. When the news ran round Peterswood that horse-thieves had been to Peter's house, the rest of the members came rushing down to find out what had happened! Peter took them all down to the little meeting-shed.

The members sat down expectantly, all agog to hear everything. 'The milkman told *me*,' said Pam. 'And I rushed round and told the others – but most of them knew, Peter, what happened? Are the horses safe?'

'Perfectly,' said Peter. 'But I have a fresh piece of news for everyone. The night before they came to us, they went to Mr Dinneford's – and took his three *best* horses! And nobody knows where they are yet.'

'Serve him right,' said George, and the others nodded in agreement. 'Horrid man! Well, he lost Tolly through his bad temper and meanness – and now he's lost three of his horses. Will the horses be all right?'

'Oh yes – they are too valuable to be ill-treated by the thieves – they'll be all right except for a fright. But goodness knows where the thieves have taken them to – or who has bought them!'

'Well – I just *can't* feel sorry for Mr Dinneford,' said Peter. 'When I think how he spoilt dear old Brownie's hind legs through making him work with an over-loaded cart, I just think to myself, "Well, serve him right!" '

'I think we all feel like that,' said Barbara. 'Peter, did you find out when Brownie's birthday is?'

'Oh yes – that's really what I wanted to call a meeting about,' said Peter. 'It's on Friday. I've spoken to Dad about it, and he says he'd like to join in too, and make it a real good day for Brownie and Tolly. And don't you think we ought to ask Bob too? It was he who told us about Brownie and Tolly.'

'Yes – of course ask him – fine!' said George, and the others nodded in complete agreement.

'Dad says that he thinks it would be a good idea to spend most of the money we have left on helping to buy a decent saddle for Brownie,' said Peter. 'Then Tolly can ride him in comfort, and Brownie will love that. Dad also said that we must get a really good one, and so *he* will put some money towards the saddle too, as he feels so grateful to Tolly for saving our horses last night.'

'Good idea!' cried everyone, very pleased, and Colin added, 'Jolly decent of your father!'

'Well, there'll be plenty of money left for a very fine party,' said Peter. 'I vote we have it in the stable yard, so that all the horses can look out of the stable – and see us – and we can give them sugar lumps so that they can feel they're in the party too.'

'Hurray!' cheered everyone, getting really excited. 'Hurray!'

And that is why they are now all sitting down to a long table set out in the stable yard. Brownie's birthday has arrived. He is thirteen years old today, though he doesn't know it. He can't *imagine* why everyone is making such a fuss of him – and look at the garland of flowers he's wearing – doesn't he look fine! Dear old Brownie – everyone loves you!

Hanging in the stable is a fine new saddle, just right for Brownie to wear. That's what Peter's father and the children bought for Tolly – and he's so proud of it that he can hardly wait to put it on Brownie's back and ride him.

There's a birthday cake too, with 'Happy Birthday, Brownie!' on it. Well, well – if ever a horse could be proud, Brownie could be today!

But he's not at all conceited. There he stands, look, his big brown eyes as kind as ever, his coat shining beautifully. Ah – sugar lumps! Good! And a slice of iced cake – even better! And a fine handful of the very best corn from Tolly's horny hand – a very nice titbit indeed.

'Hrrrumph, hrrrumph, hrrrumph!' says Brownie, and everyone laughs as Brownie nods his head politely.

'He says "Thanks, thanks, thanks!" ' says Janet. 'Tolly – I really do think he's the nicest horse in the world!'

'You're right there, Missy you're right!' said Tolly, taking Brownie another piece of cake, and look, Brownie is nuzzling into his ear, just as if he is whispering to the old man.

'He says he reckons there's no children like *you*!' reported Tolly, and that made everyone laugh.

Well, I think Brownie's right, Secret Seven. I really do think he's right!

In 1904, Franklin became engaged to Eleanor Roosevelt, a niece of then-president Theodore Roosevelt. They married in 1905, TR giving away his niece. Franklin spent the next three years with a Wall Street law firm. He entered politics in 1910, running from Dutchess County (where Hyde Park is located), a heavily Republican county. But Roosevelt campaigned energetically, and to his advantage, the Republicans were split that year between conservatives and progressives, and he was elected. In the state senate, he assumed the leadership of the progressive wing of his party and became enmeshed in a struggle between upstate Democrats and Tammany Hall over the election of a U.S. senator. Eventually, a compromise candidate was chosen, and Roosevelt went on to espouse the interests of upstate farmers and workingmen, becoming a spokesman for good government groups and conservationists. He was able to further the goals of the latter when he was named the chairman of the Committee on Fish, Forest and Game, and he attempted, vainly, to push through legislation that would have placed limits on tree cutting on private land.

He ran for reelection in 1912 but soon was involved in presidential politics, becoming the leader of the progressive anti-Tammany Democrats who backed Woodrow Wilson's nomination for the presidency. When Wilson won, Roosevelt was awarded the post of assistant secretary of the navy. After seven years in office, he established himself as one of the few young (he was thirty-one when he was appointed assistant secretary of the navy) bright lights among the progressive Democrats. Busy in his post, in 1918 he made a wide-ranging tour of navy facilities in Europe.

In 1920, he accepted his party's nomination to run on the ticket with the Democratic nominee for president, James M. Cox. Franklin campaigned vigorously throughout the nation, but the voters had wearied of the Democrats, and Republican candidate Warren G. Harding won handily.

So after ten years in elective and appointive office, Roosevelt was a private citizen. In New York, he became vice president of the Fidelity and Deposit Company, a bonding business, and returned to the practice of law. Then in August 1921 he was struck down with infantile paralysis. It was a severe attack that left him a lifelong cripple. In the years that followed he struggled to regain the use of his legs, but to no avail. Still, he remained active in party politics, and in 1928 he ran for governor of New York.

As a governor (he served two terms between 1928 and 1932) he molded his legislature agenda to appeal to as wide a swath of the electorate as possible. Thus he focused on public electric power development, a popular

Rogers's poetry creates an indirect effect on the reader through the power of language, rather than a direct effect by dictating views. Her words are never rigid, didactic, or uncompromising. She believes that "productive poets and scientists are humble in the face of the universe," and she approaches her writing as if she were "sewing a garment and holding it up to nature to see if it fits." "The garment may need to be taken apart and redesigned. Nature makes the judgment, and scientists are willing, as are poets, to adjust their work as necessary."

In 1996, Rogers was asked to participate in "Watershed Writers: Nature and Community," a six-day conference cosponsored by the Orion Society and the Library of Congress that brought together noted novelists, poets, and storytellers to discuss writing, nature, and community. Prominent among those who took part were Gary Synder and Joy Harjo. Rogers's contribution to the conference was "Animals and People: The Human Heart in Conflict with Itself," a poem that meditates on the complex relationship that exists in our environment.

In collaboration with Joellyn Duesbury, well known for her vibrant landscape paintings, Rogers published *A Covenant of Seasons* in 1998, which unites a literary and visual response to the recurring spectacle of "nature passing through the metamorphoses of the four seasons." In *The Dream of the Marsh Wren* (1999), she focuses on "rapidly changing technology, social structures, and environmental concerns."

Rogers's literary work includes numerous poems and essays that intersect science and nature, such as *Intimate Nature* (1998), *Verse and Universe* (1998), *The Measured Word: On Poetry and Science* (2000), and *A Chorus for Peace* (2002). She has also made important contributions to numerous environmental journals such as *Whole Terrain* (1995–1996), which explores ecological and social issues, and *EnviroArts*, an online review that promotes activism through the arts. In addition, she devotes much of her personal time and effort to various organizations that seek community activism toward the environment. She serves on the advisory board for the Orion Society and was an avid participant in their Forgotten Language Tour, a national tour in which top writers and poets promoted nature literature, meant to help individuals achieve a better understanding of their relationship to the natural world.

In 1998, she joined a group of Utah high school students and fellow poet Linda Hogan in the River of Words Project, an interdisciplinary expedition involving writing lessons, painting, photography, animal tracking, bird-watching, and river ecology. She also added her voice to the Writer's Residency Project, a one-week stint in the fall of 2005 to encourage long-term ecological reflections. Jim Sedell, a developer of the project, was moved to remark: "What are many advocates doing? They're reading Pattiann Rogers and other writers who can connect the public with science in many ways better than scientists can."

Rogers has bestowed on the environmental movement not a critique of the human condition but an endless pursuit of literary exuberance and exploration of the beauties of the world and what we must do to preserve them. "The more we observe," she stresses, "the more alert we are to the details of the physical world around us, and the more we must do to value and revere it."

During an interview with *Timeline Magazine*, she continued:

We are physical creatures immersed in a physical world, a world we come to know through our bodies, through our senses. We were born from the Earth and have inherent connections with it. . . . We are surrounded by and within the physical world, sunlight and shadows, wind or the still lack of it, the motion of clouds in the sky, the fragrance of rain, the silence of snow, the sound of a river, a bird calling in the background, grasses covered in frost, grasses in the wind, a fly at the window, a flowery weed by the roadside, the outline of a familiar tree at dusk, the sound of a door slamming, a dog barking in the distance, frogs or chickens or locusts beginning their calls as night comes on.

REGINA CORALLO

"An Interview with Pattiann Rogers." *Timeline Magazine*, no. 78
(November–December 2004).
Rogers, Pattiann. "Small and Insignificant, Mighty and Glorious." *Spiritus:
A Journal of Christian Spirituality* 2.2 (2002).
———. "Twentieth-Century Cosmology and the Soul's Habitation." *The Measured
Word*, ed. Kurt Brown. Athens, GA, 2001.
Wile, Kristin. "River of Words." *River of Words Organization*, May 2007.

Roosevelt, Franklin Delano (January 30, 1882–April 12, 1945).

Wholly aside from his other achievements, Roosevelt was known for his ardent support of the Civilian Conservation Corps (CCC), known as

"Roosevelt's tree army," an innovative program, and his signing o[f] Conservation Act. Nor should we ignore the national parks and monuments established while he was president.

Franklin, the son of James Roosevelt, a lawyer and railroad m[an] and Sara Delano Roosevelt, was born on his father's Hyde Park The Roosevelts were an old (the first Roosevelt arrived in America i[n] Establishment family who were comfortably fixed. James was $900,000 in an era of multimillionaires. He practiced law briefly and sequently was a railroad manager. His wife's father, Warren Delano, rich in the China trade (that is, the opium trade) and lived on an estate Newburgh, New York. Despite his resistance to their union, his twenty-year-old daughter married James, a widower, who was twice her age. T were a close-knit family, protective of their son, and this surely contribu to the sense of confidence Franklin developed that saw him through b[oth] private and public crises.

At the same time, Franklin led a rather untraditional childhood for a American child. He was taught at home by a tutor, and as early as the age three, he traveled with his parents to Europe. Indeed, these European so journs became part of his education, and as a child, he learned German and French.

While his mother took charge of the boy's management and discipline, his father introduced him to the pleasures of the out-of-doors, taking him on hikes in the woods. James knew the variety of trees on his estate (he owned a thousand acres of farmland and forests) and insisted that only diseased trees be cut down. Doubtless, Franklin's lifelong regard and respect for forests was due to his father's influence. He also acquired an interest in birds and became an avid bird-watcher. (It should be noted that historically, and with few exceptions, birders and sports fishermen have been conservationists.) In fact, presented with a gun when he was eleven, Franklin shot and, for a time, stuffed birds, developing quite a collection.

In 1896, having been tutored at home until then, Franklin was enrolled at the newly opened and exclusive Groton School. The instruction was rigorous and thorough. Four years later he went on to Harvard, where few of the professors interested him—though Harvard at the time had an impressive faculty—and was content to maintain a "gentlemanly C" average. He received his A.B. degree in 1903 and entered Columbia Law School; here he did fairly well. Passing the bar exam in the spring of the third year, he decided not to finish his courses and take a law degree.

program in the 1920s; farm legislation, chiefly by lifting the tax burden from the farmers; and old-age legislation, sure to appeal to urban residents. But scarcely had FDR moved into the governor's mansion than the 1929 Depression struck the country. Roosevelt dealt with the crisis in a number of ways. For instance, he sought legislation to shield small depositors from bank failures. He also employed jobless men, under the auspices of the state Temporary Relief Administration, to plant trees. The Relief Administration anticipated the CCC that was to be a significant part of the New Deal, and by 1932, the Relief Administration had 10,000 men planting trees.

Roosevelt's record as governor won him the Democratic nomination for the presidency. The nation was mired in the 1929 Depression, the worst economic crisis in the nation's history. President Herbert Hoover (1928–1932), in turn, had won few plaudits for his response to the Depression. Indeed, many Americans had despaired of the democratic process. Amid such despondency and economic want (fully a third of the wage and salary workers were jobless), FDR was elected with an overwhelming popular and Electoral College vote (472 to 59).

Immediately on taking office, FDR forged ahead with his famous "100 days" agenda. The Democratically controlled Congress complied, usually with alacrity, and bills sent to Congress were normally passed easily and quickly and signed by the president—from unemployment relief and Home Owner's Insurance to the National Industrial Recovery Act and the CCC.

The legislation creating the CCC was hurried through Congress, was signed by the president in March 1933, and was in operation by early April. A hugely popular program, the measure employed men in the country at the sort of labor that had interested Roosevelt since he was a child, protecting and improving America's forests. The law provided for the utilization of physically fit unemployed men, both white and an impressive number of black Americans between the ages of eighteen and twenty-six whose families were on relief. The CCC offered employment for young men, many from urban areas, to work in the country, something FDR found deeply appealing. They were to be paid $30 a month, of which $25 was sent directly to their families (thus relieving some of the pressure on the states that were attempting to deal with the cost of relief). Even this modest salary met objections—later overcome—from William Green, president of the American Federation of Labor, who feared that the income paid the CCC workers might undercut the wages of his union members.

In fact, by zealously stating his long-held view on what one can only describe as the moral value of the CCC, FDR asserted that more important than the material gains were the moral and spiritual values of such work. The large majority of unemployed Americans, FDR believed, who were now walking the streets and receiving private or public relief would definitely have preferred to work. We could have placed a vast army of these unemployed, he averred, into healthy surroundings. We could also have eliminated, to some extent at least, FDR maintained, the threat that enforced idleness brought to spiritual and moral stability. It was not a panacea for all the unemployed, he stressed, but it was an important step in this emergency.

After some discussion within the administration, a division of labor was agreed on. The War Department would build the camps, supervise the men, and supply tents and mess kits; the Labor Department would furnish the men; and the National Forest and National Parks Services would provide the work. By mid-June, 300,000 men were employed, living in 1,500 camps. And by 1935, over 500,000 men were engaged in the tasks assigned to them.

Their work involved flood control through the erection of dams; reforestation (the CCC planted over 2 trillion trees in national parks and national forests, as well as in state parks); and clearing firebreaks of obstructions and erecting observation towers, principally to search for fires. For instance, when a severe forest fire erupted in Montana, the CCC workers helped to battle it. Moreover, in Wyoming they extinguished a coal-mine fire that had been burning for seventy years. Additionally, CCC workers built 800 state parks, and they were used by the states to construct lakes in state parks and restore Revolutionary and Civil War battlefields. They constructed several thousand miles of horse trails and restocked rivers and lakes with almost a million fish. They also built campgrounds and drained swamps. In all, over 3 million men passed through CCC camps between 1933 and 1942.

There were of course problems and criticisms. Some of the camps were mismanaged (unfortunately, poor patronage appointments, though rare, did occur). And some of the city-bred youths were unskilled in what they were doing—planting seedlings, for example, that never sprouted. In Pennsylvania, moreover, poison was planted in the woods to exterminate porcupines, an action that resulted in the killing of deer.

Still, as Ted Morgan writes in *Franklin Delano Roosevelt: Champion of Freedom*, the CCC was "a hugely imaginatively and successful program."

Among the CCC's major accomplishments, aside from those already enumerated, was the substantial growth in the public domain, provided for when Congress appropriated $25 million to purchase forest land. At FDR's insistence, the CCC code stipulated that "no discrimination shall be made on account of race, color or creed." Of course, especially in the South, segregation was strictly enforced. On the other hand, black Americans were employed in numbers not far from their proportion of the nation's total population. The CCC took unemployed, and sometimes illiterate, youths and made them literate wage earners. Finally, the CCC workers were used to combat soil erosion—the major goal of the Soil Conservation and Domestic Allotment Act of 1935. It should be noted that farmers' compliance with the law was voluntary, and the government paid subsidies to farmers to allow their land to lie fallow and to plant crops, such as alfalfa, to return nitrogen to the soil.

At any rate, erosion was a problem that manifested itself in the 1930s when farmers plowed up the native anchoring grasses to plant their wheat and corn. The difficulty arose after the harvest, when farmers failed to sow an anchoring crop, such as alfalfa, and in the late autumn and winter, winds swept across the Great Plains particularly in Texas, Oklahoma, Kansas, Colorado, and New Mexico that carried the topsoil away. The result was the 1930s Dust Bowl, a difficulty compounded by a fierce, decade-long drought.

To deal with the problem, Congress passed, and Roosevelt signed, the Soil Conservation and Domestic Allotment Act. The law authorized the secretary of agriculture to provide financial assistance to agricultural producers to implement conservation and environmental measures. The act had an array of objectives, including preservation and improvement of soil fertility, advancing the retention of topsoil, and the conservation of land through dry farming. The law also established the Soil Conservation Service (SCS)—placed under the aegis of the Department of Agriculture—to fulfill the law's goals.

Several New Deal agencies were employed to carry out the aims of the law, including the Work Project Administration, the Drought Relief Service, and the CCC. In the case of the latter, for example, virtually all the CCC camps in Nebraska were working on soil conservation projects. By 1941, CCC workers had drained over 248,000 acres of swampland, replanted almost a million acres of grazing land, and protected 40 million acres of farmland from erosion. The SCS, in conjunction with the CCC, used various methods to avert soil erosion. Among these techniques were crop rotation, contour plowing, and where called for, the conversion of cropland to pasturage and woodlands. Moreover, reforestation, in the Dust Bowl states in particular, was crucial in curbing the effects of the wind and retaining moisture.

No chronicle of FDR's contributions to conservationism would be complete without some mention of the six national parks and eight national monuments established during his tenure in office. At the outset, it should be remarked that national and state parks used thousands of CCC personnel at numerous tasks, including rehabilitation and construction projects. As far as the national parks and national monuments were concerned, FDR established, with congressional compliance, six national parks and eight national monuments (based on the Antiquities Act of 1905). Of the national parks, Shenandoah National Park, established in Virginia in 1935, stands out for its natural splendor and significance in the nation's history. Moreover, the state of Virginia added to the park by purchasing almost 4,000 acres, acquired piece by piece and presented to the federal government as a gift.

What is striking about the eight national monuments, aside from their obvious historical value, is that there was no controversy surrounding seven. But the eighth, Jackson Hole in Wyoming, met intense opposition from the congressional supporters of timbermen, hunters, cattlemen, and other local interests. Bills were even introduced and passed by Congress to abolish the Antiquities Act, which FDR vetoed. The opponents then challenged the proclamation in court, but they were unsuccessful. Eventually, in 1950, a compromise was reached, and subsequently the bulk of Jackson Hole National Monument and Grand Teton National Park were incorporated in a new Grand Teton National Park.

The CCC was the most important part of FDR's contributions to environmentalism. It was enthusiastically backed by him, and although the CCC was terminated with the outbreak of World War II, the results of its reforestation program have lasted. Indeed, the CCC's reforestation program was so extensive that it can be credited with planting more than half the trees on public and private land in American history. The SCS, on the other hand, survived, though in a different guise, having been replaced by the National Resources Conservation Service. This agency has continued to offer advice and material assistance to farmers. Enduring, too, were the national parks and national monuments established during FDR's tenure in office. Over the years, millions of Americans have received pleasure, exercise, and education from their visits to the national monuments in particular. All in all, Roosevelt made a major contribution to American conservation.

RICHARD P. HARMOND

Brant, Irving. *Adventures in Conservation with Franklin D. Roosevelt.* Flagstaff, AZ, 1988.

Fridel, Frank. *Launching the New Deal.* Boston, MA, 1973.

Lacy, Leslie A. *The Soil Soldiers: The Civilian Conservation Corps in the Great Depression.* Radnor, PA, 1976.

Ward, Geoffrey. *Before the Trumpet: Young Franklin Roosevelt.* New York, 1985.

Roosevelt, Robert Barnwell (August 7, 1829–June 14, 1906). A sportsman, lawyer, politician, congressman, author, and raconteur, Roosevelt was born and reared in a mansion on Fourteenth Street in New York City. His father, Cornelius Van Schaack Roosevelt, a plate-glass importer and real estate investor, was one of the wealthiest men in the city; and RBR, as Robert was called, enjoyed a privileged upbringing that included servants and private tutors, sailing boats, and travel. Neither his father nor his mother, Margaret (Barnwell) Roosevelt, was, as far as is known, especially interested in the outdoors or nature. RBR, however, evinced a love of fishing and hunting, and his early books—*Game Fish of the Northern States of America and British Provinces* (1862), *Superior Fishing: or the Striped Bass, Trout, and Black Bass of the Northern States* (1865), and *Game Birds of the Coasts and Lakes of Northern States of America* (1866)—reveal how much he was absorbed in these activities.

Love of rod and gun drew RBR into the early conservation movement. He saw the damage being done to various species of game, from salmon and shad to quail and woodcock, by overfishing and overhunting, as well as by population pressures and industrial development. In *Superior Fishing* he wrote of the harm to wildlife and warned fellow sportsmen that "if they would retain for their old age and leave to their children the best preserver of health, a love of field sports, they must protect game-birds and fish."

Giving substance to this conviction, RBR was active in, and then in 1877 became president of, the New York Association for the Protection of Game, an organization active foremost in schemes for protecting game. Moreover, after his election to Congress as a Democrat from New York City (1871–1873),

RBR, a staunch and well-informed advocate of artificial fish propagation, enthusiastically backed experiments in pisiculture by the newly formed U.S. Commission of Fish and Fisheries.

In terms of public service, RBR's greatest contribution came during his twenty years on the New York State Fisheries Commission (a body that evolved into the current Department of Environmental Conservation). He was a member of the commission from its inception in 1868, and he headed the agency from 1879 until 1888 (when he stepped down to take an appointment from President Grover Cleveland as minister to the Netherlands, 1888–1889). Over a span of two decades, RBR, working with fish culturist Seth Green and others, launched successful experiments in pisiculture and helped establish several fish hatcheries. RBR and his fellow commissioners were also aware of the importance of educating the populace about fish restoration and conservation; so in 1874 they staged an exhibit "of fish and the process of fish hatching" at a number of state fairs. Many thousands saw the exhibit, reported the commissioners, "and went from it with new ideas and freshly awakened interest in our valuable fish."

Winning public support for fish and game laws through his books and other writings and drawing public attention to their importance through such activities as the fish culture exhibit are chief among RBR's legacies to the conservation cause.

In later years, RBR, a man of sensuous appetites, high spirits, and multiple interests, was less active in conservationism. But his nephew, Theodore Roosevelt, who founded the Boone and Crockett Club some six months before his uncle's retirement from the Fisheries Commission, took up the torch. Indeed, it would seem that RBR helped to shape TR's interest in nature and conservation.

RBR, who lived long enough to see his nephew become president and achieve major gains in the conservation field, died at his home in Sayville, Long Island. According to family tradition, his last words were: "The insects will inherit the earth."

RBR married Elizabeth Ellis in 1850, and they had three children, Margaret Barnhill, John Ellis, and Robert Jr. On the death of his first wife, he married Marion O'Shea Fortescue in 1888.

RICHARD P. HARMOND

Harmond, Richard. "Robert Barnwell Roosevelt and the Early Conservation Movement." *Theodore Roosevelt Association Journal* 14 (1986): 34–48.

McCullough, David. *Mornings on Horseback*. New York, 1981. In this biography of Theodore Roosevelt, the energetic personality of Robert Barnwell Roosevelt is covered in some detail.

🦌 **Roosevelt, Theodore** (October 27, 1858–January 6, 1919). A statesman, hunter, trust buster, aristocrat, cowboy, explorer, gentleman, ranchman, intellectual, soldier, historian, president, police commissioner, Rough Rider, imperialist, and conservationist, Roosevelt (TR) assumed many roles throughout his lifetime. His father, Theodore Roosevelt Sr., came from a wealthy New York family with Dutch origins. Roosevelt Sr. married Martha Bulloch, a southerner from Georgia, on December 22, 1853. TR was the second of their four children and was known to have frail health and asthma. Despite periodic bouts of ill health, Roosevelt developed an avid and active interest in wildlife and natural history at a young age by camping, exploring, walking, going abroad, reading, and collecting specimens. Time outdoors was respite from his ill health; he spent the summers of his childhood in the Hudson Valley and Long Island, where he nurtured his passion for ornithology. His childhood experiences began what would be a lifelong association between personal health, strength and masculinity, science, patriotic duty, progressive behavior, and conservation. Conservation was not just one aspect of his life and worldview: it was integrally connected to the other roles he would play in national history throughout his lifetime.

The Roosevelt family had a background in conservation. Roosevelt Sr. helped to found the Society for the Prevention of Cruelty to Animals and the American Museum of Natural History. Roosevelt's uncle Robert Barnhill Roosevelt was the author of *Game Fish of the Northern States of America and British Provinces* (1862) and *Game Birds of the North* (1866) and also was a figure in American conservation and New York political circles. Roosevelt would continue the family's involvement in the institutionalization of the study and conservation of wildlife through involvement with organizations like the American Museum of Natural History, the National Zoological Park in Washington, DC, and the Bronx Zoo or the New York Zoological Gardens.

From a young age, TR also experienced nature through institutions and scientific study. When he was but nine years old, he began the Roosevelt Museum of Natural History in his room. Other members would eventually include his brother Elliott Roosevelt and his cousins James West Roosevelt and William Emlen Roosevelt. The museum had members and directors, was "incorporated," and allocated a budget for the purchase of specimens. Minutes were also taken at the meetings. Its primary purpose, in addition to the association created by the common interest, seems to have been the collection of wildlife and natural specimens. By 1868, the museum had a total of 250 specimens.

Roosevelt was always an avid wildlife collector. To give an idea of how many birds Roosevelt either shot or bought and stuffed, TR donated 622 bird skins to the Smithsonian Institution in the spring of 1882 after a correspondence with Spencer F. Baird, the secretary, who knew both his father and uncle. He also donated 125 bird skins and four mounted birds to the American Museum of Natural History. Before he entered college, Roosevelt also wrote a number of notebooks and journals on his lists, findings, observations, and specimens of birds, fauna, and animals. The notebooks listed sightings of animals with remarks on their descriptions.

According to historian Paul Russell Cutright, Roosevelt's journals demonstrate a clear desire to be scientific, with a preference for order, method, and discipline. Since he was apparently familiar with Linnaeus's classification system, TR had a zest for efficiency. These writings and his early concerns for creating institutions reflect a very particular response to nature—amassing and collecting nature, learning about it, organizing it, and conquering it. His interest in natural history led to the codification and disciplinization of knowledge and nature.

While a student at Harvard, TR continued his associations with those also interested in natural history. He joined the Nuttal Ornithological Club and was vice president of the Harvard Natural History Society. He also published his first book, *The Summer Birds of Adirondacks in Franklin County, New York* (October 1877), with classmate Henry Minot. Additionally, during his time at Harvard, Roosevelt joined many different clubs and developed other interests, in particular, political economy. Despite his childhood desire to become a naturalist like John James Audubon and other distinguished men of the field, Roosevelt entered Columbia Law School after graduating from Harvard. He also became engaged to Alice Lee, the daughter of George Lee, a banker with the investment firm of Lee, Higginson & Co. and a Boston Brahmin. They were married on his birthday, October 27, 1880. The following year, Roosevelt was elected New York assemblyman and began a long career in politics.

From 1889 to 1895, Roosevelt was a civil service commissioner. He served as New York City police commissioner from 1895 to 1897. In 1897, he was appointed an assistant secretary of the navy by William McKinley. In 1898, he and Leonard Wood founded the U.S. Cavalry regiment known as the Rough Riders to fight in the Spanish-American War. That year he also was elected governor of New York State. He wrote a number of books during this period that reflected his myriad interests, including *Thomas Hart Benton* (1887), *Gouverneur Morris* (1889), *Winning of the West* (4 vols., 1889–1906), *New York* (1891), and *Oliver Cromwell* (1900). Roosevelt was McKinley's running mate in 1900 and became vice president of the United States in 1901. He became president after McKinley was assassinated in September of that year. He was president from 1901 to 1909.

Throughout his political career Roosevelt continued to devote time and interest to the study and exploration of wildlife and natural history. After a trip in 1883 to hunt and camp in the Dakota Badlands, Roosevelt invested in the cattle business. He also built a home he called Elkhorn Ranch, though he stopped ranching in 1887 after a bad winter killed his cattle. Though his business was not successful, it did not diminish his interest in the West. After the tragic deaths of both his mother and his wife Alice in February 1884, Roosevelt began a new period of traveling through the United States' remaining natural spaces. Two years later, he married childhood friend Edith Kermit Carow, and they had five children.

Between 1884 and 1892, Roosevelt took a number of trips out West. They include trips to the Two-Ocean Pass and Big Horn Mountains in Wyoming, Sellkirks in British Columbia, and Yellowstone National Park. Roosevelt recorded these experiences in what was known as a trilogy of the West, *Hunting Trips of a Ranchman* (1884); *Ranch Life and the Hunting Trial* (1888); and *The Wilderness Hunter* (1893). Some speculate that the West signified a masculine "refuge" for Roosevelt—and in his case, a refuge from personal tragedy. The changes wrought by the end of the nineteenth century due to industrialization, changes in women's roles, the rise of urbanism, the changes in class, and the rise of immigration, among other issues, led many Americans to be skeptical of civilization and its "progress." Degradation of human life and resources could be seen not only in the urban environments but also in the effects on the wilderness as the place where the frontier and the American individual were supposed to be made. Often, these observations had racial and class overtones and were expressed through fear and nostalgia for American traditions and character and popular writings on the primitive. These conditions influenced Roosevelt's understanding of masculinity with its racial and class undertones.

In *The Strenuous Life* (1900), TR wrote that the United States needed "a thoroughly manly race—a race of strong, virile character." According to historian Gary Gerstle, Roosevelt's particular nationalism combined a contradictory racial ideology that celebrated the diversity of the American people, albeit one with severe limitations, and the aggression and extermination of native peoples considered "savage." Central to his views on nation building was the aggressive male warrior. Homosocial bonds created by shared experience of warfare were bases for national leadership.

TR, as seen in his participation in male associations, cultivated spaces for male interaction; his views on masculinity and conservation were intertwined. In addition, the battlefield, urban politics, sports such as boxing and hunting, and exploration also provided those spaces. He supported the Young Men's Christian Association (YMCA) and the Boy Scouts of America, in particular. The Boy Scouts, founded by Sir Robert S. S. Baden-Powell, was developed for the United States by Ernest Thompson Seton, who argued that American boys' estrangement from nature by industrialization led to the degeneration of the American people. Roosevelt was the vice president of the Boy Scouts of America and their only Chief Scout Citizen.

TR was also president of the Boone and Crockett Club, another prominent association, from 1888 to 1893. In 1887 he and George Bird Grinnell created the plan to found the club for big game sportsmen. Grinnell and TR had met after Grinnell commented, unfavorably, on TR's book *Hunting Trips of a Ranchman*. Grinnell was the nature editor and later owner and editor in chief of *Forest and Stream,* a magazine founded in 1873. According to Grinnell, the purpose of the Boone and Crockett Club was to address their concerns around the preservation of game. TR helped to bring men of great power into the club. They included longtime friend and colleague Senator Henry Cabot Lodge, TR's secretary of state Elihu Root, J. P. Morgan, and TR's assistant secretary of state Robert Bacon.

The Boone and Crockett Club was concerned with events like the establishment of Glacier National Park, and it published a number of texts, which Roosevelt and Grinnell edited, including *American Big-Game Hunting* (1893), *Hunting in Many Lands* (1895), and *Trail and Camp Fire* (1897), to which Roosevelt contributed three articles, "Coursing the Prongbuck," "Hunting in the Cattle Country," and "On the Little Missouri." The Boone and Crockett Club was also concerned with Yellowstone National Park, the impact of the lumber industry, and tourism. Grinnell, in particular, was instrumental in fomenting public opinion against the encroachment of Yellowstone, an opinion that eventually culminated in the passage of the Lacey Act, also known as the Park Protection Act.

In addition to Grinnell, TR had relationships with other prominent men in the field of conservation who often had competing definitions of what *conservation* meant. Men like John Muir, with whom TR was a friend, defined it as preservation rather than development, even if it was a kind of development that was either scientific or planned. While TR was civil service commissioner, he met Gifford Pinchot, who is often noted as being the greatest influence on TR's political policies on conservation. Pinchot would also become a member of the Boone and Crockett Club and the secretary of the National Forest Commission. Pinchot's father, James M. Pinchot, was at one time the vice president of the American Forestry Association. Pinchot, who believed in scientific management of natural resources, had a contentious relationship with preservationists such as John Muir with whom he served on the National Forest Commission.

Both Grinnell's and Pinchot's influence on TR can be seen in part in Roosevelt's record as New York State governor. While in office, Roosevelt investigated the record of the Fisheries, Forest and Game Commission. He was explicit on the need to protect forests from fire due to their central role in maintaining the water supply; the need to protect wildlife, including fish, deer, songbirds, and game birds, from being decimated disproportionate to their natural increase; and the need to restrain railroad encroachment, timber abuses, and indiscriminate hunting—all policies that Pinchot supported. Pinchot's influence on Roosevelt's views on conservation management, rather than preservation, would continue while Roosevelt was president of the United States.

At the same time, TR's environmentalism was part of the Progressivism of the time and built on the work of Presidents Benjamin Harrison and Grover Cleveland before him. According to Cutright, Roosevelt had three conservation objectives as president: "(1) reclaiming arid lands through irrigation; (2) setting aside additional timberlands as forest reserves; and (3) creating wildlife refuges." During his administration, the Reclamation Act (1902) was passed. In 1911, the Roosevelt Dam, Arizona, was completed, which had been started during his administration. In 1904 the newly centralized Bureau of Forestry, which focused on education, was created. The new bureau actively publicized issues pertaining to forestry. Its message was that natural conservation was the measurement of a society's level of civilization and posterity. If that was the message, then TR was certainly the president to follow it.

During his presidency, Roosevelt "added almost 150 million acres of timberland to the reserves, thereby more than trebling the acreage set aside by preceding presidents." He also created the first federal wildlife refuge of Pelican Island in 1903. In all, he created fifty-one wildlife refuges. During his administration, both the Inland Waterways Commission (1907) and the Country Life Commission (1908) were founded. Congress also created five national parks, including Crater Lake, Oregon; Wind Cave Park, South Dakota; and Mesa Verde National Park, Colorado. After the passage of the National Monuments Act in 1906, Roosevelt also declared eighteen national monuments during his presidency, including Devil's Tower, Wyoming; Muir Woods in California; and the Grand Canyon in Arizona. In 1908, Roosevelt also held a conservation conference at the White House for governors, scientists, statesmen, and others. One result of the conference was the founding of the National Conservation Commission whose job it became to make an inventory of national natural resources. Just before his presidency ended, Roosevelt held the North American Conservation Conference at the White House in 1909 for statesmen from Canada, Mexico, and the United States.

In 1910, TR went to Africa with his son Kermit and three naturalists, Edgar Alexander Mearns, Edmund Heller, and John Alden Loring, on a Smithsonian-sponsored expedition. Though he returned to politics and unsuccessfully ran for the presidency on the Progressive/Bull Moose ticket, he continued to live an active life of exploration. In 1913, TR embarked on an expedition to South America with naturalists George Knuk Cherrie and Leo Edward Miller. He never lost his childhood fascination with collecting specimens in the name of science. The expedition gathered over 3,000 specimens for the American Museum of Natural History.

Throughout his many careers and roles, TR continued a lifelong interest and concern for matters dealing with the natural environment. Whether that association began from scientific inquiry, concerns over personal health, or progressivism, conservation became very much a part of his life and legacy.

SUSIE JIN PAK

Cutright, Paul Russell. *Theodore Roosevelt: The Making of a Conservationist.* Chicago, IL, 1985.

Gable, John Allen. "Theodore Roosevelt." *Biographical Dictionary of American and Canadian Naturalists and Environmentalists*, ed. Keir B. Sterling, Richard P. Harmond, George A. Cevasco, and Lorne F. Hammond. Westport, CT, 1997.

Miller, Nathan. *Theodore Roosevelt: A Life*. New York, 1992.

O'Toole, Patricia. *When Trumpets Call: Theodore Roosevelt after the White House*. New York, 2005.

Testi, Arnoldo. "The Gender of Reform Politics: Theodore Roosevelt and the Culture of Masculinity." *Journal of American History* 81.4 (March 1995): 1509–1533.

Rothrock, Joseph Trimble (April 9, 1839–June 2, 1922). A physician, botanist, and forester famous as the "Father of Pennsylvania Forestry," Rothrock was born in McVeightown, Mifflin County, Pennsylvania. His father, Dr. Abram Rothrock, was a physician who practiced in McVeightown. His mother, Phoebe (Brinton) Trimble, was related to well-known botanist William Darlington, and she herself was highly interested in the local flora and fauna. Young Rothrock attended local public schools and nearby preparatory schools. His delicate health, however, prevented a speedy completion of his early education. Nonetheless, in 1860 he was admitted to Harvard College, where he studied under the famous scientists Asa Gray and Louis Agassiz.

His studies were interrupted by the Civil War. He enlisted in the Pennsylvania volunteers as a private and was discharged in January 1864 as a captain in the Pennsylvania Voluntary Calvary, which he had helped to organize. He returned to Harvard and received his Bachelor of Science degree in July 1864. That fall, he became a student at the Medical School of the University of Pennsylvania.

Again his studies were halted. He accepted a request by the Smithsonian Institution to accompany a group who were to map and study British Columbia and Alaska. Rothrock was to collect botanical samples. Regrettably, the specimens were lost on the trip on the turbulent Fraser River. He left the group in the winter of 1865–1866. This trip, scientific in nature, may well have supplied the information that led to the purchase of Alaska in 1867.

On his return, Rothrock reentered medical school. He also completed a report for the Smithsonian Institution on the journey. His notes, "Sketch of the Flora of Alaska," appeared in the *Annual Report of the Smithsonian Institution* (1867). That same year, he completed his medical studies. From

1867 to 1869, he served as a professor of botany and human anatomy at the State Agricultural College (now Pennsylvania State University).

In May 1869, he married Martha E. May. They had five children; three survived to adulthood. One, Dr. Addison May Rothrock, helped his father in sanitorium work. They moved to Wilkes-Barre, Luzerne County, Pennsylvania, to establish a medical practice. The elder Rothrock was one of the founders of the Wilkes-Barre City Hospital and appeared to be well regarded as a physician. He was disappointed, however, at the state's failure to provide medical care for the miners in the area who were disabled by lung irritation caused by coal dust. In 1873, he abandoned his medical practice when his health deteriorated. Rothrock did not appear to have any real physical maladies; he just preferred the outdoors.

He joined another exploratory expedition as a botanist and medical officer. He became a member of the Lieutenant George N. Wheeler Expedition of the U.S. Geographical Survey. The purpose was to explore, map, and provide an inventory of the area south of the 39th parallel. Rothrock devoted most of his time and energy to botany for the period 1873 to 1875. His botanical report was extensive and took up a full volume (volume 6) in a seven-volume report published in 1878: "Reports on the Botanical Collections," *U.S. Geographical Surveys West of the 100th Meridian.* In providing his report, Rothrock gave full credit to Professor Asa Gray, to Dr. George Vasey of the Commission on Agriculture, and to distinguished ornithologist Henry W. Henshaw.

As a result of his travels in the Southwest, Rothrock became convinced of the benefits of outdoor living for sickly boys. Thus, in 1876, he established the North Mountain School of Physical Culture in Luzerne County, which remained open for three years. When Rothrock returned home after the Wheeler Expedition, he served in 1876 as the principal of a girls' school in Wilkes-Barre. The following year he was appointed a professor of botany at the University of Pennsylvania, where he remained until 1893. While Rothrock maintained an interest in health-related matters as well as in botany, his attention began to shift to the problem of forestry and its decline and degradation, especially in his home state of Pennsylvania.

In 1880, Rothrock went to Germany to study under world-famous botanist Henrich Anton De Bary (1831–1888). Rothrock was impressed, as other American foresters had been, by the care and concern of the German government and its people for their forests, which renewed his interest in the protection of the American forests. On his return from Germany, Rothrock was appointed to the Pennsylvania State Forest Commission. Now he became fully engaged in an effort to salvage and reforest the Pennsylvania landscape. He began to gather data on the decline of Pennsylvania's forests and proposed a commission to study the matter in his *An Act Relative to the Forestry Commission* (1893). He was appointed the botanist member of the commission, a full-time position, which necessitated his retirement from the University of Pennsylvania. In his new position, Rothrock stressed the need to preserve the forests for the present as well as for the future and to protect the present forests from the danger of forest fires. He made a number of suggestions to the state legislature to encourage the preservation of existing forests and reforestation in the future by the purchase of private lands, allowing tax relief and subsidies to private landowners to encourage their role in preservation and reforestation. He reported on his early findings in the "Forests of Pennsylvania," published in the *Proceedings of the American Philosophical Society* (1894).

Rothrock saw the need for a more active state role. In the *First Annual Report to the Pennsylvania Department of Agriculture* prepared by him and William F. Strunk in 1895, they hardily recommended that the state purchase certain private lands for forest reserves. They provided information that there were a growing number of barren and unproductive acres in Pennsylvania that would be helped by forest cover. In this report, the authors stressed the importance of forests in maintaining flood control as well as an adequate supply of drinking water. The state legislature reacted positively, and in 1897 they established a forestry reservation commission authorized to purchase 40,000 acres of land. That same year, legislation established a fire warden system to handle forest fires. Additional legislation recommended by Rothrock established tree nurseries that provided trees for planting. Before his death in 1922, well over 30 million trees were provided to private owners.

In addition, Rothrock wanted to see implemented what he had noted in Germany: forestry education. He encouraged the University of Pennsylvania to establish a school, or even a department, where young men could prepare to be forestry agents. Finally, in 1903, he succeeded, and the state named him commissioner of forestry, with the authority to establish what came to be called the State Forest Academy. He continued as commissioner until 1904.

Rothrock's greatest contribution was his sounding the alarm to the dangers that the forests of Pennsylvania faced. He successfully aroused public awareness to the degradation of deforestation and the absolute necessity of protection and reforestation. A man of commitment, a man of indefatigable energy when it came to forestry, he proved essential to the preservation of Pennsylvania's state forests and is justifiably remembered as the Father of Pennsylvania Forestry.

JUDITH M. CURRAN

Dudley, Susan, and David R. Goddard. "Joseph T. Rothrock and Forest Conservation." *Proceedings of the American Philosophical Society* 117 (February 1973): 37–50. Contains a list of his most significant writings.

Kelly, Howard A. *Some American Medical Botanists.* New York, 1914. Contains an autobiographical sketch of Rothrock's career.

Wirt, George H. "Joseph Trimble Rothrock." *Journal of Forestry* 44 (June 1946): 442–443.

Ruckelshaus, William Doyle (July 24, 1932–). Over his forty-year career, Ruckelshaus exerted a great influence on the development of domestic environmental policy in the United States at multiple levels of government and in the private sector. He is perhaps best known for establishing the goals and maintaining the mission of the U.S. Environmental Protection Agency (EPA) as the agency's first (1970–1973) and fifth (1983–1985) administrator. Today, his contributions to environmentalism and the environmental movement go beyond that of the federal government. As an attorney and civil servant, Ruckelshaus has led or served on countless private and public environmental policy organizations, including the U.S. Commission for Ocean Policy, the World Commission for the Environment and Development (established by the United Nations), the World Resource Institute, and the National Council for Science and the Environment.

Ruckelshaus is known for his keen understanding of the interplay between public opinion, environmental problems, and governance. Although residual effects of troubles within the Nixon administration would lead him away from federal politics and into private business, his acumen for effective environmentalism through democracy ensures his place as an adviser and environmental actor on a range of issues. His contributions to environmentalism continue today as he highlights corporate environmental responsibility through his business leadership and writes and speaks out about environmental issues, science, and democracy in modern society.

Born into a family legacy of lawyers in Indianapolis, Indiana, he was the middle child of John K. and Marion (Doyle) Ruckelshaus. Directly out of high school, he began his public service career by enlisting in the U.S. Army and served for two years. In 1955, at the age of twenty-three, he entered Princeton, from which he was graduated with a Bachelor of Arts degree. Directly following, he attended Harvard Law School, where he earned an LL.B., graduating in 1960.

He then returned home to Indianapolis, passed the state bar, and began practicing law at the family firm of Ruckelshaus, Bobbitt, and O'Connor. At the age of twenty-eight, he was appointed deputy state attorney general and was assigned to the Indiana Board of State Health, working as counsel to the Indiana Stream Pollution Control Board. Here Ruckelshaus would gain his first major environmental experience with what would later become a large part of his adult life: ensuring corporate and federal stewardship of natural resources in the interest of ecological and public health. Ruckelshaus would later explain that he never saw himself as an environmentalist but as an enforcer of the law. Over the next four years, the young lawyer would quickly move up the public service ladder in the state of Indiana, culminating with his position as chief counsel for the General Attorney's Office.

In 1964, Ruckelshaus ran for a state congressional seat in Indiana as a moderate Republican but lost in the primaries. Undaunted, Ruckelshaus ran again in 1964, this time winning his party's selection and earning a seat in the Indiana House of Representatives. This success would continue, and he quickly became majority leader his first year in office. In 1968, Ruckelshaus won his party's nomination again, but this time for a seat in the U.S. Senate race. The election, however, went to his Democratic opponent. Although moderately successful in politics, Ruckelshaus would later find his strengths were more in government administration and corporate leadership, rather than running in political races.

By 1970, at the age of thirty-eight, he had already had considerable experience at varying levels of government, which would prove helpful as he navigated through various bureaucratic waters of federal administration. Ruckelshaus occupied a series of highly visible federal administration positions after being called to Washington, DC, by Richard Nixon during the start of his presidency to serve as assistant U.S. attorney general for the Civil Division, overseeing all federal government litigation proceedings. While in Washington, Ruckelshaus refined his political, administrative, and law skills and quickly became a well-respected member of the federal government. In 1970, the president's Executive Council on Administration recommended that federal involvement with environmental issues be consolidated into a single governmental institution. This decision, known as Reorganization Plan Number 3, would undergo intense congressional scrutiny during the planning phase but would ultimately result in the development of the U.S. Environmental Protection Agency. Due to his high visibility, administrative successes, and experience regulating environmental issues, Ruckelshaus was a prime candidate to lead the new agency and was confirmed as the EPA's first administrator on its first day of operation, December 4, 1970.

He had considerable success with the nascent agency. He is credited with defining the mission, hiring the leaders, and outlining environmental policies, much of which still exist today. These priorities, based on his experiences, include his personal philosophies that environmental policies must be determined in part through public consensus, and it is the government's responsibility to mitigate industrial pollution through monitoring, regulation, and litigation on behalf of the citizenry. During his first tenure with the EPA, he was effectively able to fortify the agency with his personal integrity while largely establishing the role of the agency: protecting domestic ecological and public health through governmental regulation and policy. Among other accomplishments, he is credited with overseeing the three-month hearing and subsequent ban on the hazardous pesticide DDT. During these proceedings, Ruckelshaus led discussions that addressed both the economic impact of the chemical ban and the growing public distrust of the scientific and industrial communities taking place in America during this time. He would later write about the role of trust in science and implementing favorable policy. Ruckelshaus would continue to champion emerging environmental issues with the EPA until April 30, 1973, when the Watergate scandal would bring political turmoil and with it a remarkable reshuffling of the federal government. The resignation of several presidential loyalists left vacant high-level positions that Ruckelshaus was more than qualified to fill. Ruckelshaus decided to leave the EPA in exchange for a position as the director of the Federal Bureau of Investigation. This position, however, would be short-lived, as cascading effects of the Nixon administrative foibles would end in mass resignations, later known as the "Saturday Night Massacre," Ruckelshaus included.

Understandably, Ruckelshaus left Washington, following the unfavorable events of the Nixon administration, for the greener pastures of private business, not likely expecting to return to the turmoil of civil service in Washington. It would not be long, however, before he received a call back to federal government. In the ten years following Ruckelshaus's absence, public trust of the EPA would wane, and in 1983, Ronald Reagan's chief of staff would ask Ruckelshaus to return to Washington to restore integrity to the agency. He would again act as agency director but would stay just long enough to get the EPA back on its feet. Ruckelshaus had final say over filling the top positions with quality people and redirecting the wayward agency back to its original mission of bolstering trust with the American citizenry while ensuring corporate environmental accountability of polluters. Once he felt that stability was restored, he would leave the EPA for a second time on February 7, 1985, which coincided with the beginning of Reagan's second term as president. Again, Ruckelshaus moved away from federal positions into the private sector, and although he would no longer direct American environmental policy as an administrator, he would continue to keep environmental responsibility near, holding several high-level positions at law firms and industrial companies, working to ensure the sustainability of our shared natural resources.

Today, the long-standing contributions of Ruckelshaus have extended far beyond his initial role of establishing environmental governance through the EPA. Ruckelshaus has transitioned into several roles as corporate environmental steward and author. Throughout his many years in private business, Ruckelshaus has played a large part in defining the role of corporate environmental responsibility and mitigating resource use and ecological stability because, in his words, "it is the right thing to do." He has also written and spoken extensively on issues that revolve around the history of environmentalism in America and tracked its changes from the rhetoric demonstrated in the 1960s to the implementation of legislation meant to curb pollution in the 1970s and 1980s. Ruckelshaus is known as a knowledgeable and opinionated author whose writings and speeches about environmentalism, the role of trust in government, and policy have been seen in popular periodicals like the *New York Times* and *Business Week* and in academic journals such as *Environmental Toxicology, Risk Analysis,* and *Scientific American.*

Throughout his career in private business, he has been a sought-after leader, pursued by many 500 companies to oversee business management while bringing his distinct sense of environmental accountabilities to their operations. One noteworthy characteristic of Ruckelshaus that accounts for at least some of his success in government and in business is his candor when speaking and writing about the interplay between environmental responsibility, public opinion, and democracy.

Ruckelshaus continues to mitigate natural resources issues through his involvement in several for-profit corporations while volunteering his time and expertise for many governmental organizations and environmental think tanks. Currently, he is serving as the director of several corporations, which include Cummins Engine Company, Pharmacia Corporation, Coinstar Inc., Solutia Inc., Nordstrom Inc., and Weyerhaeuser Company. He lives with his wife Jill in Seattle, Washington, where he remains committed to sustainable natural resource management, volunteering his time advising local and national environmental committees for the federal government and for nonprofit organizations.

STEVEN GRAY

"Ruckelshaus, W. D." *Business Week*, June 18, 1990.

"Ruckelshaus, W. D." *New York Times*, November 30, 1988.

Ruckelshaus, W. D. "Risk, Science, and Democracy." *Issues in Science and Technology* 3 (1985).

———. "Risk in a Free Society." *Risk Analysis* 4 (1984).

U.S. Environmental Protection Agency. "William Ruckelshaus: Oral History Interview." EPA 202-K-92-0003, January 1993. http://epa.gov/adminweb/history/publications/ruck/index.htm.

Safina, Carl (May 23, 1955–). An eminent ecologist and oceanic conservationist, Safina is known not only for the *Song for the Blue Ocean* (1997) and other books but also for such initiatives as establishing, in 1990, the Living Oceans Program at the National Audubon Society.

Safina, son of Carlo Safina, a New York City high school teacher, and Rose Safina, was born into a middle-class family in the Ridgewood area of Brooklyn. Like many other environmentalists, Safina had pets as a child, including a flock of homing pigeons in his family's backyard. He possessed an instinctual predilection toward animals, and his father, who raised canaries, supported his penchants by trips to the Bronx Zoo and the Museum of Natural History. When Carl was ten, his family moved to Syosset, Long Island; he loved roaming in "the woods" in nearby Woodbury, looking for birds, snakes, toads, and other animals. But one day bulldozers appeared and destroyed the woods; this incident had a significant impact on the youngster, persuading him that anything of value might be lost.

"On warm spring evenings in the rich light before sunset . . . my father would take me down to the pebbly shore of Long Island Sound to hunt striped bass," Safina recalls. "I thought that my father and I, with our secret fishing spot, were very, very lucky," Safina notes. "When one is growing up with a sense of place, the world seems secure and filled with promise" (*Song for the Blue Ocean*). These trips to Long Island Sound were also the source of Safina's love of fishing. Indeed, fishing, overfishing, and the consequent threat of species extinction dominated Safina's career as an oceanic conservationist.

Safina attended Syosset High School, where a classmate enlisted him to assist in a bird-banding study on Fire Island (off the south shore of Long Island). The experience was the source of Safina's fondness for wild birds (which he labeled "living jewels").

After graduating, Safina enrolled in the State University of New York, at Purchase, earning a B.A. degree in environmental science in 1977. (As a teenager, Safina had learned to play the drums, and he worked his way through college playing at weddings and private parties.)

He next trained hawks and, for a short time, falcons for the Peregrine Fund (a nonprofit association). Subsequently, he enrolled in a graduate program of study at Rutgers University and gained an M.S. (1981) and Ph.D. (1982) in ecology. His doctoral dissertation was on the interconnected behaviors and yearly cycles of the common tern and bluefish, both of which consume the same small watery prey.

While working on his dissertation, Safina observed a decline in fish species, including striped bass, tuna, marlin, sharks, and other denizens of the deep—as well as sea turtles. Safina began to realize that fish required as much protection as terns and falcons. "People never thought of fish as wildlife," he told an interviewer. "They just thought fish was something that wound up in the fish store or on a plate in a restaurant" (*Newsday*, June 19, 2002). One day in 1989, while fishing in the Atlantic, Safina took note of some anglers taking "ridiculous amounts" of bluefin tuna, reported Safina. "Somebody got on the radio and said, 'Guys, maybe we should leave some for tomorrow.' Another guy came on and said, 'Hey, they didn't leave any buffalo for me'" (*New York Times*, September 22, 1998). That terse remark stirred Safina deeply, since he understood that because of overfishing a whole fish species might actually disappear. He began speaking of global overfishing as "the last buffalo hunt."

In 1990 Safina started the Living Oceans Program at the National Audubon Society, serving for ten years as vice president for ocean conservation. At the same time, between 1991 and 1994, he was on the Mid-Atlantic Fisheries Management Council of the U.S. Department of Commerce. In 2003 Safina co-started and was president of the Blue Ocean Institute, an institution committed to encouraging among humankind a closer connection with the ocean and assisting people with appreciating its beauty and power. The idea behind founding the institute was to devise a "sea ethic" comparable to Aldo Leopold's "land ethic," as well as to stimulate in people a greater regard for the oceans and their denizens.

Song for the Blue Ocean, Safina's first book, earned the enthusiastic plaudits of reviewers. It was described by various reviewers as "prescient and powerful," "engrossing and illuminating," "a thought-provoking narrative [that] describes species, sketches local history, and introduces the key players to tell their side of the story"—a book, in sum, that is a "must-read for anyone concerned about the future of marine fisheries." "What Rachel Carson's *Silent Spring* [1962] did to spur public outrage over pesticides, we can only hope Carl Safina's magnificent, profoundly disturbing book will do to halt over-fishing and the catastrophic depletion of marine species," another critic wrote.

Song for the Blue Ocean was (and remains) as this and more. Traveling to the northeastern and northwestern United States, as well as Asia, Safina unflinchingly and authoritatively recounted the dismal story of the sharp diminution of a host of fish species. That host, as of the mid-1990s, included bluefin tuna, blue marlin, white marlin, eastern Atlantic yellowfin tuna, albacore tuna, bigeye tuna, and swordfish. All these fish species were "at the lowest levels in history." Other fish species under duress in New England waters were cod, haddock, and pollock. In the northwestern United States, species of salmon were in trouble. Indeed, wrote Safina: "Less than 5 percent and even with hatcheries about 75 percent of the original number of runs in the Northwest are either going or gone." In the case of salmon, the construction of dams (which made it difficult for salmon to swim up steams to spawn) and overfishing were the culprits.

In the years since I began these travels in the early 1990s, the two possible fates for the world's oceans have, indeed, been duking it out, and the forces of good have landed a few solid punches.

Prompted by the combined voices of hundreds of conservation-minded people—ranging from environmental organizations—the United Nations enacted a worldwide ban on large-scale drift net in the early 1990s. In 1995 the U.N. also agreed upon historic new standards for fishing on the high seas. Once this agreement enters into force (though only thirty ratifications are required and more than fifty countries intend to ratify it, the process takes several years), no area of the world's seas will be lawless any longer. The agreement includes a concept called the "precautionary principle," which says, in effect, that we must err on the side of caution—the first time a large scale treaty has carried this concept. The United Nations also passed a fisheries Code of Conduct, setting out strongly worded guidelines.

In the United States, fisheries reform grew into a major conservation issue in the 1990s. Over 125 groups (perhaps the largest coalition ever assembled to work on an environmental issue on America) united to overhaul the federal law governing fishing in the U.S., the Fisheries Conservation and Management Act. The law now requires fisheries managers to end overfishing for most species and requires rebuilding of depleted populations (bluefin tuna are one of the few exceptions, unfortunately).

In New England, strict new regulations have finally halted overfishing for most groundfishes, and some are showing increases for the first time in many years. Some sharks even got a break, with increasing attention at CITES [Convention on International Trade in Endangered Species] meetings; halving of catch quotas off the U.S. East Coast; protection for great white, whale and basking sharks in several countries; and scientists from around the world pooling their efforts to assemble a global action plan for shark conservation. The World Conservation Union in 1996 placed over a hundred species of marine fishes on its "Red List of Threatened Animals," a gesture that greatly raised the visibility of, and underscored the importance of, ocean depletions.

To cap a decade of real progress and to acknowledge how fundamentally the seas unify the world, the U.N. designated 1998 as the Year of the Oceans. For me personally, nothing speaks more eloquently about the possibilities for renewal than seeing the return of plentiful runs of striped bass coursing through my home water, spectacular success proving that tough management and respect for science really can turn depletion into abundance within a human lifetime.

Today many people are sensing that the seas need sympathy and that people who rely on the seas need action. In many ways the 1990s emerged as the decade when people finally began discovering the oceans. In 1995, *National Geographic's* ten million subscribers worldwide read about the imperiled state of the world's seas. And as a fitting precursor to 1997's designation as International Year of the Reef, *Time* magazine's October 1996 international edition featured corals and fishes on its cover, as well as twelve pages of articles to go with the cover headline:

Global Agenda
TREASURES OF THE SEAS
We've plundered the oceans' gifts.
Can we now protect them?

Good question. A better one would be, "Will we choose to?" And perhaps we can help answer that by posing another question: "What if we don't?"

It has been said that the economy is a wholly owned subsidiary of the environment. Certainly, the salmon fishers in the Northwest know this—and live it. When we speak of saving the oceans, then, I offer this: We need the seas more than they need us.

For each of us, then, the challenge and opportunity is to cherish all life as the gift it is, envision it whole, seek to know it truly, and undertake—with our minds, hearts, and hands—to restore its abundance. It is said that where there's life there's hope, and so no place can inspire us more hopefulness that the great, life-making sea—that singular, wondrous ocean covering the blue planet.

Song for the Blue Ocean was selected as a *New York Times* Notable Book of the Year and a *Los Angeles Times* Best Nonfiction Selection and earned Safina the Lannan Literary Award for Nonfiction.

Safina's next book was *Seafood Lover's Almanac* (written with Mercedes Lee and Suzanne Indicello; 2000), which is a guide for those who eat seafood but are disquieted by depleted fish and shellfish stocks. Critics lauded the book and welcomed the tips about how to balance a seafood diet with a conservationist ethic.

The Seafood Lover's Almanac was succeeded by *Eye of the Albatross: Visions of Hope and Survival* (2002). The book, acclaimed by reviewers, trailed a Laysan albatross (named "Amelia" by Safina) through a single breeding season, describing the various perils the albatross confront, as well as the striking exploits they achieve, such as flying stupifying distances and living as long as sixty years. In 2005 *Eye of the Albatross* earned the John Burroughs Medal, given yearly to books that provide scientific accuracy, depictions of fieldwork, and inventive natural history writing.

Safina's most recent book is *Voyage of the Turtle: In Pursuit of the Earth's Last Dinosaur* (2006). This book, lauded by reviewers (for instance, "a marvelous account," an "engaging literary exploration," and "a wonderful chronicle"), might almost be subtitled "a tale of two oceans." The turtles—leatherbacks, in particular—face two problems: "drowning in fishing gear" and having the female turtles' "eggs taken by people." Pacific leatherbacks have plummeted "from an estimated 90,000-plus adult females living in the 1980's to fewer than 50,000 by the threshold of the new millennium." In fact, "between 1980 and 2000, the leatherback turtle lost an estimated 70 percent of its worldwide population." Still, the Atlantic leatherback population had generally stabilized by 2000, "with some populations clearly increasing" from former lows. In the Pacific, where the situation has been quite bleak, there is some reason for hope. In Malaysia, for instance, the sea turtle has made a comeback. Why not elsewhere in the Pacific?

Safina has won numerous honors. In 2000 he was awarded a MacArthur Foundation Fellowship, also known as the "genius grant." He used the prize money to support his research and travels. He has also received several honorary doctorates, been chosen by Rutgers University as the most distinguished alumnus to graduate from the school's ecology and evolution program, and been selected by *Audubon* magazine as one of the most influential environmentalists of the twentieth century. He has been the recipient of the International Game Fish Association Conservation Award and the American Fisheries Society's Carl R. Sullivan Conservation Award.

If not optimistic, Safina is at least hopeful about the future of the oceans. He observes that "the oceans and the living world are in trouble." He realizes that some fish species have been lost, and still more will vanish. But others will "likely" be saved. Moreover, with "climate change" as the "defining environmental issue for the foreseeable future," awareness has developed among Americans that "we are all connected by the things we do." This new consciousness may well make people more receptive to other environmental matters, such as the oceans. Finally, as Safina observes, fish species that were once "very depleted" have recovered, including striped bass in local waters and sea turtles in the Caribbean.

Safina, who lives in Amagansett, Long Island, remains a fisherman. But he sharply limits his catch to what he requires for dinner or "enough bluefish to smoke and give away as holiday gifts."

RICHARD P. HARMOND

"Safina, Carl." *Current Biography*. 2005.
The author wishes to thank Dr. Safina for materials provided that are quoted in this entry.

Sargent, Charles Sprague (April 24, 1841–March 22, 1927). An arboriculturalist and dendrologist, Sargent was born to Henrietta (Gray) and Ignatius Sargent, the youngest of three children. In an era when family position largely determined one's place and success in the social order, Sargent arrived in the world with impeccable credentials. His father was a wealthy Boston merchant and banker, and the family was counted among Boston's elite.

There is scant information about Sargent's childhood years. He grew up on the family estate in Brookline, 130 acres of carefully planted parkland

and gardens, which were actively planned and tended by his father. He attended private schools and entered Harvard College in 1858, to graduate four years later with an undistinguished record in classical studies. The Civil War claimed his next three years. He served as an infantry officer for the North and was honorably discharged in 1865. Three years of European travel preceded his return to Boston and his marriage to Mary Ellen Robeson in 1873. They subsequently raised a family of two sons and three daughters.

It does not seem to be either a simple lack of information or a pervasive and persistent personal reticence on Sargent's part that leaves one with very little sense of his early primary interests and direction. Intellectual matters had not sparked him, although his college years had been marked by the advent of Charles Darwin's *The Origin of Species* (1859). Nor had the experiences of war moved him nor an extended period under the stimulus of foreign travel. A true product of his time and place, Sargent was concerned with order, particularly as it was represented in the natural world. When he returned to Boston in 1873, he came home to take on the management of the family estate (Holm Lea) and especially the feature thereof to which he was most drawn—its trees.

Estate horticulture was at this time a pursuit of wealthy individuals who had both the resources and the leisure to transform large areas of land into competitive showcases. Sargent's neighbors in Brookline were to serve as powerful mentors in his chosen endeavor, providing him with the network of contacts that he used both to initiate and to sustain his career.

In 1873 Sargent was appointed as curator and subsequently director of Harvard's newly endowed Arnold Arboretum. He was also named director of the Botanic Garden in Cambridge, being initially hired into these positions to reduce the workload of celebrated American botanist Asa Gray. Sargent gave up the directorship of the Garden in 1879 to devote his energies to the Arboretum. The administrative, political, and financial negotiations that preceded the first permanent plantings in 1886 were numerous, but Sargent's commitment and perseverance brought the Arboretum to the attention of a public hitherto little concerned with trees.

On a larger scale, the early 1880s saw Sargent's appointment as coordinator of a census investigation of U.S. forests for the Department of Agriculture's new Division of Forestry. These investigations produced the 1884 *Report on the Forests of North America*. This, Sargent's first major publication, was well received and provided not only a comprehensive, descriptive botanical reference but also a much-needed authoritative baseline from which conservationists and legislators could produce recommendations.

Other surveys in which Sargent took part were the Northern Pacific Transcontinental Survey of Northwest forests and another of Adirondack forestland for New York State. While strongly aware of the need to secure federal protection for forest resources, Sargent was discouraged by the political battles and often inauspicious outcomes of the legislative process. After a final, disappointing engagement in a Congressional Commission under President Grover Cleveland to set aside thirteen new forest reserves, Sargent retired from the political fray in 1897 and returned his attentions to the Arboretum.

Fortunately, the negative conservation experience had in no way blunted Sargent's enthusiastic and successful botanical investigations. His studies resulted in the fourteen volumes of *The Silva of North America* (1891–1902), *Forest Flora of Japan* (1894), *Manual of the Trees of North America* (1905), and production of the weekly magazine *Garden and Forest* (1888–1897), which served to popularize forestry issues in the United States. Sargent continued in his scholarly pursuits and in active direction of the Arboretum until the month of his death in 1927.

Strictly speaking, Sargent's greatest contribution in the service of his beloved trees was neither as a conservationist nor as a botanist (for example, his classification of the genus *Crataegus*, or hawthorne, was in error and has tarnished his taxonomic reputation). His many detailed, descriptive publications and his successful management of the Arnold Arboretum as a natural platform for the public presentation of information brought forestry issues into the public domain for the first time. His work bridged the gap between the scientific theories of botany and the practical knowledge of the gardener and was instrumental in establishing a critical initial assessment of America's forest resources.

KAREN HOVDE

"Sargent, Charles Sprague." *Dictionary of American Biography.* Vol. 8. 1963.

Sutton, S. B. *Charles Sprague Sargent and the Arnold Arboretum.* Cambridge, MA, 1970.

Seton, Ernest Thompson (August 14, 1860–October 23, 1946). A naturalist, artist, author, early Boy Scout leader, and lecturer, Seton was the

leading nature writer of his generation, best known for his many books of exciting animal stories, which were illustrated with his evocative drawings and quick sketches. A founder of the Woodcraft Indians (1902) and the Boy Scouts of America (1910), he inculcated generations of boys with the enjoyment and challenges of outdoor life, a fascination with Native American lore, and the importance of conserving natural resources.

Born in South Shield, a seaport town near Newcastle, England, Seton was the twelfth of fourteen children born to Joseph Logan and Alice (Snowden) Thompson. Seton's father, a stern Scots Calvinist and a fierce disciplinarian, was inclined to flog his offspring. Young Ernest was christened Ernest Evan, after a relative who had been a famous Scots hunter, but used the names Ernest E. Thompson and, in response to his mother's plea, Ernest Thompson Seton, which he adopted legally after her death in 1901.

In 1866, his father's once prosperous shipping firm failed owing to a series of business reverses, and the family moved to Canada. There Joseph planned to establish himself in the manner of an English country squire on a hundred-acre farm near Lindsay, Ontario. But Ernest's father lacked the aptitude for farming, and his older sons quit as soon as they had the opportunity. In 1870, Joseph sold his property to William Blackwell, a neighbor, moved his family to Toronto, and took up a career as an accountant.

Ernest's years in the Canadian countryside had given him his goal in life, to become a naturalist, though his father opposed this. In 1876, Seton was apprenticed to a hack portrait painter, his father having evidently concluded that Ernest could best earn his living in that fashion. But Ernest continued his studies for several years at the Ontario School of Art, where he won a gold medal at age eighteen.

He persuaded his father to advance the money for his passage to London in 1879, where he studied mammalian anatomy at the London Zoo and the British Museum (Natural History). Late in 1880, he won a substantial scholarship at the Royal Academy School of Painting and Sculpture, but he attended classes there for less than a year. Struggling to stretch the inadequate funds received from his father, his health suffered, and he returned to Toronto in November 1881.

The following spring, Seton helped his brother Arthur build a house on the latter's property near Carberry, Manitoba, and in 1883, he took up a land claim of his own in the Fort Pelly region. But he was not yet ready to settle down. Except for periods of time in Toronto, and two visits to New York and one to Chicago, where he underwent a successful hernia operation,

Seton spent nearly five years on the great plains of Manitoba, homestead-ing, hunting, trapping, and collecting. The years in Manitoba matured Seton's talents for field research. As Manitoba's appointed government naturalist, Seton produced his first scientific publications, *Mammals of Manitoba,* in 1886, and *The Birds of Manitoba,* in 1891.

Seton was invited to join the recently organized American Ornithologists' Union (AOU) in 1884 by its dynamic young secretary, C. Hart Merriam, and met the AOU's three cofounders, Joel Asaph Allen, William Brewster, and Elliott Coues, all distinguished ornithologists. Spencer Fullerton Baird, a senior AOU member and second secretary of the Smithsonian Institution (1823–1887), was one of Seton's staunchest supporters. Seton became par-ticularly close to Frank Chapman, then Allen's young assistant at the American Museum of Natural History in New York. Seton contributed to, and illustrated, Chapman's *Handbook of Birds of Eastern United States* (1895) and his *Bird Life* (1896). He also began contributing articles to the AOU's journal, the *Auk.* In one article, Seton, ever the popularizer, argued that while scientific names were entirely in the hands of the scientists, pop-ular names were "just as completely in the hands of the people . . . to be popular [they] must be distinctive, and in accord with the genius of our language." Scientists might advise, he added, but not dictate on this point. Thrush, heron, rail, hawk and night jar were good examples of popularly devised names, said Seton, but "Black Ptiligonys," "Semipalmated" "Tat-tler," and "Fascinated Tit" represented efforts by scientists to impose their ideas on the popular mind.

Merriam had complained that he knew of no artist in America "who could make a decent drawing of an animal," but Seton's work soon elicited Merriam's high praise. He used one of Seton's sketches in his *Mammals of the Adirondacks,* published in 1884, and commissioned additional draw-ings, which were later used in various U.S. government publications. This helped Seton get started in his chosen profession. Another boost to his ca-reer came about when he met W. Lewis Frazer of the *Century Magazine,* for whom he made 1,000 nature drawings for *The Century Dictionary* (1889–1891). In 1891, Seton was back in Paris for additional training at Julian's Academy and independent anatomical study. His oil painting of a sleeping wolf was exhibited at that year's Grand Salon. His anatomical research bore fruit with the publication of his *Art Anatomy of Animals* (1896).

Seton found another basis for his calling as naturalist in 1892 when he accepted a job as wolf killer for a wealthy rancher living in Clayton, New

Mexico. He used steel traps and poisoned baits with great effectiveness but also began learning more about the birds and mammals of the American Southwest, a section of the country he came to love deeply. His experiences were turned into one of the first of his famous animal stories, "The King of the Currumpaw," first published in *Scribner's* in 1894. It dealt with Lobo, a gray wolf of unusual size, strength, and cunning, who finally fell victim to Seton's traps only because of his loyalty to his mate, the white wolf Bianca.

A similar pattern marked the other successful stories Seton began writing at this time: a particular mammal or bird, named and endowed by Seton with certain strengths and understandings culled from his field experiences with several animals of the same kind, triumphs over a series of perils and in the end, perhaps, perishes bravely. Seton once wrote that "for the wild animal there is no such thing as a gentle decline in peaceful old age. Its life is spent at the front, in line of battle, and as soon as its powers begin to wane in the least, its enemies become too strong for it; it falls." The aptly titled *Wild Animals I Have Known,* first published in 1898, demonstrated the appeal of such tales, quickly became a bestseller, and founded, according to Seton, "the modern school of animal stories." This volume, still in print, was easily the author's most successful literary effort.

En route to Paris for further study in 1894, Seton met Grace Gallatin, daughter of a California financier and a young woman of both social and artistic aspirations. They were married in New York in June 1896. Their one daughter, Ann, became the novelist Anya Seton. Grace assisted her husband with many editorial tasks but also enjoyed her own career as a writer, feminist reformer, and social leader. She was willing to share Seton's interests, but he did not take easily to the settled and socially established ways his wife preferred, and their lives soon tended to diverge, although they remained on friendly married terms for thirty-nine years.

In 1897, Seton explored the Yellowstone; in 1898, the Wind River country and Jackson Hole; and in 1900 he was in Norway. In 1907, he took a 2,000-mile Canadian canoe trip nearly to the Arctic Circle with E. A. Preble, a U.S. Biological Survey scientist and Seton's guide. Preble later expressed some reservations about Seton's abilities to handle himself in the wilderness. Seton's account of this trip, which revealed, among other things, his mixed reactions to the lifestyles of the Native Americans he encountered, was published as *The Arctic Prairie* in 1911. Early editions of this book antagonized some biologists who resented Seton's failure to acknowledge Preble's contributions to the success of the trip.

During the early 1900s, Seton began making public lectures—depending, as he said, on a "naturally powerful voice and stage presence"—which earned him as much as $12,000 annually. By 1909 he had traveled in nearly all the forty-eight states and the provinces of Canada—camping out in most of them—and he had published twenty books.

About fifty of Seton's popular works appeared between 1886 and 1945, several of them in foreign-language editions and editions for the blind. Some were anthologies of articles originally published in such periodicals as *Scribner's, Century, Ladies' Home Journal, Country Life in America, St. Nicholas, American Magazine, Forest and Stream, Bird Lore, Recreation, Boy's Life, American Boy,* and *Recreation.* The best known included *Animal Heroes* (1905), *Wild Animals at Home* (1913), and *Wild Animal Ways* (1916). Books for younger readers, usually focused on a particular animal, included *The Trail of a Sandhill Stag* (1899), *Biography of a Grizzly* (1900), *Monarch, the Big Bear of Tallac* (1904), and *Biography of a Silver Fox* (1909). These were more detailed life histories, with somewhat fictionalized story lines. Seton's scientific articles about mammals appeared in the *Journal of Mammalogy,* published by the American Society of Mammalogists, beginning in 1919.

By 1910, Seton had become financially secure as one of America's foremost nature writers and illustrators. But John Burroughs, the leading American nature essayist at the turn of the century, made the most serious public challenge to Seton's writings when his article "Real and Sham Natural History" appeared in the *Atlantic* for March 1903. Burroughs cast doubt on some of the more remarkable actions of Seton's animal protagonists, suggesting that he both humanized and fictionalized them for dramatic effect. Seton later wrote of confronting Burroughs at a dinner party, where the older man was obliged to admit that he had had little firsthand experience in hunting, photographing, or any "special study" of animals, and he promised to publish a retraction. Seton invited Burroughs to his Connecticut home to see his collection of books, drawings, and notes, later asserting that Burroughs was mightily impressed by this evidence of his authority.

But Burroughs was only partially convinced, since his article in the July 1904 *Atlantic* mentioned Seton only once and that briefly. Ranking Seton as the highest among the new group of nature students "as an artist and raconteur," he added that "to those who can separate the fact from the fiction in his animal stories, he is truly delightful." Both in its praise and its caveat, this remains a perceptive estimate of some of Seton's earlier work. Seton himself had recognized this difficulty when in his *Lives of the Hunted* (1901) he referred to some of his early stories where "I used the archaic method, making the animals talk . . . since then, I have adhered to the more scientific method." But President Theodore Roosevelt's reaction to Burroughs's criticism clearly did much to galvanize Seton into a change of course. "Burroughs and the people at large," said the president, "don't know how many facts you have back of your stories. You must publish the facts."

Seton set to work, and in 1910 his two-volume *Life Histories of Northern Animals: An Account of the Mammals of Manitoba* appeared. This dealt with some sixty species found in the province and in many northwestern American states. Critical response was highly favorable, though some could not forget then or later the liberties Seton had taken with his less formal animal biographies in earlier years. The work received the Camp Fire Gold Medal as the outstanding popular natural history for the year. Seton regarded it, however, as a mere "prodrome" for the eight-volume *Lives of Game Animals,* published between 1925 and 1928, which won him the coveted Burroughs Medal in 1926 and the Daniel Giraud Elliott Medal of the National Institute of Science in 1928. Seton claimed that his *Lives* "effectively silenced all my critics" and that this work was "considered the last word and best authority on the subject"; but his earlier assessment, that they were "a starting point for other workers in the field" and that he was "merely assembling tools" in what might be considered a wide-ranging contribution to the literature, is perhaps more accurate.

In the *Lives,* Seton effectively blended his forty years of field experiences with the observations of hundreds of other observers, derived from reading various American natural histories extending back to the colonial period. He also consulted a host of recognized scientific authorities while trying to make his work both eminently readable and reflective of the most recent and accurate thinking. Though he focused on the larger and more readily recognized game species, he also included some smaller mammals. His insights into what might be termed *mammalian psychology* and his emphasis on ethological material, so often lacking in other dry and methodical tomes on the subject, placed the *Lives* in a class by themselves. They are properly regarded as classics of the genre.

Despite his considerable artistic accomplishments, Seton was never recognized as a first-rank artist by his fellow American colleagues, in his own day or since. He understood this when he acknowledged that others were creative artists while he was at best an academic painter. Many of his mammal paintings, however, are of outstanding quality and set the standard for works of this kind done in later years by such illustrators as Louis Agassiz Fuertes, Allan Brooks, and Richard P. Grossenheider. In this field, Seton had few peers. His pen and ink or brush sketches, his marginal drawings, and his quick field impressions or preliminary studies for formal work greatly contributed to the success of all his books. He had a talent for rendering mammalian anatomy, often with an admirable economy of line.

In 1910, Seton helped found the Boy Scouts of America, writing the original *Boy Scouts of America Handbook* (1910) and serving as Chief Scout until 1915, when he resigned because his pacifism was regarded as out of step with a world at war. Scouting for Seton had less to do with uniforms and mottoes than with camping, woodcraft, and Indian lore. He later broke with the other leaders of the movement to give greater attention to his own organization, the Woodcraft Indians, which he had founded in 1902. An experiment with a batch of unruly boys on his tract of woodland in Connecticut had engendered this group. He subsequently wrote a dozen books on the outdoors to stimulate interest among younger readers, among them *Two Little Savages* (1903), *How to Play Indian* (1903), *How to Make a Real Indian Teepee* (1903), *How Boys Can Form a Band of Indians* (1903), *The Birchbark Roll of the Woodcraft Indians* (various editions, 1906–1931), *The Forester's Manual* (1911–one of the best-written examples), *The Woodcraft Manual for Girls* (1916), *The Woodcraft Manual for Boys* (1917), and *Sign Talk* (1918).

Seton was as responsible as any writer since James Fenimore Cooper for celebrating and popularizing the American Indian, at least insofar as he chose to interpret them, "embodied in Tecumseh, the great Shawnee— physically perfect, wise, brave, picturesque, unselfish, dignified." Working in association with Mrs. Julia M. Buttree, a student of Indian lore, reinforced his interest. Seton acknowledged her aid to him, in helping, for example, to produce *Lives of Game Animals,* and he illustrated her book *Rhythm of the Red Man,* published in 1930. That same year, they edited *Gospel of the Red Man: An Indian Bible.*

In 1930, Seton became an American citizen and moved to New Mexico. He had long taken an interest, both practical and theoretical, in the Southwest and its architecture and landscaping. On a 2,500-acre tract near Santa Fe, he built "Seton Castle," now a museum. A thirty-room stone and adobe structure, it housed his private library of more than 13,000 books, nearly 8,000 of his paintings and drawings, and a collection of some 3,000 bird and mammal skins. Here also he established his College of Indian Wisdom, which operated until the early 1940s. At seventy Seton had realized the kind of grandiose dream that had eluded his father and had done so by steadfastly following the naturalist's life, which his father had opposed and belittled.

On January 22, 1935, four days after divorcing Grace Gallatin Seton, Seton married Julia Buttree, who was almost thirty years his junior. The couple later adopted a daughter, Dee, later Dee Seton Barber. Seton died of pancreatic cancer at age eighty-six at his home near Santa Fe. His funeral was followed by cremation at Albuquerque.

Seton was at his best when his graphic art worked to complement or supplement the pages of his stories. At such times, Seton the writer and illustrator merged into Seton the prophet and propagandist for nature, the teller of outdoor tales that depended less on accuracy and plausibility than on their power to evoke excitement, wonder, and belief. To a society rapidly becoming so urbanized and dependent on technology that it was losing touch with the natural world, Seton brought beguiling tales of places and wild creatures left behind—or, in the case of the wolf and buffalo, creatures that were swiftly vanishing. Though Seton seldom mastered the look of flight, he devised the field identification system for birds later developed and popularized in the field guides of Roger Tory Peterson and others. He also performed an invaluable service to natural science by including much Native American lore concerning the species he dealt with.

KEIR STERLING

Anderson, H. Allen. *The Chief: Ernest Thompson Seton and the Changing West.* New York, 1988.

Keller, Betty. *Black Wolf: The Life of Ernest Thompson Seton.* New York, 1984.

Lutts, Ralph H. *The Nature Fakers: Wildlife, Science and Sentiment.* New York, 1990.

Samson, John G., ed. *The Worlds of Ernest Thompson Seton.* New York, 1976.

Seton, Julia B., ed. *By a Thousand Fires: Nature Notes and Extracts from the Life and Unpublished Journals of Ernest Thompson Seton.* New York, 1967.

Wadland, John Henry. *Ernest Thompson Seton: Man in Nature and the Progressive Era, 1880–1915.* New York, 1978.

Wiley, Farida A., ed. *Ernest Thompson Seton's America.* New York, 1954.

Shelford, Victor Ernest (September 27, 1877–December 27, 1968). A zoologist, naturalist, conservationist, and ecologist, Shelford was born in Chemung, New York. On graduation from a rural school two miles from his home, he attended a normal school at Cortland, New York, and then taught in New York State public schools.

In the fall of 1899 he entered the University of West Virginia to pursue a career in medicine. He lodged with an uncle who taught him the joys of insect collecting and botanizing. At the university, he had the good fortune to study under Dr. John B. Johnson, a gifted biologist, who interested Shelford in ecology. Close association with his uncle and study under Johnson made young Shelford realize that his interest and aptitude were in the area of natural science rather than medicine.

Shelford chose the University of Chicago for his graduate work. Here his chief mentors were Charles Child and Henry Cowles, both of whom had a profound influence on his scientific development. For his work with tiger beetles (Cicindelinae), Shelford was awarded the Ph.D. and was appointed to the faculty in 1907. The following year his doctoral thesis on tiger beetles, twenty pages long, was read at the Linnaean Society in London.

A close observer of animal life, Shelford learned that to understand how an animal functions, one must have an intimate knowledge of its habitat. He put his powers of observation, intuition, and imagination to work in his classic studies of the ecology of ponds and streams near the southwestern shores of Lake Michigan. Changes in pond plant and animal life as well as pond chemistry, he noted, were primarily due to actions of the animals and plants in their own environment, making each set of coexisting species in a particular pond less fit for itself and more fit for its successors—classical community development, that is, succession.

In 1913, Shelford published *Animal Communities in Temperate America*. In his work he emphasized a physiological (functional) approach; the figures used were meant to demonstrate interrelationships among species. Concepts he presented were forerunners of certain functional aspects of ecology that are so popular today, though they did not become part of ecological science until the mid-1950s.

Shelford left the University of Chicago in 1914 to join the faculty at the University of Illinois, where he was provided with a modern laboratory in a newly constructed vivarium. He was also given three research laboratories and additional space in a portion of a rear greenhouse. Nothing inhibited his work, and he became a pioneer in the new science of ecology, which he dubbed "new natural history." He was now a progressive conservationist who believed in the application of technical and ecological knowledge to resource management.

In 1915, Shelford was elected the first president of the Ecological Society of America. He convinced his colleagues of the need to inventory the natural areas of North America. Nine years later, his personal work *A Naturalist's Guide to the Americas* was published. Then followed *Laboratory and Field Biology* (1929). He continued his study of tiger beetles and went on to investigate the life cycle of the codling moth, a pest of apple trees, and chinch bugs, which damaged cereal crops. In addition, he studied marine communities at Puget Sound Biological Station.

He collaborated with the premier plant ecologist of his day, Frederick Clements, and they worked together for some twelve years. Their labor resulted in *Bioecology* (1938). Both scientists were engaged with ecology on a larger scale and were concerned with the "biome," though they failed to agree on what constituted a biome. But they agreed that there was a need to train biologists in a "unified approach" to the study of plants and animals.

During the 1930s, Shelford pressed to create a National Grasslands Movement. It was obvious that unsound farming methods and overgrazing were ruining native grasslands; such excesses had greatly exacerbated the terrible droughts of the decade. He had hoped to create the National Grassland Movement in northeastern Nebraska and southwestern South Dakota, but he failed to reach his goals.

All through the following decade, Shelford was concerned with the problem of preservation. The officers of the Ecological Society of America felt otherwise; indeed, an executive committee recommended that it should not become involved with politics, that the society should not take direct action "to influence legislation on its own behalf." Disappointed, Shelford founded a new society, the Ecologists Union. Encouraged by his leadership some eighty-three ecologists became charter members. By December 1946, the union had increased to 158 members. A constitution was drawn up, and their stated objective became the preservation of natural biotic communities and the encouragement of research in such areas. In 1950, the Ecologists Union changed its name to the Nature Conservancy. Today, the organization boasts a membership of over 500,000 individuals and of having preserved approximately 4 million acres of land.

In 1964 Shelford was cited by the Conservancy at its annual meeting for "his twenty years as Chairman of the Ecological Society's Committee on the Preservation of Natural Conditions, his establishment in Trelease Woods of the first University ecological research area in America, his participation in the foundation of the Nature Conservancy, and for his scholarly writing." Such recognition came to Shelford about the same time his last book, *Ecology of North America* (1963), was the recipient of highly favorable reviews. In 1968, he was named Eminent Ecologist of the Year by the Ecological Society. Shortly thereafter, at age ninety-one he died of uremia and pneumonia.

Shelford married Mabel Brown on June 12, 1907; they had two children, Lois and John.

RICHARD STALTER

Croker, Robert A. *Pioneer Ecologist: The Life and Work of Victor Ernest Shelford.* Washington, DC, 1991.

Kendeigh, S. C. "Victor Ernest Shelford, Eminent Ecologist." *Bulletin of the Ecological Society of America* 49 (1968): 97–100.

Waford, N. Review of *Ecology of North America*, by Victor E. Shelford. *Journal of Animal Ecology* 33 (1969): 532–533.

Shiras, George, III (January 1, 1859–March 24, 1942). A wildlife authority, naturalist, biologist, lawyer, congressman, author, and amateur photographer, Shiras was born in Allegheny, Pennsylvania. He spent his boyhood summers in northern Michigan, where he became acquainted with the wilderness of the Upper Peninsula and developed a deep love for the outdoors. With a broad education that included public schools and Phillips Academy (Andover, Massachusetts), Cornell, and Yale Law School, Shiras practiced law in his father's firm from 1883, when he was admitted to the Pennsylvania bar, until 1892, when his father was appointed as a justice of the U.S. Supreme Court. He then continued his profession until 1904 as a member of Shiras & Dickey in Pittsburgh.

After serving a term in the Pennsylvania legislature from 1889 to 1890, Shiras was elected to the 58th Congress in 1903. His devotion to wildlife made him an early advocate of protective legislation for wild animals and birds, resulting in many of Michigan's game laws. Shiras made a study of pollution and of game bird migration and, in 1904, introduced a bill to protect migratory birds in the United States. It was ten years before the subject was brought to a vote as the Weeks-McLean bill. Supported by the American Game Protection Association, the Boone and Crockett Club, and forty of the Game and Fish Commissions, the law was enacted in 1913. Originally intended to cover only migratory game birds, the bill was amended at the insistence of the Audubon Society to include insectivorous birds, songbirds, and plummage birds as well. Shiras is viewed as a major figure in the history of federal protection of migratory birds.

A photographer and biologist rather than a hunter, Shiras took expeditions to Newfoundland, Ontario, Alaska, Hawaii, Florida, Lake Superior, Mexico, Panama, and the West Indies. A pioneer of hunting wild game with a camera, he is credited as the originator of flashlight photography of wild animals. Several of his flashlight photographs were exhibited at the Paris Exposition in 1900, where they received a gold medal, and at the St. Louis Fair in 1904, where they received a Grand Prize. The pictures were taken by one of two methods that Shiras developed. One technique involved taking pictures with a flash fired by hand when the animal was in focus and in the best position. With the other technique, pictures were taken automatically when the animal pulled a piece of bait attached to a string connected to the flashlight and camera setup. He made it a point never to photograph animals in parks and reserves but in the wild where he studied their habits carefully and observed them for hours and even days before setting up his camera and flashes. His techniques were based on the conviction that "it is not necessary to convert the wilderness into untenanted and silent waste in order to enjoy the sport of successfully hunting wild birds and animals."

The author of numerous articles in the *National Geographic, Forest and Stream*, and other outdoors and sporting magazines, Shiras's written works include "One Season's Game Bag with the Camera," "Wild Animals that Took Their Own Pictures by Day and Night," and "The Wild Life of Lake Superior, Past and Present." He also contributed "How Birds Can Take Their Own Portraits" to *The Book of Birds*, published by the National Geographic Society in 1927. He is probably best known for his own book *Hunting Wildlife with Camera and Flashlight*, a two-volume work describing his pioneering technique of nighttime, trip-wire photography, published in 1935.

In addition to his legislative and literary endeavors, Shiras was actively involved in public service. For more than thirty years, he was an officer of the American Game Protection Association, a trustee of the National Geographic Society, and an advisory board member of the Migratory Bird Treaty Regulations Board of the Department of Agriculture. Other memberships and interests that benefited the environmental cause included the Ornithology Union, Audubon Society, American Bison Society, Boone and Crockett Club, National Parks Association, Society of Foresters, and

Explorers Club. Beyond organizational involvement, he also left a legacy to conservation when he presented a clubhouse to the Marquette (Michigan) Federation of Women's Clubs and a municipal swimming pool and extensive lakeshore frontage, now called Shiras Park, to the city of Marquette.

In 1885, Shiras married Frances P. White, the daughter of Peter White, one of the early developers of Upper Michigan's ore, lumber, and shipping industries. They had two children, Ellen Kennedy and George Peter. Shiras is buried in Park Cemetery in Marquette, Michigan.

GWEN GRIFFIN

Hawes, Harry Barton. *Fish and Game: Now or Never.* New York, 1935.

Who's Who in America. Shiras, George III 1906–1907.

Who Was Who in America. Shiras, George III 1943–1950.

Silko, Leslie Marmon (March 5, 1948–). Humans' interactions with the natural world has been a main theme in many of Silko's stories and novels. Her writing often connects historical injustices committed against Native Americans with similar abuses of America's natural resources. It also challenges the traditional ways in which Americans view property rights—suggesting that shared property and resources would lead to a more coherent, universal valuation of the earth and the people on it. Though Silko has some legal education, she made the decision that storytelling is a more effective way to convey her environmental message.

Silko was born in Albuquerque, New Mexico, to Leland Marmon and Mary Virginia Lee Leslie. She is of mixed Mexican, Laguna Pueblo, and white ancestry. Silko is the name of her husband, John, whom she married in 1971. They had a son in 1972. She attended the Bureau of Indian Affairs (BIA) school at Laguna through the fourth grade, then attended private Catholic school Manzano Day School in Albuquerque. Her parents, who had not forgotten their negative experiences at BIA schools, made a commitment to driving the hour commute to get Leslie to and from her private school. She later graduated Phi Beta Kappa from the University of New Mexico in 1969 with a B.A. in English. Leslie also attended law school at the University of New Mexico but left before completing her degree. After taking a creative writing seminar, she realized that writing had the potential to achieve the impact that she had been looking to make in law. Currently, she holds academic appointments at the University of Arizona and the

University of New Mexico. She has won a MacArthur "genius" grant, a National Education Association Discovery Grant, and the Pushcart Prize for Poetry.

In her writing Silko challenges the traditional ways in which readers view genre and the line between prose and poetry, and her characters defy traditional American gender stereotypes. The women of her novels are often strong and self-sufficient, playing many of the roles that a reader might expect men to play. She credits her tendency to confound expectations of gender roles to the way she was raised in the Laguna Pueblo tradition. Silko's writing and storytelling challenge the way we think about such important issues as environmental justice, gender roles, political and physical borders, and even the accuracy of the historical record. Her steady engagement with environmental issues in her storytelling brings new audiences—literary scholars, critics, and everyday readers—to important scientific and sociopolitical discussions.

Associating identity closely with place, Silko weaves that connection into her stories and frequently brings up the importance of place in interviews with literary scholars. She brings to environmental writing a different perspective than mainstream environmentalism. Instead of viewing the natural world as physical place separate from human beings, she blends her characters' identities with the ecosystems in which they reside. Natural resources also play a larger role in the plots of her stories than in those of many fiction writers; sometimes events will happen as a direct result of abuses to the earth. Silko asks readers to imagine how they might feel about land and water if they were dealing with nuclear waste facilities while feeling that the land had been stolen from them in the past. Responding to a question about the upcoming American bicentennial in 1976, and her feelings about it, Silko reminded readers that much of America's wealth and success were built on stolen Indian lands and resources. Ellen Arnold, who has interviewed and written about Silko extensively, claims that she is "resolute in her exposure of the destructive systems of thought and practices that drive the consumption of the natural works and indigenous peoples by Western colonialism and capitalism." Silko does not always directly criticize what she sees as problems in American history. Instead, she provides an alternative version of events where justice is found.

Family is important to Silko, both in her personal life and in her stories. Frequently mentioned by her in interviews and referenced in autobiographical works are her great aunt Susie Marmon and her Grandma Lillie,

Francesca Stagner Marmon. These two women were especially strong influences in Silko's absorption of the Laguna Pueblo oral storytelling tradition, which she has continued in her writing. Yet another way in which she goes against expectations is that while she has long credited the influence of stories told by her grandmother, aunts, and other family members, Silko has never identified herself as part of the Native oral storytelling tradition. Instead, she emphasizes the written tradition, which she believes belongs as much to Native storytellers as the oral tradition. She writes moving, innovative, and ethically challenging fiction, poetry, and nonfiction that all cause us to carefully consider our core beliefs as Americans—property rights, the American dream, traditional concepts of time, and the ways in which we think about—or ignore—nuclear testing and weapons issues.

In interviews she has suggested that her stories show the ways in which people are "related to the land in a familiar way" as sisters, brothers, and parents would be. "Landscape, History, and the Pueblo Imagination," one of her most famous essays, begins to connect land, culture, and storytelling, a tradition that carries through in nearly all of her work. The essay is included in Cheryll Glotfelty and Harold Fromm's foundational 1996 anthology *The Ecocriticism Reader,* placing Silko easily in the first wave of recent writers to be identified by ecocritical scholars for a focus on earth and the environment.

In 1969, "The Man to Send Rain Clouds," Silko's first short story, was published in the *New Mexico Quarterly.* By 1974 several of her poems were collected into a volume called *Laguna Woman: Poems.* A collection of her short stories appeared in an anthology called *The Man to Send Rain Clouds,* edited by Kenneth Rosen and published in 1974.

Ceremony, published in 1981, is one of Silko's most transparently environmental works. Tayo, the protagonist, must learn again how to read the natural world as he comes home from World War II to face a series of conflicts with the Laguna people and his home environment. The book ends with Tayo, in close proximity to some of the nation's nuclear facilities, coming to a new realization about the balance between humankind and the forces of destruction that it has created. This book was written while Silko lived in Ketchikan, Alaska, and her homesickness manifested itself in some of the most vivid descriptions of the desert Southwest that appear anywhere in her oeuvre.

Silko's 1981 book *Storyteller* combines short essays and poems with photos of Silko's family and ancestors. Seen by many critics as a heavily autobiographical work, it is divided into five smaller sections, or chapters. One of those, "Storyteller," involves earth's retaliation for abuses of the tundra land and resources, and several other stories involve tales of Yellow Woman, a recurring character in both Native tales and Silko's stories who connects to the earth through water and spirits for the sake of her people.

Appearing in only one collection, Simon Ortiz's *Earth Power Coming: Short Fiction in Native American Literature*, Silko's 1983 short story titled "Private Property" is of interest to environmentalists. Told with multiple narrative voices, it interweaves the various understandings of property and possessions through the story of a family—and their feuds—in a small town.

Almanac of the Dead, published in 1991, caused more controversy than most of Silko's other work combined. The thick tome (reduced to 763 pages by her editors) creates a future in which the ghosts of indigenous peoples of the Americas rise up and take back the land on which they lived many years before. This book is also significant in that it predicts, very closely, the uprising of indigenous peoples in Chiapas, Mexico, that would happen two years after the publication of the book. While many critics and readers took offense at what they considered an angry and disorganized book, some critics suggest Silko creates this scenario as a story of the possibilities for the earth if we were to broker international agreements to reclaim environmental responsibility and social justice.

An important text in considering Silko as an environmentalist is her 1993 book *Sacred Water: Narratives and Pictures*, a book of poems and photographs first assembled in her home. A similar book, *Rain* (1996), combines photographs by Leslie's father, Lee Marmon, with her own work.

Silko's 1996 *Yellow Woman and a Beauty of the Spirit: Essays on Native American Life Today* is one of her few collections of nonfiction essays. In these short pieces, she explores contemporary politics as well as the history of the Laguna Pueblo people. She criticizes both tribal politics and U.S. international relations, particularly with Central and South America.

Gardens in the Dunes, published in 1999, exhibits Silko's strength in historical fiction writing. The protagonist, a young Indian girl, runs away from boarding school, loses her mother at a Ghost Dance ceremony, and winds up with a well-off woman who is involved in literary scholarship and Victorian plant collecting. Each of the female characters draws on a cultural gardening tradition, but by the end of the book those traditions have been combined to make a new garden in the dunes. Discussions between characters and events throughout the novel address scholarly and personal issues such as religion, feminism, and race and cultural relations in the United States.

Already, Silko has brought to light the many different voices that together can create effective dialogue about the environment and our shared natural resources. While some of her work has been called inflammatory by critics, she encourages conversations about land and people that are necessary and that might otherwise not occur. Her prose also creates vivid visual images for readers who may not have visited the places about which she writes, allowing them to share in her appreciation of the aesthetic and emotional values of those places.

LESLIE WOLCOTT

Arnold, Ellen L. "*Dictionary of Literary Biography.*" Vol. 275. 2003.

——, ed. *Conversations with Leslie Marmon Silko.* Jackson, MS, 2000.

Barnett, Louise K., and James L. Thorson, eds. *Leslie Marmon Silko: A Collection of Critical Essays.* Albuquerque, NM, 1999.

Fitz, Brewster E. *Silko: Writing Storyteller and Medicine Woman.* Norman, OK, 2004.

Salyer, Gregory. *Leslie Marmon Silko.* New York, 1997.

Snyder, Gary Sherman (May 8, 1930–). Renowned primarily for his environmental poetry and prose, Snyder has often been compared to such important historical figures in the environmental movement as Henry David Thoreau and John Muir. As author of over thirty books and hundreds of articles, and winner of such prestigious awards as the Pulitzer, Frank O'Hara, and Levinson Prizes as well as the American Book Award, he has long been recognized as one of the environmental movement's most significant and influential literary voices.

Snyder, a logger, fire lookout, trail crew member, award-winning poet and essayist, and contemporary environmental philosopher and activist, makes his home on the San Juan ridge of the Yuba watershed in the Sierra Nevada range of northern California. A native of the Pacific Northwest, Snyder grew up on a small farm in Oregon and spent much of his boyhood rambling through the forests and mountains of Oregon, Washington, and California. Early in his life, Snyder witnessed the wanton destruction of his beloved western forests and found a love for the study of Native American culture and lifeways, Japanese landscape painting, and Zen philosophy, as well as mountaineering and ecology. Over the intervening years, Snyder has successfully cobbled together this seemingly eclectic combination of interests into a firm foundation for his philosophy and practice—a "riprap of things"—a sure-footed trail designed to lead readers toward a sacred and sustainable relationship with the natural world.

Snyder was born in San Francisco to Harold Alton Snyder and Lois (Wilkie) Snyder and attended public schools in Seattle and Portland, while growing up in the Pacific Northwest. He augmented his formal education with hours of outside reading and exploration, a practice he would continue throughout his life. As a young boy, Snyder regularly attended summer camp at Spirit Lake at the foot of Mount St. Helens, and as a teenager he joined the Mazamas, a rigorous mountaineering club that required an ascent of a snow-covered peak with a living glacier as one of several criteria for membership. During his teens, Snyder served as the associate editor for *Mazama* and published a number of articles on mountaineering in the magazine. After high school, Snyder attended the prestigious Reed College and graduated with a B.A. in literature and anthropology in 1951; he also studied at Indiana University and divided his extracurricular time between working as a lumberjack, trail crew member, fire lookout, and emerging poet. Snyder married Allison Glass while still in school, but their short-lived marriage was ended after a year in 1951.

He attended graduate school at the University of California at Berkeley from 1953 to 1956, specializing in the study of Oriental languages while beginning to lay the foundation for his literary career. As a founding member of the Beat Generation, Snyder participated in San Francisco's famed Six Gallery Reading in October 1955, along with Allen Ginsberg, Philip Lamantia, Michael McClure, and Philip Whalen, and firmly secured his place in this growing, yet revolutionary, literary tradition. In 1956, Snyder moved to Japan to study Zen Buddhism and Asian languages and lived abroad almost continuously for the next twelve years. During that time, he practiced Zen Buddhism religiously, published his first book of poetry, *Riprap* in 1959, and married and divorced his second wife, Joanne Kyger.

Snyder was married a third time from 1967 to 1989 to Masa Uehara with whom he had two boys, Kai and Gen. In addition to exploring themes of environmental sustainability, Zen Buddhism, and indigenous lifeways, much of Snyder's poetry from this period also focuses on the simple and sacred life of the family. In 1985 he accepted a position teaching at the University of California, Davis, and in 1991 married his current wife, Carole

Koda. Today Snyder lives with Carole at Kitkitdizze, the bioregional home place he and his friends constructed, and continues to write and speak out on behalf of the environment.

Snyder's greatest contribution to the environmental movement is, perhaps, his least direct. Although an active member in a wide variety of environmental defense associations, who has dedicated much of his own money, time, and labor to specific environmental causes, Snyder's literary work has had the most influential impact of any of his efforts on the American landscape and the policies and people who affect it. In his work, Snyder practices what has been called "mythopoetics," or the attempt, through literature, to change the foundational myths of a culture. According to Snyder, and many other scholars, these foundational myths, although often hidden and unexamined, exert a tremendous influence over the practices and policies of the people who hold them. From this perspective, then, replacing outdated and deleterious American myths with more accurate and beneficial beliefs is the most effective method for creating lasting cultural change. Replacing such myths, for example, as the belief in progress and continuous growth with the values of a stable state system, or anthropocentrism with ecocentrism, or globalization with localization, is a necessary first step toward crafting policies that support these more ecologically sound and socially just values.

Snyder views the function of poetry—his primary activist tool—from an anthropological perspective, arguing that literature carries on important cultural work and can both reflect and direct our attitudes, values, and actions. In *A Place in Space* he argues:

> For at least a century and half, the socially engaged writers of the developed world have taken their role to be one of resistance and subversion. Poetry can disclose the misuse of language by holders of power, it can attack dangerous archetypes employed to oppress, and it can expose the flimsiness of shabby made-up mythologies. It can savagely ridicule pomp and pretension, and it can offer—in ways both obvious and subtle— more elegant, tastier, lovelier, deeper, more ecstatic, and far more intelligent words and images.

While Snyder admits, in *The Real Work* that poetry "has indirect effects, not direct effects if you want to talk about 'masses,'" he believes, with good reason, that these "indirect" effects can be quite powerful and enduring. According to Snyder, the images and ideas contained within socially active poetry can evolve over time into common ideology and political policy. This evolutionary process from poetic metaphor to public policy may be understood by exploring the implications of Snyder's frequent personification of trees. In "Two Logging Songs" (*No Nature*), for example, he writes:

> Forestry. "How
> Many people
> Were harvested
> In Viet-Nam?"

> Clear-cut. "Some
> Were children,
> Some were over-ripe."

In this stanza, Snyder equates the indiscriminate "harvesting" of trees with the indiscriminate murder that necessarily follows war. Humans and trees are metaphorically conflated, linking the emotional power and tragedy of war with the destruction of our native forests.

These poetic metaphors, which imaginatively link human sentience and morality with the lives and rights of nonhuman nature (in this case, trees), enter our cultural consciousness, germinate, and grow, until they flower into full-fledged ideology and policy. As Snyder explains in *The Real Work*:

> Thus, you proceed from an animistic idea that you can hear voices from trees. And a few decades later a lawyer like Christopher Stone, writes a *legalistic* argument—"Should Trees Have Standing"—arguing that trees should be involved in the democratic process. . . . And you push it forward a generation or two in the future you can actually feel on a gut level that nonhuman nature has rights. And that will be the work of the poet, to set that direction.

Snyder's poetry synthesizes ecological insights and Native American wisdom with Buddhist teachings and practice to offer an alternative paradigm for Americans who wish to "reinhabit"—or become native to—their own home places. As he states in the same interview, "My political position is to be a spokesman for wild nature. I take that as a primary constituency." Just as we have advocates to represent the interests of such exploited or underrepresented classes as the poor, children, minorities, and women, Snyder sees himself as representing the "'classes' which have so far been overlooked—the animals, rivers, rocks, and grasses—now entering history" (*Practice of the Wild*).

Snyder's first two books of poetry, *Riprap* and *Myths & Texts,* were published in 1959 and 1960, respectively; both relied heavily on his experiences growing up in the Pacific Northwest, exploring such issues as trail construction, wilderness travel, logging, forest fires, and the stories that shape our relationships to the natural world. *Riprap* was republished in 1965 under the title *Riprap & Cold Mountain Poems* and included Snyder's own translations of the works of Chinese poet and hermit Han Shan. Over the next few years, Snyder produced a number of influential collections of environmental poetry including *The Backcountry* (1967), *The Blue Sky* (1969), *Regarding Wave* (1970), *Manzanita* (1971), and *Piute Creek* (1972). By 1975, when Snyder was awarded the Pulitzer Prize for his 1974 publication *Turtle Island,* his literary career and reputation as a prominent American environmental activist were both firmly established. In 1983 and 1986, respectively, Snyder published *Axe Handles* and *Left Out in the Rain: New Poems,* which continued to explore personal and cultural responses to the escalating environmental crisis. A major collection of Snyder's poetry, *No Nature: New and Selected Poems,* was published in 1992, and in 1996 he completed *Mountains and Rivers without End,* a single, long poem, over twenty-six years in the making.

Snyder's literary work also includes a number of essay collections and prose pieces that explore issues in mythology and ecology and advocate for cultural and political transformation. In 1969 he published *Earth House Hold: Technical Notes and Queries to Fellow Dharma Revolutionaries*, and in 1977, *The Old Ways: Six Essays;* both illustrate Snyder's fusion of Eastern and Western philosophies and lifeways and his continuing preoccupation with finding sustainable cultural mythologies for Americans to live by. *The Real Work: Interviews and Talks (1964–1979)* was published in 1980 and has become a seminal text for environmental activists working within the bioregional movement today. Snyder's two most recent and significant works of prose, *The Practice of the Wild* (1990) and *A Place in Space: Ethics, Aesthetics, and Watersheds* (1995), continue to explore the vital connections between the stories we tell in our culture and the lives we lead on our land.

Snyder's work has enjoyed both critical acclaim in the academy and popular success with the general public, an exceedingly rare feat for contemporary authors. This dual success has led to Snyder's current role as a leader in the American environmental movement. Snyder has often been called "an elder of the tribe" by many prominent environmentalists including Dave

Foreman, Wendell Berry, and Wes Jackson, as well as many other environmental educators, poets, and scholars. Along with Deep Ecology's founder, Norwegian philosopher Arne Naess, Snyder is recognized as one of the movement's foremost American proponents; his work, in fact, was extremely influential in shaping George Sessions and Bill Duvall's writing of *Deep Ecology* in 1985.

Snyder has always seen his work as being integrally involved with the underlying philosophy behind, and direct practices of, the American environmental movement. For the first Earth Day, in 1970, for example, Snyder worked with David Brower to publish and distribute *The Environmental Handbook*, a collection of essays from such authors as Paul Erlich and Lynn White. Snyder provided two pieces for the publication, "Four Changes" and "Smokey the Bear Sutra," for free and continued to support the distribution and republication of these pieces by allowing them to be reproduced without copyright (an activist practice he would repeat throughout his career).

To reduce his and his family's ecological impact, Snyder built, with the help of friends, a bioregional home (a house built sustainably out of local materials) on the Pacific slope of the Sierra Nevada. In fact, both his writing and his personal example have been credited with inspiring the back-to-the-land movement of the late 1960s and 1970s. Today, he continues to engage in biological surveys, clear brush to prevent wildfires, and plant trees to restore damaged landscapes, all in an effort to develop a reciprocal relationship with the land upon which he lives, a lifeway that gives as much to the land as is taken from it.

In addition, Snyder has often served on boards and as an active member of a variety of environmental organizations; as Ryo Imamura notes, when Snyder was treasurer of the Buddhist Peace Fellowship Board, he gave a poetry reading and donated all the proceeds to get the books back into the black. Others have noted Snyder's consistent practice of quietly donating a portion of his performance fees (earned while giving public readings) to local environmental groups working in each area he travels to. He also served on the California Arts Commission at the request of Governor Jerry Brown and acted in an informal capacity as an adviser to the governor on a variety of matters. For Snyder, such involvement with one's community, or *sangha*, represents not only a political practice but also a spiritual way of life.

In a 1979 interview from *The Real Work*, Snyder detailed his long-term vision for environmental activists everywhere to defend the planet and direct us toward a sustainable future, but he could just as accurately have been describing the way in which he has chosen to live his own personal life. He asserts:

> The fact is that the dynamics of industrial capitalism are still so enormous that until it slows down of its own glut there isn't much we can do except holding actions, and try to keep our heads clear about what can be and should be.... And as it does so we would be well advised to have in mind what kinds of skills we really need and what it means to be self-governing, and to increasingly take responsibility for our own lives, our own neighborhoods, and our own communities.

As Snyder's professional work and personal life attest, these are precisely the goals he has been working toward throughout his career, and they represent his most lasting contributions to the environmental movement. As author of over thirty-three different books of poetry and prose, and hundreds of articles, essays, and poems in a wide variety of literary journals, popular magazines, newspapers, and anthologies, Snyder represents one of the most persistent and respected voices of the American environmental movement today. Over the last fifty years, his writings have been directly responsible for countless "conservationist conversions" and have supplied much-needed emotional inspiration and intellectual direction for a large number of contemporary environmental leaders. Snyder's most valuable gift to environmentalists today has come not from his negative critiques of modern industrial capitalism but from his positive example of a life and career lived sustainably, simply, and locally. In "For the Children" he offers environmentalists a final piece of sage advice: *"stay together / learn the flowers / go light"* (*No Nature*).

COREY LEWIS

Halper, John, ed. *Gary Snyder: Dimensions of a Life*. San Francisco, CA, 1991.

Lewis, Corey. *Reading the Trail: Exploring the Literature and Natural History of the California Crest*. Reno, NV, 2005.

Murphy, Patrick, ed. *Critical Essays on Gary Snyder*. Boston, MA, 1991.

———. *A Place for Wayfaring: The Poetry and Prose of Gary Snyder*. Corvallis, OR, 2000.

Stanwood, Cordelia Johnson (August 1, 1865–November 20, 1958). With a nineteen-year career as an art and nature study teacher, in 1904

Stanwood returned to her family's home in Ellsworth, Maine, to launch her vocation as an ornithologist, writer, and photographer of chickadees, woodpeckers, warblers, and thrushes. "I never had time to study the birds until I stopped teaching," she wrote of bird work. An authoritative voice published in the *Auk*, the *Wilson Bulletin*, and the *Journal of the Maine Society of Ornithology*, among others, her reputation as a knowledgeable authority brought her increasing recognition as "Ellsworth's Famous Bird-woman." Known primarily for her popular photographic portraits of chickadees and other passerines, Stanwood was also known for her comprehensive field observations of warblers, titmice, woodpeckers, and vireos, as well as insects.

An author of both popular and serious ornithological articles, her work is recorded in numerous compendiums of the life histories of birds published in the mid-twentieth-century United States. As a partner in scientific discovery, the National Academy of Natural Science named a crane fly in her honor, *Limnophilia stanwoodoe*. Stanwood was also an avid nature study advocate, active both as a teacher in the classroom as a young woman and then later leading children and others on nature walks from her home "Birdsacre." A conservation activist, Stanwood was instrumental in the passage of the Lacey Act in 1913 from her home state of Maine.

Stanwood was born in Ellsworth, Maine, to Roswell Stanwood of Ellsworth, Maine, and Margaret (Maggie) Susan (Bown) Stanwood of Cape Eskasoni of Cape Breton Island, Canada. She made her home at her family homestead in Ellsworth for most of her life. Her early childhood was spent on her sailing captain father's vessels; when she was eight years old her father retired to the family home in Ellsworth, where he could participate in family life. There in the bosom of her family, Stanwood learned the homesteading practices of her New England and Canadian ancestors, where in the late nineteenth century the landscape of Stanwood's childhood was deeply imprinted by human intervention. Its forests were lumber resources; its fields were created by the labor of human hands. Commercial schooners and dories rimmed its beaches; shingles, staves, and sawdust choked its rivers. The duration of this human tampering was long enough so that young Stanwood was already witnessing the decay of the human fingerprint in rotting mills and breached dams. From an early age, Stanwood played in this "natural" landscape that was thickly embroidered by New England culture, its geographic contours shaped by the hand of human kind. For Stanwood, there was no artificial distinction between "nature" and "culture"—unlike today, nature was not set aside as a place to be untouched except for recreation. Stanwood's forests, fields, coastlines, and oceans were economic resources for her family and the community. From the time she was a child, nature had a history, and its boundaries were defined by how far she could walk, the distant horizon of the cleared field, or how far her father could sail.

The natural world was a congenial place for Stanwood, as she preferred wandering the woods, fields, and streams of the Down East Maine coast to the domestic space of the parlor or kitchen. Stanwood's understanding of the importance of habitat destruction was heightened by this environment, for most of the countryside had been deforested, its trees felled for boards, bobbins, clapboards, and shutters. Even as she grew up, the productive extractive economy of Ellsworth was in decline.

At fifteen Stanwood left Ellsworth to live with her aunt in Providence, Rhode Island, where she completed her high school education and her teacher training. There, Stanwood witnessed the growth of the city and the surrounding urban environment at the same time as she was entertained at her uncle's country farm on the shores of Long Island Sound. Her enthusiasm for the natural world is footnoted by her valedictory speech, "The Language of Trees," at her high school graduation.

A talented artist, Stanwood refined her teacher training at the Massachusetts Normal Art School (later the Massachusetts College of Art), where she learned the pedagogy of drawing from nature. As a young teacher, she also participated in summer teacher training institutes at Martha's Vineyard, where she learned the principles of nature study for children from its leaders such as Liberty Hyde Bailey, who coined a new kind of teaching based on drawing from the natural world called "nature study." This training heightened her already strong interest in the natural world and encouraged her to pursue a career as an art teacher in the practice of nature study. She worked in several schools in Rhode Island, Massachusetts, and New York State, notably the Quincy School, which was wholly based on the "nature study idea," one that encouraged active learning in fields and gardens, releasing children from the captivity of the nailed-to-the-floor classroom seat and connecting them to their community. The Quincy School experience offered her the opportunity to converse and entertain the naturalists and writers John Burroughs and Ernest Thompson Seton, who both came to her classroom to see her pupils' work inspired by the natural world.

As a young woman, however, her teaching, which required driving a buggy from school to one-room school over hilly New England terrain in harsh icy winters, proved to be too much for Stanwood, and after nineteen years, in 1904 she retired from teaching to return to Ellsworth, where she could care for her aging parents. Once in Ellsworth, indicating the seriousness of her approach to nature, she named her home Birdsacre. There, she began serious fieldwork and started keeping a lifetime of observation notes until she was in her late eighties. These field notes described bird behavior, development, and habitat observations of numerous species; these she developed into both serious ornithological and lighter popular ornithology articles, illustrated with her photographs.

Stanwood's ornithological expertise and her skill with the camera provided a foundation for her work as an activist in bird protection and conservation. As a bird expert she lent credibility and leadership to the popular movement of bird conservation, writing to congressional leaders, circulating petitions, and gaining support for successful legislation for the protection of birds, enabling the successful passage of the Lacey Act.

Her "Bird Notebooks" chronicled the nesting habits of the resident birds in her coastal Maine habitat. With them she laid the groundwork for the newest form of scientific writing, the birdlife study. Her nature diaries, discrete observations written in economical prose and structured by the passage of time, following in the tradition of the journals of Englishman Gilbert White, became an instrument of change in the development of scientific knowledge building and widespread cultural and intellectual engagement with the natural world. Furthermore, Stanwood's bird studies contributed to the refinement of the bird identification guide.

Her notes were the foundation for articles with features of the American feminine literary tradition. Without a regular means of support, and sequestered with her aging parents, Stanwood followed the social traditions for women of the nineteenth century while living in the twentieth, relying on her writing for her support. Her "Bird Notebooks" chronicle Stanwood's struggle to reconcile her traditional upbringing with her intellect, independence, and the winds of social change for women in the new century.

In addition to articles appearing in scientific publications, Stanwood also was published in the upscale *Country Life in America, House Beautiful,* and the short-lived Progressive Era magazine *Home Progress.* By the 1940s and 1950s, ornithological colleagues were compiling the birdlife histories to which she had contributed. Her observations provided material for Ralph Palmer's *Maine Birds* (1949) and Arthur Cleveland Bent's *Bird Life Histories* (1919–1968), first printed by the Smithsonian Institution. Bent's

Life Histories series is considered the most comprehensive and reliable collection of information ever compiled on the behavior of birds. It is a must for ornithologists, amateur bird-watchers, naturalists, and anyone for whom an involvement with birds does not end with identification. In its descriptions of warblers, titmice, and woodpeckers contributed by Stanwood, Bent provides careful details of virtually everything known about the life cycles and habits of hundreds of birds. Each volume is profusely illustrated with live photographs that Stanwood volunteered to publish.

While Stanwood lived at Birdsacre, she joined many other "back to the land" people who sought a simpler life, one lived didactically as an example to others that one can find peace in simplicity and in living close to nature. The Ellsworth community, while suspicious of her solitary ways, nonetheless embraced her passion for birds. Several years following her death, stalwart volunteers arranged for her property to remain a nature sanctuary in perpetuity. Today, located on the busy road to Acadia National Park, the Birdsacre Sanctuary stills stands as a quiet refuge for injured owls and nature lovers who can walk its trails.

CYNTHIA A. MELENDY

Bonta, Marcia Meyers. *American Women Afield: Writings by Pioneer Women Naturalists*. College Station, TX, 1995.

Graham, Ada, and Frank Graham Jr. *Six Little Chickadees: A Scientist and Her Work with Birds*. New York, 1982.

Norwood, Vera. *Made from This Earth: American Women and Nature*. Chapel Hill, NC, 1993.

Richmond, Chandler S. *Beyond the Spring: Cordelia Stanwood of Birdsacre*. Ellsworth, New and rev. ed. 2nd ed. ME, 1989.

Strom, Deborah. *Birdwatching with American Women*. New York, 1986.

Stegner, Wallace Earle (February 18, 1909–April 13, 1993). An American novelist, nonfiction writer, short-story writer, essayist, editor, biographer, and conservationist, Stegner was born near Lake Mills, Iowa, and spent his childhood in several locations. He was the son of George and Hilda (Paulson) Stegner. His childhood homes included Iowa, North Dakota, Washington, Montana, Utah, Nevada, and California. However, it was five years that he spent in Saskatchewan that influenced Stegner the most. There he observed one of the last great western frontiers and its groups of farmers, ranchers, cowboys, immigrants, and bad men who provided him with the characters and themes for many of his novels. The American West gave him both a literary backdrop and a lifelong avocation. Stegner sought to preserve the beauty of the West and prevent the westward expansion of big cities as a member of the National Parks Advisory Board.

Stegner received his B.A. at Utah State University and his M.A. and Ph.D. at the University of Iowa. His writing career began in 1937. He won several writing awards including the Little, Brown novelette contest in 1937 for *Remembering Laughter* and the Houghton Mifflin Life-in-America Award in 1945 for *One Nation*; he also shared the *Saturday Review*'s Anisfield-Wolf Award for *One Nation*. In 1942 and again in 1948, he won second prize in the O. Henry Memorial Award volume for short stories. He received a Guggenheim Fellowship in 1949.

Stegner became a professor of English and director of the Writing Center at Stanford University in 1945. Among his students were writers Larry McMurtry, Robert Stone, Wendell Berry, and Tom McGuane.

A prolific writer, Stegner's novels include *Remembering Laughter* (1937), *The Potter's House* (1938), *On a Darkling Plain* (1941), *Second Growth* (1948), *The Big Rock Candy Mountain* (1950), *The Preacher and the Slave* (1950), *A Shooting Star* (1961), *All the Little Living Things* (1968), *Angle of Repose* (1971), *The Spectator Bird* (1976), and *Recapitulation* (1979), as well as numerous short stories, essays, and works of nonfiction. His nonfiction works include two books on Mormon culture and numerous books on the geography, history, culture, and literary traditions of the American West. In 1981, he and his son Page published *American Places*, essays on the wilderness areas in America, and in 1992, he published a collection of autobiographical essays, *Where the Bluebird Sings to the Lemonade Springs: Living and Writing in the West*.

Stegner's fiction often portrays the conflict between eastern "culture" and western "nature." His books often focus on similar themes: the importance of place, the value of family and friends, the conflict between youth and age, and the impact of history on the present.

Stegner was also an active conservationist. His writings and speeches often called attention to the fragility of the environment and the need to protect it. He identified a strong link between the land and its people and helped to make people aware of the need to protect the dwindling frontier in the West. He joined a campaign to support the "Wilderness Act," which was signed into law in 1964, and supported legislation designed to prohibit the building of dams in national parks.

Stegner married Mary Stuart Page in 1934 and had one son, Stuart Page, in 1935.

PATIANNE DELGROSSO STABILE

Arthur, Anthony. *Critical Essays on Wallace Stegner*. Boston, MA, 1982.

Barnes, Bart. "Wallace Stegner Dies; Prize-Winning Author" [obit.]. *Washington Post*, April 15, 1993.

Colberg, Nancy. *Wallace Stegner: A Descriptive Bibliography*. Lewiston, ID, 1990.

Honan, William H. "Wallace Stegner Is Dead at 84; Pulitzer Prize–Winning Author" [obit]. *New York Times*, April 15, 1993.

Watkins, T. H. "Wallace Stegner 1909–1993." *Wilderness* 56 (1993): 8–9.

Willrich, Patricia Rowe. "A Perspective on Wallace Stegner." *Virginia Quarterly Review* 67 (1991): 240–259.

Steinbeck, John (February 27, 1902–December 20, 1968). As an author Steinbeck did a great deal to prepare the American public for the advent of the modern environmental movement. His books have reached millions of readers, and the Pulitzer Prize–winning *The Grapes of Wrath* (1939) is an American classic, topping required reading lists for students across the country. Steinbeck's intense interest in ecology, conservation, and the general interrelatedness of all life shaped his craft; in turn, his craft shaped the American imagination and forced us, as a nation, to examine our moral responsibility toward the natural world.

Steinbeck had a deep personal relationship with the soft hills of his native Salinas Valley, with his other homes in Lake Tahoe and Pacific Grove, and with the human and natural tide pools around Monterey and the Sea of Cortez. An abiding sense of place imbues his fiction and nonfiction, and *The Grapes of Wrath*, certainly, stands as a testament to the effects of environmental degradation on land and people. His internal sense of right and wrong that governed his writing was shaped by an environmental ethic that demanded stewardship and respect for the natural world.

In a 1935 *San Francisco Chronicle* sketch of the young writer, a reporter dramatizes Steinbeck's oneness with the land: "Down out of the hills he came, he said; he felt as if he had somehow always lived in them." It would be tempting to say that Steinbeck cultivated this image of himself, except that he was famously reticent to be interviewed, speak publicly, and even have his photo taken. More likely, Steinbeck genuinely felt himself to be physically and spiritually attached to the land—his childhood experiences and later interest in burgeoning ecological sciences bear this out. Jackson Benson opens his authoritative biography on John Steinbeck by reflecting on Steinbeck's childhood "communion with nature," his love of finding secret places for hours of observation around Salinas, and the family summer home in Pacific Grove, California. The imprint of his childhood places— hills, coast—on the formation of his literary imagination cannot be overstated. Steinbeck's sense of place, his deep understanding of the ways nature and identity shape each other, was also influenced by his parents and their responses to the natural world.

While not wealthy, both sides of Steinbeck's family were prosperous founding members of communities in what the writer immortalized as the "long valley." Steinbeck's mother Olive Hamilton was born in San Jose to Irish immigrant parents. Olive's father signed the Salinas Valley charter in 1872 and eventually homesteaded a large but economically unsuccessful ranch in the south end of the valley. Olive, along with the other eight Hamilton children, grew up close to the land; when Olive turned fifteen, she left the ranch to become a schoolteacher. By the time she turned eighteen she was teaching in a one-room schoolhouse south of Monterey, traveling back and forth on horseback. During a teaching assignment in King City, she met her future husband, then the manager of the King City flour mill. Olive gave up teaching and ranch life, preferring the social and physical comforts of Salinas. The gifts she gave to her four children, three sisters and little brother John, include a powerful imagination and a house full of art and literature. She appreciated the magical and the enchanted and likely stirred young John's lifelong interest in such figures as leprechauns and knights of the Round Table.

Steinbeck's father, Benson tells us, "felt the constant need to be plugged to the soil, to feel its vibrations." He may have felt this need due to his "Old Country" ancestry. The family tree took root in Jerusalem, where Steinbeck's paternal grandfather John Adolf Grossteinbeck, a German cabinetmaker, met and married Almira Dickson, daughter of a Lutheran minister. Enduring attack by a Bedouin tribe and shipwreck on the return voyage to the United States, John Adolf and Almira settled in New England. The Steinbecks, as they now called themselves, moved to Florida before the Civil War. John Adolf and his brother both fought in the war—the former with the Confederate Army, the latter with the Union Army. It was during the war that Steinbeck's father John was born, and shortly before the war ended, the family made their roundabout way to the West. John Adolf bought ten acres of land near Salinas and eventually opened a flour mill.

Steinbeck senior, an accountant and an outdoor man, in addition to feeling a deep need to be in close contact with the land, had a disciplined, pragmatic side that he passed along to his son. He instilled in his son a love of gardening—John junior always had a garden, wherever he lived—and a deep love of animals. Steinbeck's love for the natural world and for artistic, imaginative expression was certainly cultivated by his parents. He also valued his intermittent work on ranches, as a chemist in a sugar plant, and as a field hand. Although his on-again, off-again education at Stanford did not exert a major influence on his work, one remarkable summer class stands as a powerful jump start to his literary imagination.

What interested Steinbeck was the way the human and the nonhuman world existed in relationship to each other, and he had a keen journalistic eye for detail and an obsessive need to record his views. He jumped at the chance, in 1923, to enroll with his sister Mary for a summer course at the Hopkins Marine Station. His teacher that summer, C. V. Taylor, conducted the general zoology class under the influence of zoologist William Emerson Ritter. Ritter had developed his theory of "organicism" in 1918 and through his scholarship urged others to consider "nature as a whole" and to discover trends of interrelatedness. This theme would remain central to Steinbeck throughout his career. As Benson explains, "Nearly all of Steinbeck's published fiction was to reflect to some degree or another the essential principle of the organismal unity of life." It would be one of the main things that marked his work as different from that of his contemporaries.

Steinbeck's first three novels, *Cup of Gold* (1929), *Pastures of Heaven* (1932), and *To a God Unknown* (1933), did little to improve his fame and fortune as a novelist. Each novel was published by a different publishing house; each went broke during the Depression. *Cup of Gold* is an Arthurian-style romance concerning the life of buccaneer Sir Henry Morgan. In *Pastures of Heaven* Steinbeck is more subtly allegorical. The espisodic novel details life in a seemingly happy California Valley that unravels due to the arrival of the Munroe family. This novel is notable for the appearance of two Steinbeck "stock" characters: the misunderstood mentally disabled Tularecito and the matriarch Molly Morgan, modeled after his mother, Olive Hamilton. From this period, it is in *To a God Unknown* that Steinbeck most succinctly unfolds the meaning of the organismal theory of nature. Herein Joseph Wayne, the central character, is identified with the whole of nature, especially as he sacrifices himself to end a drought: "He lay on his side with his wrist outstretched and looked down the long black mountain of his body. 'I am the land,' he said, 'and I am the rain. The grass will grow out of me in a little while.'"

Although he often struggled financially during this time, he never wavered in his determination to keep writing. Perhaps it was the three bonds he formed in 1930 that kept him going. He married his first wife, Carol Henning; he began a relationship with the literary agency who would represent him his entire career, McIntosh & Otis (from which his celebrated association with editor Pascal Covici developed); and perhaps most significant, he met the remarkable Edward Ricketts. The famous friendship that ensued not only provided Steinbeck with a companion of like mind and a prototype for his most famous character ("Doc"), but it forced his thinking on "organicism" to evolve into a mature philosophy.

Steinbeck and Ricketts knew each other for eighteen years, and it was during the first few years of their relationship, when they were frequently together, that Steinbeck's most critically acclaimed books were written. When the pair first met, Ricketts owned Pacific Biological Laboratory, a Monterey-based operation that prepared mostly marine animals for exhibition and study. His lab overlooked Monterey Bay, just a few blocks from Steinbeck's home, and the two usually got together in the afternoons after Steinbeck had written a thousand words or so. They caroused, they collected marine specimens for the lab, they listened to music, and they talked art, philosophy, and evolutionary biology.

During the early 1930s, Steinbeck worked on several stories and novels that went unpublished. Finally, *Tortilla Flat* (1935), another episodic novel using an Arthurian allegory, proved to be the one to lift him from poverty and obscurity. Using stories from a local Spanish teacher, Sue Gregory, Steinbeck wove together vignettes about marginalized paisanos living on the outskirts of Monterey in a place called Tortilla Flat. Herein Steinbeck develops his ideas of a Ricketts-inspired theory, "group man." Throughout his career, Steinbeck was drawn to the way a group itself becomes a powerful entity, an organic whole. Danny, the central character in the novel, comes home from the war to find he had inherited two houses from his deceased *Viejo*. The community that springs up in Tortilla Flat (a liminal space between "wilderness"—that is, undeveloped land and the city) and their antics also provided Steinbeck a frame in which to pursue another enduring theme: the misunderstood, marginalized person (or group), shunned by dominant society but nonetheless possessing moral clarity and a generous spirit. Lennie and George in *Of Mice and Men* (1937), the Joads and other environmental refugees in *The Grapes of Wrath*, and Doc and the boys in *Cannery Row* (1945) all exemplify this trend.

After *Tortilla Flat*, Steinbeck had little trouble publishing his next twenty-seven books. He also published a multitude of nonfiction in American magazines and abroad. The subjects he wrote about included the environment, poverty, homelessness, war, and racism. He endeavored always to discover and define America in its complexity.

In 1936, Steinbeck published a series of articles in the *San Francisco News* about migrant laborers and their struggles to unionize. He took his research seriously, living and working with migrant laborers on ranches up and down California's central valley. Much of what he saw, heard, and experienced provided him with the material for *The Grapes of Wrath*, which was published in 1939. As he was writing *Grapes*, a book he expected to be a nonfiction account of migrant labor, he published *Of Mice and Men*. Like *Tortilla Flat*, *Of Mice and Men* features characters on the social margins of society who find solace and refuge in wild, natural, or liminal spaces. The novel's themes garnered even more attention when it was turned into a successful stage play late in 1937.

All the while, Steinbeck's focus became more consumed by the plight of migrant workers. His empathy with "group man" and his outrage at the environmental degradation during the Dust Bowl and beyond fueled his writing. Steinbeck, ever the seeker of allegory, told a *San Jose Mercury News* reporter that migration to California from Dust Bowl states "will change things almost as much as did the coming of the first American settlers." He goes on to develop a theme that endures into his later works. The migrant workers, he tells the reporter, "know just what they want. . . . The Californian . . . wants things. . . . The Oklahoman wants a piece of land. And he goes after it and gets it." Mindless consumerism was an American ill, Steinbeck believed, leading to all manner of immoral actions toward the environment.

The plight of the Joad family is familiar to millions of readers. They leave Dust Bowl poverty and journey to California in hopes of work and a better life. Along the way, the Joads learn about the scarcity of work from other migrants, and they endure the deaths of granma and granpa. But like the famous turtle introduced early in the book, which stands as a metaphor for the migrants, they move forward with grim determination. Steinbeck's vision is bleak—during the penultimate chapter, the family experiences rain and flood, illness and hunger, unemployment, begging, and stealing. Eventually, however, spring comes, and "tiny points of grass come through the earth." As a final gesture of finding hope in the continuance of nature's inevitable cycle, Rose of Sharon saves the life of a starving man by nursing him with the milk meant for her stillborn baby.

The Grapes of Wrath was published in March 1939; by May it was the number-one bestseller. Steinbeck was lauded for exposing the powerlessness of migrant workers and their struggles against poverty, hunger, and ruthless landowners. But *Grapes* was greeted with controversy. Steinbeck was accused of being a Communist and a gross exaggerator. Eleanor Roosevelt defended Steinbeck and took the book's message of social inequity and injustice to heart. Many believe that the power of the book's message led to the congressional hearings on migrant camp conditions and eventual changes in labor laws.

In 1940, Steinbeck escaped the controversy surrounding *The Grapes of Wrath* by traveling to the Sea of Cortez with Ed Ricketts. There they charter a ship, the *Western Flyer*, and set themselves the task of collecting marine specimens. They coauthor a book about the expedition, originally titled *Sea of Cortez: A Leisurely Journey of Travel and Research* (1941). *The Log from the Sea of Cortez*, as it later became known, was a different book for Steinbeck. Nonfiction, collaborative, and scientific minded, it collapsed the physical and intellectual journeys into one exploration.

In *The Log*, Steinbeck and Ricketts celebrate the beauty of life in a post-Darwinian universe. "We wanted to see everything our eyes could accommodate," Steinbeck and Ricketts write, "to build some kind of structure in modeled imitation of reality." What they come up with is "non-teleogical" or "Is" thinking, a philosophical approach to life that considers what is, not what should be. The universe is a holistic unit, the authors believed, and humans and nature mirror each other in their struggle for survival.

Steinbeck extends the theme of the self-contained tide pool to the human community in the novel *Cannery Row* (1945). Doc, Mark and the boys, and Dora and her girls struggle to survive; they live exuberantly and sometimes die tragically. In this novel the narrator turns a microscopic lens on the characters in the human tide pool. In doing so, Steinbeck picks up and refines his enduring themes: the interrelatedness of life, group man, and the moral clarity of the marginalized. His language is both religious and Darwinian: "Our Father who art in nature," he writes, "who has given the gift of survival to the coyote, the common brown rat, the English sparrow, the house fly and the moth, must have a great and overwhelming love for no-goods and blots-on-the-town and bums, and Mack and the boys."

In 1954, Steinbeck published *Sweet Thursday*, a sequel to *Cannery Row*, which Benson called Steinbeck's indulgence, a book he wrote mostly for himself. It seems true that much of Steinbeck's later fiction, including the celebrated *East of Eden* (1952), is nostalgic. The nonfiction *Travels with Charley* (1962), however, published the year Steinbeck was awarded the Nobel Prize for Literature, is a notable exception.

The narrative movement of *Travels with Charley* takes its rhythm from Steinbeck's year on the road in a pickup truck with his poodle Charley. He wishes, as he writes to his agent in 1960, to experience "one place in relation to another." He dubs his trip "Operation Windmills" and his truck "Rocinante," in honor of Don Quixote's horse. But his trip was not whimsical; his letters from this period underscore a determination to take the American pulse. His letters also indicate a growing discomfort with American consumerism. In a 1959 letter to Adlai Stevenson, Steinbeck describes what he calls a plague: "Having too many THINGS [Americans] spend their hours and money on the couch searching for a soul. . . . If I wanted to destroy a nation, I would give it too much and I would have it on its knees, miserable, greedy, and sick." In the opening pages of *Travels with Charley*, Steinbeck writes that he wished to "feel" his country. As in his Monterey books and earlier novels, Steinbeck creates a microcosm of vividly drawn characters. Ultimately, however, Steinbeck laments the unchecked growth and consumerist habits that may prove to be the American environmental downfall. The book, often characterized as a memoir, became an instant bestseller.

Long after his death in 1968, John Steinbeck's environmental legacy continues to unfold for readers. New critical tools allow us to read his work in fresh ways. Green Marxism can show us how the Joads and others are alienated from the natural world because of methods of production and how these very methods cause irrevocable damage to the environment. Ecological criticism allows us to read closely for the relationship between human and nonhuman nature. Deep ecology guides us in understanding Ricketts's and Steinbeck's urge to move from androcentric to ecocentric thinking. Despite these new ways of thinking about Steinbeck's literary contributions, his traditional environmental legacy carries the most weight. He challenged Americans to think about their moral responsibility to each other and the land. He had great hope for the American environmental scene. In *America and the Americans* (1966), he writes, "We are no longer content to destroy

our beloved country. We are slow to learn; but we learn. . . . And we no longer believe that a man, by owning a piece of America, is free to outrage it."

GIOIA WOODS

Beegal, Susan F., Susan Shillinglaw, and Wesley N. Tiffney Jr., eds. *Steinbeck and the
Environment: Interdisciplinary Approaches*. Tuscaloosa, AL, 1997.

Benson, Jackson J. *John Steinbeck, Writer*. New York, 1984.

Fensch, Thomas, ed. *Conversations with John Steinbeck*. Jackson, MS, 1988.

Steinbeck, Elaine, and Robert Wallsten, eds. *Steinbeck: A Life in Letters*.
New York, 1976.

Stratton-Porter, Gene (August 17, 1863–December 6, 1924). Placed
alongside early U.S. environmental activists such as Theodore Roosevelt,
whose strong conservation efforts emerged from the closing of the American frontier, Stratton-Porter, bestselling writer of twelve novels, eight nature writing books, various poems, and magazine publications, helped to
popularize the national conservation movement by writing primarily for a
middle-class and wealthy female audience who were influenced by her conservationist environmental values.

Born at the family homestead near Lagro Township in Wabash County,
Indiana, Geneva "Gene" Stratton was the daughter of Mark and Mary Stratton and the youngest of twelve children. Of English descent, Mark prided
himself on his Anglo heritage and raised his children with a strong sense of
connection to English literature and culture. He was a third-generation
American who grew up on an Ohio farm within a strict Methodist family.
At a young age, he was required to memorize and recite the Bible and became known for his rich vocabulary and eloquent storytelling. After he
and Mary married, they migrated from Wayne County, Ohio. The family
temporarily settled on the Kosciusko/Wabash county line and farmed for
five years to gain capital. Eventually they settled along the Wabash River in
Wabash County, Indiana. There, Mark purchased a large farmstead, which
he developed into a successful family farm named Hopewell. Meanwhile,
Mary, the daughter of a miller from Wayne County, followed her husband
on his mission for an independent farm and performed the crucial role of
farm mother by bearing numerous children.

In the years just prior to Gene's birth, Mark played two major civic roles
for the local community. In 1858 he was licensed as a Methodist minister,

and from 1858 to 1863 he served as a Wabash County commissioner. He loved the Wabash Valley region where he and his family had settled and instilled in his children both an appreciation for the landscape there as well as a commitment to the Methodist community in Lagro. It is little wonder that this verbose, outgoing patriarch's religious and land ethics would influence his daughter's future writing.

Because of her father's decision to rear his children in the country, Gene spent a great deal of her youth outside on the farm in the Wabash River Basin, where she gained an awareness of the local plants and wildlife that would later inform her place-based novels, nature photography, and nature essays. Her youth was marked by social ostracism because not only was she raised on a farm, but she appeared to enjoy exploring the outdoors like her male peers. She grew up during the height of Victorian influence in the United States, and she rebelled against cultural value that expected clear boundaries between masculine and feminine behavior and activities. Unlike her female peers, Gene sought out natural history and field observations and disliked being pushed into the traditional female domestic sphere. Her preoccupation with birdlife ignited her interest in advanced nature study, and this independent research served as a salve for the Victorian-style education imposed on females. Although she gained an adequate girl's education for her time, she faced constant disparagement for her interest in science-oriented nature studies. Her teachers and peers thought such studies were suitable only for males. When her mother died in 1875, Gene left high school. She never returned to graduate, but her love for reading, writing, and field research persisted beyond her formal education.

After ten years of living with her widowed father in the Wabash Valley, Gene wed Charles D. Porter in 1886. A successful druggist in Adams County, Charles bought a two-story house in the center of Decatur, Illinois. This urban lifestyle upset Gene's nature study and made apparent her antisocial tendencies, and within five years, they relocated to a smaller town, Geneva, Indiana, with their only child, Jeannette. It was here that they planned and finished their home, Limberlost Cabin, in 1895. This small house was built on a large rural lot with a garden, orchard, chicken park, and yard where Jeannette could play. Especially useful for Gene's fieldwork was the swampy area near their home, which she explored for bird-watching.

During this period, Porter juggled her roles as mother, wife, and housekeeper to pursue her professional writing. Her first book, *The Strike at Shane's*, was initially published anonymously in 1893 and is now compared to George Orwell's *Animal Farm* (1945) because of the anthropomor-phized animal characters. *The Song of the Cardinal* (1903), inspired by her indignation from finding a discarded body of a cardinal shot by a hunter to show his marksmanship, established her reputation as the "Bird Woman." When she acquired a camera in 1895, she taught herself basic photographic techniques to create images for her stories. She began publishing her photography and writing under her real name in 1900, and soon her animal and plant conservation beliefs became known to a mainstream audience.

While her writing quickly gained her fame, her research and writing left her little time to socialize, and many people in her local community saw her as an antisocial eccentric. When she did hold social gatherings in her home, she exchanged her "men's clothing" for proper feminine attire but chose to entertain in the evening rather than hold afternoon events, which was the socially acceptable behavior for a female hostess. Beyond her obvious unconventional behavior, the Porter family's wealth inspired jealousy and distrust in her female neighbors, who saw her affluence as the reason she would dare to pursue her professional writing goals despite the social conventions that deemed such work inappropriate for proper women. Although she was not popular with her female neighbors, Stratton-Porter was accepted by the lumbermen, the oil workers, and the farmers who worked the Limberlost as well as the farm women with whom she developed friendships during her nature treks. Her positive relationships with these rural people played a role in her writing because her most sympathetic characters are the rural folk. Her nature field trips through Limberlost influenced her fiction and nonfiction writing, and the commercial exploitation of the land pushed her to include a strong conservationist ethic in her work. Stratton-Porter integrated her environmental sensibilities into these narratives by creating characters who engaged directly with the natural world, both as lovers and exploiters of the land who had to confront moral or religious issues about their land use and social practices.

Unfortunately, as much as she loved the Limberlost forest, by 1913 the destruction of the area was permanent. Lumbering, oil development, drainage, and cultivation destroyed her research environment, so Stratton-Porter used her own money earned from her six successful novels and four nature books to purchase more land to prevent further decimation of the local Indiana flora and fauna. She bought a nearby 120-acre plot on the southwest end of Sylvan Lake, where she had another house built. In addition, she built a second Limberlost cabin in Rome City and bought a 14-acre plot of dense woodland bordering the lake. In the end she owned 150 acres with two miles of shoreline, acreage she named "Wildflower Woods." It was at Wildflower Woods that she persisted with her writing, completing three novels, one nature book, a children's book, and numerous magazine articles. When the Sylvan Lake region was being threatened by natural resources overexploitation, she fought, unsuccessfully, to preserve the area and had to work vigilantly to record as much about the native flora before it was destroyed. Although much of the region was developed, her private conservation effort in Wildflower Woods provided a safe habitat for flora propagation, and the numerous plant species she cultivated are in greater numbers there than in any other portion of Indiana. This local conservation effort reached her reading audience, and people sent her plant materials from all over the world. While she appreciated foreign plant propagation, Stratton-Porter cared most about the native species. Like Theodore Roosevelt, she was a realist who believed that preservation was impossible for a country such as the United States that was attempting to develop a sense of nationhood based on economic stability, so she worked to record the nature of the region before it was destroyed while calling for responsible use of the land through pragmatic land conservation policies.

The mainstream female audience appreciated her writing and its environmental messages, but Stratton-Porter received harsh criticism for the lack of scientific accuracy in her nonfiction nature writing. Deemed non-scholarly because she did not record her field observations in the traditional scientific style, she was marked as a "nature faker" by naturalists like John S. Burroughs, who believed that nature writing needed to be scientifically accurate to be respected. However, this censure from a male-dominated science community ignored the effect that Stratton-Porter's writing had on her female readers who could influence their husbands' support for conservation. A product of her time and culture, Stratton-Porter's perspective of the world was obviously filtered through female Victorian values. Although her love of the outdoors removed her from the purely domestic sphere, she wrote for a female audience with their domestic interests in mind. Eugene Pattison suggests that Porter wrote to "popularize scientific nature study, by writing about it directly and simply, or by sugar-coating it with fiction" and that she was influenced by midwestern sentimental writers as well as by English Romantic and Victorian poets and English historians, Victorian fiction, and French novelists. Stratton-Porter's focus on bird home-life studies in books such as *The Song of the Cardinal* may have anthropomor-phized animals, but it attracted women who connected the animal home with their own domestic behaviors. Despite numerous nature writers like her who defended their style of field observation and writing as respectable nature study, the nature fakers controversy eventually created a line between natural history writing and nature writing, deeming the prior as hard sci-ence and the latter as soft literature.

When World War I ended in 1919, Stratton-Porter traveled to California for the first time and finally established her own permanent home there. She purchased land on Catalina Island, where she started construction of a summer home, and in a Los Angeles suburb, where she constructed her home base that overlooked the city. During her time in California, Stratton-Porter became known as the country's top female writer. Her busy social life in Los Angeles prevented her from undertaking serious fieldwork and bird photography, but her two California novels *Her Father's Daughter* (1921) and *The Keeper of the Bees* (1925), did include extensive attention to the diverse plant life around her.

In 1924 Stratton-Porter died not in the rural countryside that had in-spired so much of her creative work but in a car collision with a street car in the urban bustle of Los Angeles. Beyond the still-protected nature preserve at Wildflower Woods, Stratton-Porter's writing and civic work as a conser-vationist inspired the Adirondack Forest Service to dedicate to her a me-morial grove of 10,000 white pines at the base of Tongue Mountain on Lake George, New York. While Stratton-Porter may have faced criticism for her sentimental novels and nature essays, her environmental ethics filtered through her writing and photography, and she played a significant role in popularizing conservationist principles at a time in the United States when rampant exploitation of the nation's natural resources threatened to de-stroy much of the wilderness and less-populated lands. By expressing her values through less-scholarly popular novels and nature writing, Stratton-Porter spread her ideas to a broad audience whose own Victorian values helped them connect to her conservation ethic.

GWYNNE MIDDLETON

Birkelo, Cheryl. "The Harvester and the Natural Bounty of Gene Stratton-Porter."
    Such News of the Land: U.S. Women Nature Writers. Hanover, NH, 2001.
Long, Judith Reick. *Gene Stratton-Porter: Novelist and Naturalist.* Indianapolis,
    IN, 1990.

Pattison, Eugene H. "The Limberlost, Tinker Creek, Science and Society: Gene Stratton-Porter and Annie Dillard." *Pittsburgh History* (Winter 1994–1995): 160–172.

Philippon, Daniel L. *Conserving Words: How American Nature Writers Shaped the Environmental Movement.* Athens, GA, 2005.

Phillips, Anne K. "Epiphanies and Poets: Gene Stratton-Porter's Domestic Transcendentalism." *Children's Literature Association Quarterly* 19.4 (1994): 153–158.

Richards, Bertrand F. *Gene Stratton-Porter.* Boston, MA, 1980.

⚶ Swallow, Ellen Henrietta (Richards) (December 3, 1842–March 30, 1911).

By the standards of any era, Swallow would have been recognized as a remarkable individual, but the magnitude of her contribution to the formation of the fledgling science of the environment has earned her the title of "First Lady of Science and Technology." The quality of her talents and achievements and the comprehensive scope of her influence are all the more remarkable because she lived in an environment that neither encouraged nor rewarded such activities on the part of women.

Swallow was the only child of Peter and Fanny Swallow, teachers who, at the time of Ellen's birth, were engaged in farming in Massachusetts. While it is possible to overestimate the influences of one's early childhood experiences, the place and tenor of Ellen's first sixteen years unquestionably had a profound impact on her intellectual capacities and the directions in which she focused her growing talents for observation and analysis.

A frail child, she was encouraged to pursue activities out-of-doors. Her parents conducted her first schooling at home, and her father included field studies with the more traditional textbook and domestic subjects. Thus, she was from an early age intimately familiar with the natural environment; and her curiosity and examination of the world around her were not impeded but systematically directed and enlarged. When Ellen was sixteen the family moved so that she could benefit from a more formal education at Westford Academy. While assisting at her father's new general store, Ellen became interested in the human element of the universe—on what basis people made their choices, their buying habits, and the composition and purity of the store's products.

Swallow entered Vassar College and graduated in 1870 with a bachelor's degree. It was while at Vassar that she discovered the science of chemistry.

Her desire to pursue this subject led her to apply to the Massachusetts Institute of Technology (MIT), an institution that did not as yet admit female students. Her eventual acceptance was considered by MIT to be something in the nature of an experiment. She was to pay no fees of any kind. Should her course of study fail, MIT would bear no official responsibility for her presence. Despite her highly successful and lifelong association with MIT, that institution would hesitate until nearly the year of her death to bestow any higher degree than the initial B.S. that she earned in 1873. (Her master's came from Vassar in the same year.)

Swallow was retained by MIT as an instructor in various divisions, and from 1876 to 1911 she produced works of consequence in both established and emerging disciplines. In the field of water science and analysis Swallow was without peer. Her early involvement in a Massachusetts water purity study (the first of its kind) led to the Great Sanitary Survey of Massachusetts Water and Sewage and to the Normal Chlorine Map of the United States, both of which provided the first tools to demonstrate and combat water pollution. Her mineralogical studies earned her international renown, and even fire came under her laboratory investigation, as inquiry was made into the ignition levels of industrial oils.

Swallow's greatest contribution to the emerging environmental sciences, even beyond the pioneering analytical tools and guidelines that she developed, lay in her aptitude for holistic thought and synthesis. Water, air, and soil studies did not exist in a vacuum. They were an investigation of elements as they lay, in situ, in an environment composed of both natural and human variables. For Swallow, water pollution was not simply an index on a sample. It was an integral part of the unhealthy physical and social environment of the late nineteenth century. Her efforts to bring those conditions and their scientific solution to public attention created such practical spin-offs as the New England Kitchen (a working laboratory for producing nutritious and inexpensive food), plans for home and institutional sanitation and air circulation, the founding of the first commercial sanitary laundry, and the creation of a correspondence school for women. She served as an expert consultant to numerous institutions and organizations, including U.S. government departments and committees.

The principles that Swallow promoted in public she espoused also in her private life. After her marriage in 1875 to Robert Hallowell Richards, a professor of mining engineering at MIT, she established a home that was both a laboratory and showcase for the art of healthful living. The couple had no

children, and their marriage was characterized as being one of true sym-
biosis, providing a source of mutual support and inspiration for both of
their careers.

Swallow's combined efforts in the home sciences and her continued interests in the education of women as agents of change for better living conditions culminated in the establishment of the discipline we now know as
home economics. While acknowledging Swallow as its founder, home economics has largely abandoned the environmental element for which she
had intended it as a vehicle. Swallow published (under her married name of
Richards) an extensive series of titles in this area: *The Cost of Cleanness*
(1908), *Air, Water, and Food—From a Sanitary Standpoint* (1900), *The Chemistry of Cooking and Cleaning* (1882), and many others on the topics of food
and nutrition, consumerism, shelter, and cost of living.

A single overriding precept drove all of Swallow's accomplishments, the
idea that physical and human environments must exist in partnership—
that the process of discovery and documentation of the intricacies of their
nature and relationship can and must be used to improve both these conditions. Human beings not only interact with and affect their environment;
they must be taught to do so in ways beneficial to them and the environment. Scientific knowledge must come to terms with economic compulsion
through the process of environmental education. These were unique, even
radical, ideas in Swallow's time. She sought in her latter years to compose
and publicize these concepts in a work titled *Euthenics—the Science of Con-
trollable Environment* (1910).

Swallow's legacy to the environmental sciences lies in this element of
comprehensiveness. She worked to bring the bits and pieces of emerging
environmental inquiry together and to endow them with strict scientific
and academic credentials. She also sought to show how interdependent this
new world was with human affairs and how education and information
were necessary to achieve the best balance. She was a pioneer not only in
the documentation of environmental problems but in the proposal of suggested solutions that form the basis of environmentalism today.

KAREN HOVDE

Clarke, Robert. *Ellen Swallow: The Woman Who Founded Ecology.* Chicago, IL, 1973.
Ogilvie, Marilyn Bailey. "Richards, Ellen Swallow." *Women in Science: Antiquity
through the Nineteenth Century.* Cambridge, MA, 1986.

Teale, Edwin Way (June 2, 1899–October 18, 1980). A self-taught naturalist, photographer/illustrator, and staff writer (*Popular Science*, 1928–1941), Teale was the perennially popular describer of "The American Seasons" in *North with the Spring* (1951), *Autumn across America* (1956), *Journey into Summer* (1960), and *Wandering Through Winter* (1965). This final volume in his 100,000-mile, fifteen-year-project with his wife Nellie won the Pulitzer Prize for general nonfiction in 1966.

Teale is best known for combining absolute accuracy of reported observations with a lucid, descriptive style similar to the caption style of *Life* magazine. In his very popular books, the photographs and the commentary seamlessly complement one another. Teale also was the first to use the building of America's transcontinental road system and consequent access to national parks to give his readers a friendly armchair view of America's then-little-known natural history. He said, "We tend to date events by our cars. That was when we had the Model T."

Through his thirty books he convinced average Americans that they had a stake in the preservation of America's varied ecological zones. By combining motor travel, photography, and his intentionally folksy, plain style of narrative, he showed a new group of prosperous Americans (the new suburbanites) how to "experience" and how to "appreciate" nature. Therefore, Teale's work in general can be seen as a historical bridge in sensibility between the more austere Henry David Thoreau, John Muir, and Donald C. Peattie through the 1950s and 1960s to younger philosophical naturalists.

In his autobiography *Dune Boy: The Early Years of a Naturalist* (1943), Teale wrote of his happy boyhood at "Lone Oak," his grandfather's Indiana farm. Here he taught himself to learn from careful observation of prairie insects, and he mastered simple photography. At age twelve he changed his name from Edwin Alfred to Edwin Way, one he believed would be more distinguished for a photographer/writer. This early sense of gravitas never left him and is evidence of the meticulous planning and organizing that 1950s. American readers admired and supported in his works.

In his first book on insects, *Grassroots Jungles* (1937), his combination of observation with philosophical musings set the pattern for his success. In

1941 he became a full-time popularizing naturalist. Teale's natural history autobiographies continued in *The Lost Woods* (1945), *Days without Time* (1948), *A Naturalist Buys an Old Farm* (1974), and his last book, *A Walk through the Year* (1978). He also edited Thoreau's *Walden* (1946), William H. Hudson's *Green Mansions* (1944), *The Insect World of J. Henri Fabre* (1949), and *The Wilderness World of John Muir* (1955). He was awarded the John Burroughs Medal for distinguished nature writing in 1943.

In his books, the mature Teale carefully built toward a summarizing passage that would give his readers a harsher view of the natural world than they got from another popularizer of the 1950s, Walt Disney. For example, in *Journey into Summer: A Naturalist's Record of a 19,000-Mile Journey Through the North American Summer* (1960), Teale accepts the gulf between a rattlesnake and modern man as he leans from his powerful, protecting car's window:

> Looking down on the flat, weaving head, in the slide of the coils, . . . I gazed at this fellow creature on earth across an unbridgeable gulf. Nature is not always as we would have her on a pleasant day. Goodwill toward all living creatures is not enough. Understanding that the deadly serpent was born with its fangs and venom—that it did not invent them, that the credit for that belongs elsewhere—is not enough. The mental threat remains. The man of goodwill turns away . . . with a troubled mind.

The bleakness of these descriptive discussions is present in Teale's four-volume *The American Seasons*, for he was a realist, but they are always counterbalanced by his appreciation of the joy (anthropomorphic or not) that he found in all natural events. Once he overheard an elderly man repairing an electric light ask:

> "What does *he* do?"
> This question . . . infinitely varied, was always the same wherever we went. If a man drives a truck . . . everyone understands. But if he spends his days roaming a field observing nature . . . his activity is mysterious. At times, the response, half-incredulous, has been: "What a wonderful way to make a living!" and to that only one reply has ever came to mind: "It is, indeed" (*Journey into Summer*).

In his later works, Teale, like Peattie and Richard Jeffries, taught his readers that nature could provide meaning to those who sought it: "The question of a lifetime returns with renewed force. Why should there be so much suffering in the world? On this March day [this was his last book and he was seventy-seven], I come to this old question from a different viewpoint, the viewpoint of nature."

Teale's eloquent answer is in perhaps his wisest book, a distinguished addition to American nature writing, *A Walk through the Year*. The voice of a decent, kind, believable man is present in all of Teale's work. By being the eyes and ears and legs for workaday Americans, Teale convinced many of them to support national parks and the conservation movement. He also convinced many to return to Thoreau and Muir and repopularized their ideas of the true value of the natural world.

In 1925, Teale married Nellie Donovan, his close companion as well as his chief botanizing partner. Their only son, David Allen, was killed in World War II.

RODNEY SMITH

"Edwin Way Teale Is Dead at 81." *New York Times*, October 21, 1980.

Miller, David Stuart. "An Unfinished Pilgrimage: Edwin Way Teale and American Nature Writing." *Dissertations Abstracts International* 43.8 (1983).

Zwinger, Ann, and E. W. Teale. *A Conscious Stillness: Two Naturalists on Thoreau's Rivers*. New York, 1982.

Train, Russell Errol (June 4, 1920–   ). A tireless advocate for global environmental concerns, Train served as the agency administrator for the Environmental Protection Agency (EPA) during the Nixon and Ford administrations. Later he became founding trustee and president of the World Wildlife Fund (WWF), which he helped to build from a relatively small organization into one of the largest and most powerful conservation foundations in the world. Today he serves as chairman emeritus for the WWF.

Train was born in Jamestown, Rhode Island, on Acushnet Island in Narragansett Bay, where his parents were renting a summer house. The Trains' home was in Washington, DC, where both his parents—U.S. Navy Rear Admiral Charles R. Train and Errol C. (Brown) Train—had grown up, but in the summertime, the family went north to enjoy what Train calls the "more salubrious climate" of the Northeast. The Trains vacationed for several summers near Elizabethtown, New York, and Russell and his older brothers spent much of their youth exploring the woods along the Bouquet River and climbing several of the nearby peaks in the Adirondack Mountains.

He also spent time at Pochet Island on Cape Cod, where he learned to swim, sail, fish, ride a horse, and dig for crabs. Memories of these early experiences would play an important role in the development of Train's environmental ethic later in life.

Like his brothers before him, Train attended the Potomac School before eventually graduating from St. Albans in 1937. He then attended Princeton University and in 1941 received a bachelor's degree in politics. While at Princeton, he joined the Army Reserve Officers' Training Corps (ROTC), which his father reluctantly allowed only because the university had no naval ROTC. During World War II, Train served in the United States and Okinawa, rising to the rank of major. After his army discharge, prompted by the example of his uncle, prominent New York federal judge Augustus Hand, Train attended Columbia University Law School and earned his J.D. in 1948.

Train married Aileen Bowdoin in 1954, and the couple had four children: a son, Charles "Bowdy" Train; and three daughters, Errol, Nancy, and Emily. The family resided in the Washington, DC, area throughout Train's career in government. He spent the first part of his career as an attorney and jurist for various legislative committees and executive departments. From 1948 to 1957 he served in several positions: legal adviser for the Congressional Joint Committee on Internal Revenue Taxation (where he became an expert on tax law); chief counsel, then minority adviser, to the House Ways and Means Committee; and assistant to the secretary of the treasury and head of the department's legal advisory staff. In 1957 President Dwight Eisenhower nominated him to preside over a U.S. Tax Court, an appointment that was renewed by President John Kennedy and that Train held until 1965.

During this early period in Train's career, he and his wife visited Kenya, Rwanda, the Belgian Congo, and Uganda on two safaris in 1956 and 1958, on which he hunted elephant, buffalo, gazelle, leopard, and antelope. It was on these excursions that Train first became interested in African wildlife. He describes his encounters with mountain gorillas as "heart-stopping events," and he meditates at length on what he saw as the romantic wildness of the African continent: "the cold early mornings, the heat of midday spent in the shade of an acacia, the incessant calling of the doves, . . . the nights full of stars, the occasional roar of the distant lion, the call of a hyena." Train's interest in wildlife conservation eventually influenced his radical career shift into environmental work. In 1959 he founded the African

Wildlife Leadership Foundation, which helps developing nations in Africa to establish wildlife parks and reserves. The foundation, which still maintains offices in Nairobi and Washington, DC, remains one of the main international organizations involved with conservation in Africa.

In 1965 Train resigned his position on the Tax Court and became president of the Conservation Foundation. Under Train's leadership, the organization worked to find ways in which environmental considerations could be brought into the policy-making process in Washington. Train's experience with the Conservation Foundation drew the attention of Senator Henry "Scoop" Jackson of Washington, then the chair of the Senate Interior Committee, which at the time was considering how to build environmental factors into government decision making. On the Conservation Foundation's advisory board was Lynton "Keith" Caldwell, a political scientist at the University of Indiana, who was offered a consulting position with the committee to address these issues. In large part due to Train's influence, Caldwell became the chief architect of the Environmental Impact Statement (EIS) and the National Environmental Policy Act (NEPA), two of the most significant documents for environmental protection in U.S. history.

After three years in the private sector, Train was appointed in 1968 to the seven-member National Water Commission. When Richard Nixon was elected president in November of that year, Train—as a notable Republican and conservationist—was asked to chair a task force on resource and environmental issues, which he did until January of 1969. The task force's report recommended a White House office of environmental policy, an idea that culminated in the passage of NEPA. Train's work on the environmental task force prompted Nixon to appoint Train to the post of undersecretary of the interior.

After the enactment of NEPA, Nixon established the Council on Environmental Quality (CEQ) and named Train as its first chairman. The CEQ advised the president on policy, drafted legislation, coordinated federal environmental initiatives, and prepared an annual report to Congress on the state of the nation's environment. While at the CEQ, Train pressured the Nixon administration to concentrate the government's environmental responsibilities in a single, high-visibility agency, rather than assigning them to a larger bureaucracy such as a new Department of Natural Resources, a plan that the White House favored at the time. Train's view ultimately prevailed, and the EPA was formed in 1970 to serve this important function.

Initially, the CEQ focused on policy formulation, while the EPA and its first administrator, William Ruckleshaus, concentrated on implementing these policies. One of the most significant results of their joint efforts was the creation of the Clean Air Act of 1970. By 1973, however, the EPA had come to assume the dominant position between these two agencies, much as Train had envisioned. When Ruckelshaus resigned from EPA to become acting Federal Bureau of Investigation director, Train announced his interest in becoming EPA administrator, and in 1973 Nixon appointed him to the position, which he held until the start of the Carter administration in 1977. During Train's tenure, the agency expanded its interest in international affairs and encouraged the passage of several pieces of important environmental legislation, including the Endangered Species Act. Also during this time, the EPA implemented several important pieces of legislation, most notably the Clean Air Act and Clean Water Act. Additionally, even at the height of the Arab oil embargo during the mid- 1970s, Train and the EPA fought—with some success—to keep environmental concerns at the forefront of policy decisions.

After concluding his career of public service, Train was named president and chief executive officer of the World Wildlife Fund. At the time that Train joined the WWF, the group had only about 30,000 members and an annual endowment of $2 million. One of Train's first actions was to increase WWF's program staff, with the goal of improving the organization's fund-raising potential. By the year 2000, thanks in large part to Train's efforts, WWF-U.S. had increased its membership to 1.3 million and had an annual operating budget of about $100 million. During his nearly three decades with the WWF, Train has led a variety of international efforts to protect endangered species and their habitats.

After co-chairing the Environmentalists for Bush committee during the presidential campaign of 1988, Train was awarded the Presidential Medal of Freedom by President George H. W. Bush four years later. Part of the citation for the medal read, "America honors an ardent conservationist, whose efforts help preserve Nature's treasures in this country and around the world."

Since his retirement from the WWF in 1994, Train has remained active in the organization as chairman emeritus, and he has continued to write and speak publicly on behalf of environmental causes. His 2003 book *Politics, Pollution, and Pandas: An Environmental Memoir* recounts his experiences at the CEQ and the EPA; it also serves as a rejection of the G. W. Bush administration for its environmental policies. In recent years, Train has become critical of the younger Bush, and he has gone as far as labeling his environmental agenda "ideological antagonism." Indeed, after a lifetime working for Republican presidents, Train concluded that he could not support the Republican platform in 2004. His stance emphasizes an important consistency in his life: his genuinely nonpartisan concern for the natural world amid the inherently partisan climate of Washington.

Train's legacy is one in which concerns for the environment and conservative politics, rather than being seen as antagonistic to one another, are in fact complementary. He is, furthermore, responsible for helping to create and maintain many of the agencies that remain the backbone of American environmental policy and for promoting the conservation of endangered species across the globe.

JAMES E. BISHOP

"Conversation with a Conservative: Russell Train." *Mother Jones*, October 21, 2004.

Shabecoff, P. 'Mr. Conservation.' *The New York Times Biographical Service* V. 15 (June 1984) p. 862

Train, Russell E. *Current Biography* H. W. Wilson Co., 1970.

Train, Russell E. *A Memoir.* Washington, DC, 2000.

———. *Politics, Pollution, and Pandas: An Environmental Memoir.* Washington, DC, 2003.

Udall, Stewart (January 21, 1920–). Secretary of the interior under Presidents John F. Kennedy and Lyndon B. Johnson, Udall was one of the most influential figures in the history of American environmental protection. During his eight-year tenure Udall oversaw the addition of four national parks, six national monuments, eight national seashores, nine national recreation areas, twenty historic sites, fifty-six wildlife refuges, and numerous other environmental programs. Udall was an important intellectual on the environment and author of *The Quiet Crisis* (1963). He argued that Americans needed to view the environment as a whole and not as an infinite supply of resources to be extracted. He particularly stressed the importance the environment played in the quality of life to all citizens of the nation.

Udall was born to Levi S. and Louise Lee Udall in the small town of St. John's, Arizona. The town was a Mormon community founded by Udall's grandfather. This personal attachment and sense of place instilled in Udall a deep reverence for the western land. At an early age Udall became an avid hiker, fisherman, and mountain climber. For several generations the Udall family had been politically active; Levi, for example, served as a judge on the Arizona State Supreme Court. In 1940 Stewart left St. John's to attend Arizona State University. During World War II he served in the Army Air Corps as a gunner on a B-24 bomber, flying fifty missions and reaching the rank of sergeant. After the war he returned to the university, where he excelled at basketball. In 1946 he was named all conference guard. Two years later he graduated with a law degree and established a practice in Tucson with his brother Morris.

In 1954, Udall followed his father's footsteps and entered into politics by seeking election as a Democratic candidate to Congress. He would be reelected three more times before resigning in 1961 to accept a position in the cabinet. During his time in Congress Udall advocated fair treatment to Native Americans, labor rights, and increased federal education spending. Regarding conservation, Udall supported the Colorado River Basin Project, which included the controversial construction of Glen Canyon and Echo Park Dams. Udall also voted in favor of federal aid to desalinization plants and to the purchase of lands that the courts had ordered removed from the Coconino and Sitgreaves National Forests.

Although a relative junior in Congress, Udall became an influential figure as a conciliator between liberal and moderate factions within the Democratic Party and between the Democrats and Republicans. His intellectual power, willingness to hear all sides of an argument, ability to build consensus, and long hours of work accounted for his quick accumulation of influence. In the House Education Committee, Udall surprised observers when he led a successful coup against the arbitrary rule of Chairman Graham Barden of North Carolina. During the 1960 Democratic presidential convention, Udall was instrumental in convincing the Arizona delegation to support John Kennedy of Massachusetts instead of fellow southwesterner Lyndon Johnson of Texas.

Udall resigned from Congress in 1961 to become secretary of the interior under President Kennedy. Although neither an easterner nor an Ivy Leaguer, Udall fit the model of Kennedy's best and brightest in another important respect. During his time in Congress, Udall was considered one of the leading intellectuals of the House of Representatives. He cultivated many literary associations, including a close friendship with poet Robert Frost. It was Udall who suggested that Frost read a poem at Kennedy's 1961 inauguration.

President Kennedy gave Udall free reign to shape the administration's environmental program. However, the president was largely uninterested, and Udall had difficulty getting Kennedy's attention. International crisis, civil rights, and lack of influence in Congress hampered the administration's environmental program. Udall was able to convince Congress to create Petrified Forest National Park and Cape Cod National Seashore and to continue the Eisenhower administration's national park and forest improvement program known as Mission 66. In response to Rachel Carson's *Silent Spring* (1962), Udall suspended the use of pesticides in the 750 million acres of land managed by the Interior Department. During the Kennedy term, Udall lobbied Congress to approve the Wilderness Act. Udall first took an interest in the measure when it was introduced in 1958 while he was still a member of Congress. By the time it became law in 1964 it had undergone several serious revisions. Although Udall was pleased by the long-delayed passage of the Wilderness Act, which protected 9.1 million acres, he regretted that the final version was somewhat watered down from the original introduced by Howard Zahniser.

In 1963 Udall's book *The Quiet Crisis* was published with the assistance of author Wallace Stegner. It is an important work in the development of ideas and policy surrounding the environment. Udall used history to illustrate that Americans historically believed in what he dubbed the "myth of super-abundance." According to Udall, this myth led to wholesale degradation of the environment that was no longer sustainable. Americans needed to understand that their natural resources were finite. However, environmental protection, in his opinion, needed to progress past the strict economic focus of traditional conservation. Instead, he proposed shifting the focus of environmental protection to quality-of-life issues, such as clean air and water, the recreational and psychological value of wilderness preservation, and restricted use of pesticides. Udall was following a trend that John Kenneth Galbraith set forth in *The Affluent Society* (1958). Galbraith argued that Americans' exceptional wealth meant public policy needed to focus less on wealth distribution and more on improving the quality of life for all citizens through increased investment in education and health care. With *The Quiet Crisis*, Udall advanced the importance of the environment to the emerging liberal agenda. *The Quiet Crisis* complemented *Silent Spring* by Rachel Carson in stimulating the burgeoning environmental awakening of the 1960s.

Following the assassination of President Kennedy, President Johnson asked Udall to remain in the cabinet. Under the prompting of Udall and First Lady Claudia "Lady Bird" Johnson and based on his own childhood experiences, the president made environmental issues an important part of his ambitious Great Society domestic reform agenda. On February 8, 1965, in a special message to Congress on conservation, Johnson outlined a bold and sweeping environmental agenda that included much of what Udall had requested. Unlike Kennedy, Johnson was actively involved and personally interested in his administration's environmental program. It was Udall's responsibility to work with administrative agencies, Congress, and lobbying groups to advance this agenda. Principal achievements included the Wilderness Act, Endangered Species Act, Highway Beautification Act, National Trails Act, Solid Waste Disposal Act, and Canyonlands, North Cascades, Petrified Forests, and Redwood National Parks. As part of his public relations campaign Udall wrote magazine articles to introduce the Americans to their new national parks and to persuade them to change their perceptions of the environment.

There were several projects that Udall was much more closely identified with within the Great Society. In 1965, with Johnson's support, Congress created the Land and Water Conservation Fund. Under this program Congress set aside money for Udall to dispense to the states as matching funds for environmental projects. It was important to Udall that access to natural wonders not be confined to the West. Although the National Parks created under his tenure as secretary of the interior were in the West, he labored to use the money available under the Land and Water Conservation Fund to assist states in the East to create open space and parks, such as the Delaware River Gap. During the first years of operation the fund provided between $100 and $150 million for matching funds. In 1968 Udall persuaded Congress to include additional sources of revenue, such as money from offshore oil leases, to increase the amount of funds available. Another Udall initiative was the Wild and Scenic Rivers Act for which he battled three years with feisty Colorado Congressman Wayne Aspinall to get it passed. Udall also succeeded in getting Congress to revise surface mining legislation, although his reforms fell short of completely rewriting the 1872 Mining Act, which he believed to be inimical to sound environmental policy. When disputes erupted in Alaska, Udall froze all land sales on federally owned lands until the Congress or the courts could sort out the mess. Such a measure protected the environment and the interests of the Natives. Congress addressed the issue in 1971 with the Alaskan Native Claims Settlement.

Despite his successes, Udall did suffer some disappointments as secretary of the interior. First, he had a difficult time getting other federal agencies to follow his lead. Although Udall stopped pesticide use on land under his jurisdiction, he could not convince the Department of Agriculture to do the same. He also could not cajole the Department of Transportation to consider environmental impact as a factor in road construction projects. Although he worked on creating the National Environmental Policy Act, legislation that required impact statements, it was enacted in 1969 after he left office. Second, he had very uneasy relations with environmental groups. In 1963 Udall supported a massive water reclamation project that would place dams at Bridge Canyon and Marble Gorge in the Grand Canyon. Environmental groups resolutely opposed this project on the grounds that the Grand Canyon was of such exceptional beauty that damming it at any point would be a crime against nature. Detractors accused Udall of placing the interests of his home state over that of the nation. In 1967 Udall took a rafting trip down the Colorado River in the Grand Canyon and conceded that he had erred. He completely reversed his position, and in 1968, a new law he had advanced was passed that banned the construction of any additional dams on the Colorado River between the already existing Hoover and Glen Canyon Dams. Nevertheless, his standing among environmental groups suffered significantly. Finally, the president occasionally disappointed Udall. In the closing days of the Johnson administration, Udall urged the president to place an additional 7.5 million acres in the National Park System. After notifying the press of this increase, Udall was stunned and embarrassed to learn that Johnson denied his request and placed only 384,500 acres into the system.

Udall left office in 1969 after Richard Nixon became president. He formed an environmental consulting company and continued to speak out and write concerning environmental issues. His syndicated column "Udall on the Environment" was carried in newspapers nationwide. During the early 1970s he joined a growing chorus concerned about the exploding human population on the earth. During the 1980s he vehemently opposed the policies of the Reagan administration. In 1990 a federal compensation act rewarded his fourteen years of pro bono work on behalf of claimants exposed to nuclear weapons testing in the Southwest. Udall has also written several histories of the West. He lives today in Santa Fe, New Mexico.

GREGORY J. DEHLER

Hays, Samuel P. *Beauty, Health, and Permanence: Environmental Politics in the United States, 1955–1985.* New York, 1987.

Smith, Thomas G. "John F. Kennedy, Stewart Udall, and the New Frontier Conservation." *Pacific Historical Review* 64 (August 1995).

Stewart Udall Papers. Univ. of Arizona, Tucson,

Udall, Stewart. "National Parks for the Future." *Atlantic Monthly* 207 (June 1961).

Vogt, William (May 15, 1902–July 12, 1968). An ornithologist, conservationist, internationally renowned writer, and population control expert, Vogt was born to William and Frances Belle (Doughty) Vogt in Mineola, New York. Vogt studied languages and journalism at St. Stephens (now Bard) College, where he won the poetry prize and edited the literary magazine. He graduated with honors in 1925. Before turning to a career in environmentalism, Vogt worked as a journalist and drama critic and served as assistant editor at the New York Academy of Sciences from 1930 to 1932.

Vogt's interest in environmental issues can be traced back to his readings of Ernest Thompson Seton's work and his participation in Christmas bird counts and social activities with the Bronx County Bird Club, a group associated with the Linnaean Society of New York. The Bird Club brought Vogt into close contact not only with birds and field activities but also with such ornithologists as Roger Tory Peterson, Joseph Hickey, and Allan D. Crukshank, men who would have a profound impact on the direction of his professional life. While the connections forged through birding were influential through much of Vogt's career, Vogt himself was an influential figure in the club. Peterson credits Vogt with persuading him to create his famous bird guides, with pursuing magazine and book publishing leads for the guides, and, in short, with serving as "midwife" for publication of Peterson's works despite the Depression. Peterson also credits Vogt with overcoming the physical effects of childhood polio and taking an active role in bird counts and other field trips, on which he taught Peterson flower identification in exchange for lessons in bird identification.

Vogt's earliest forays into ornithology include a study of the willet—begun while enrolled in a seminar at the American Museum of Natural History and later awarded the Field Research Prize of the Linnaean Society—and a paper with Robert Cushman Murphy on dovekies. In 1932, after impressing New York City's director of parks (reportedly while registering a complaint), Vogt became head of the Jones Beach State Bird Sanctuary, living on-site in a former hunting shack with his wife Johanna (Von Goeckingk) and entertaining ornithologists and conservationists. While at Jones Beach, Vogt edited the National Association of Audubon Societies' magazine *Bird-Lore* (which later became *Audubon Magazine*). His interests grew from listing birds to studying their behavior, and he wrote articles on studies of bird behavior for *Auk*.

In 1935, Vogt left the sanctuary to become a field naturalist and lecturer for the Audubon Societies, a post he held until 1939. During his tenure as Audubon naturalist, Vogt gathered and annotated Audubon illustrations and wrote the introduction for the 1937 edition of *Audubon's Birds of America*. That same year he wrote *Thirst for Land*, a pamphlet on water conservation, marking his broadening interest in conservation as well as ornithology.

Dismissed (along with several colleagues) after a 1939 political shuffle at Audubon, Vogt became a consultant to the Peruvian Compañia Administradora del Guano, where he further expanded his work in ornithology to address broader issues in the conservation of natural resources and management of population growth. In Peru, where guano had been used as fuel, Vogt studied the effects of the oceanographic force El Niño on bird populations and guano production, investigating the impact of overpopulation as well as weather systems on cormorants, boobies, and pelicans. Increasingly, he applied to human populations his observations on the links between environmental devastation and overpopulation. In his ecological studies in Peru, Vogt also turned toward comparative studies of farmers using traditional methods for subsistence and those using modern technological farming methods for export and profit. These issues would emerge nearly a decade later in his pivotal book *Road to Survival* (1948).

Having become an authority on Latin American issues, Vogt returned to the United States to work in various capacities throughout the 1940s, drawing on that expertise. In 1942, Vogt served the U.S. Department of War as consultant on South America, and from 1942 to 1943 he served the Office of Coordinator of Inter-American Affairs as associate director of the division of science and education. From 1943 to 1950, he worked with the Pan American Union (later the Organization of American States) as chief of the conservation section, studying the environments and agricultural practices of Costa Rica and El Salvador. In 1945, he wrote "Hunger at the Peace Table" for the *Saturday Evening Post*, drawing readers' attention to the links he increasingly saw between the soil erosion of traditional farmers, problems of overpopulation, and conservation issues in industrial countries. During his tenure with the Pan American Union, Vogt also wrote several environmental studies in Spanish and English, including in 1948

El Hombre y la Tierra (Man and the Earth) and *The Population of Costa Rica*, a monograph in which he posited illness as a metaphor for understanding the potential destruction of the earth. That same year he published his internationally acclaimed *Road to Survival*, drawing on his major concerns about population, environmental destruction, traditional and modern farming methods, and what he called the "waster's psychology" of modern industrial life. The book is especially noteworthy for its lively voice, depiction of individual characters, and attempt to enable readers to view environmental issues (and their own behavior) from many angles, including third-world and old-world perspectives.

In the next few decades, Vogt turned increasingly toward population issues. From 1950 to 1951, supported by Fulbright and Guggenheim fellowships, Vogt traveled to Norway, Sweden, and Denmark to study population problems and their solutions. From 1951 to 1961, he served as director of the Planned Parenthood Federation of America, on several occasions taking direct action to protest discrimination against that organization or physicians who supported it and consistently serving as a vocal advocate for population planning. His 1960 book *People: Challenge to Survival* drew on his many years of travel and study to posit the centrality of excessive population growth and industrialization in endangering the environment. From 1964 to 1968, Vogt was secretary of the Conservation Foundation, writing such studies as "Comments on a Brief Reconnaissance of Resource Use, Progress and Conservation Needs in Some Latin American Countries."

Throughout his career, Vogt remained active in professional environmental organizations such as the Soil Conservation Society of America, the New York Zoological Society, the American Association for the Advancement of Science, the American Ornithologists' Union, the American Geographical Society, the British Ecological Society, the Ecological Society of America, the Conservation Foundation, and the Sociedad Mexicana de Historia Natural. His work won many prizes, including in 1948 the Mary Soper Pope Medal from the Cranbrook Institute of Science; in 1949, the First National Conservation Award of the Izaak Walton League of America and a Gutenberg Award for *Road to Survival*; in 1951, the Albert and Mary Lasker Foundation Award in Planned Parenthood.

In 1968, after a disabling stroke, Vogt ended his life and was cremated.

In his 1945 *Saturday Evening Post* article, Vogt wrote that "man, though he is apt to forget it, is a creature of the earth." Much of his career was spent reminding people—in lively, dramatic, personable prose—of that belief. Vogt persisted in taking action on his concerns for the environment, rebounding from organizational politics and repositionings, maintaining his pursuit of knowledge of conservation, and working to open the public's eyes to the increasing dangers he observed. An advocate of social and political action, often tracing political problems back to their ecological roots, Vogt prefigures the environmental movement of the 1970s by reminding urban dwellers that they depend on the environment as much as any traditional, rural farmer, even though that dependence may at times seem invisible.

JOCELYN BARTKEVICIUS

Duffy, David Cameron. "William Vogt: A Pilgrim on the Road to Survival." *American Birds* 43 (1989): 1256–1257.

Lord, Russell. "The Ground from Under Your Feet." the *Saturday Review*, (August 7, 1948), 13, 33–35.

Peterson, Roger Tory. "William Vogt: A Man Ahead of His Time." *American Birds* 43 (1989): 1254–1255.

Wallace, Henry (October 7, 1888–November 18, 1965). An agriculturist, plant breeder, businessman, political figure, and humanitarian, Wallace was born in Adair, Iowa, where both his grandfather and father were farmers and journalists and active in agricultural politics. His grandfather, Henry Wallace, founded *Wallace's Farmer*, a journal that his father Henry Cantwell Wallace eventually edited as well.

Wallace was by all accounts a smart, somewhat shy young man, with an aptitude for scientific investigation and a love for plant breeding. As a child, he became friends with George Washington Carver, who at the time was studying at Iowa State University and who became the university's first black graduate. Wallace graduated from Iowa State University himself in 1910, with a concentration in genetics and plant breeding. His experiments with hybrid corn led to the development of hardy, disease-resistant strains that he successfully marketed. He founded the Pioneer Hi-Bred Corn Company, the success of which made him a wealthy man, although he lived a relatively austere life, generally rejecting many of the accoutrements of wealth. While a believer in the scientific manipulation of corn varieties to increase yields, Wallace was also an advocate of conservation measures, especially in terms of finding ways to stem soil erosion, which he recognized as a significant long-term problem in the agricultural Midwest.

When Henry Cantwell (known as Harry) took a job as secretary of agriculture in the Harding administration, his son took over as editor of *Wallace's Farmer*. He used the position to promote principles of scientific agriculture and to advance policies that he believed would help American farmers. Specifically, Wallace supported McNary-Haugenism. The McNary-Haugen Farm Relief Bill sought to provide for a fair return on commodity prices by having the federal government buy excess production. President Calvin Coolidge vetoed versions of the bill three times. He was supported in this by his secretary of commerce Herbert Hoover, who rejected government interference in commodity pricing. McNary-Haugenism's influence extended beyond a specific piece of legislation, evolving into a philosophical position that suggested limits on free market principles in the agricultural sector. McNary-Haugenism was the precursor to rural reforms measures that would be advanced during the New Deal and that would be spearheaded by Wallace himself.

The Wallace family, like most midwestern farm families in the post–Civil War era, was committed to the Republican Party. But the farm crisis of the 1920s, and Calvin Coolidge's unwillingness to respond directly, began to drive farmers into the Democratic camp, with significant defections occurring in the 1928 campaign between Herbert Hoover and Alfred A. Smith. Wallace, although nominally a Republican, supported the candidacy of Democrat Smith.

On winning the presidency in 1932, Franklin Roosevelt appointed two Republicans to his cabinet, Wallace and Harold Ickes. Farmers had been devastated by the Depression, many losing their land in foreclosure actions. Wallace, as secretary of agriculture, wrote the Agricultural Adjustment Act (AAA), based on principles of McNary-Haugenism. Paying farmers for reducing production, in an attempt to stabilize or increase prices, became national policy. Wallace encouraged cotton farmers to plow under their fields, and hog farmers to slaughter their animals, both of which occurred, earning him the nickname "The Greatest Butcher in Christendom." The AAA and the National Recovery Act (NRA) were the centerpieces of Roosevelt's programs to contend with the economic plight of Americans during the Depression. Like the NRA, the AAA was deemed unconstitutional by the Supreme Court. In *U.S. v. Butler* (1936), the Court ruled that the AAA provided an improper extension of the powers of the national government and that its taxing mechanism was unconstitutional because rather than being an instrument for raising revenue, it was essentially a pretext for fashioning social policy. A second version of the bill, passed in 1938, funded from the general tax system rather than from a levy on food processors, was deemed as constitutional by the Court. Set-asides as a mechanism to maintain farm price stability remained the cornerstone of farm policy in the United States until the 1970s.

Given his contributions to New Deal policy, and his writings, which included the book *New Frontiers* (1934), Wallace was sometimes considered to be the "Philosopher of the New Deal." Given his tireless devotion to the interests of American farmers, he is also often considered the greatest secretary of agriculture in American history.

In 1940, Franklin Roosevelt rejected John Nance Garner as his running mate and chose Wallace instead. Roosevelt favored Wallace because of his commitments to New Deal principles and also partly due to the Republican

Party's decision to run, as Wendell Wilkie's running mate, Charles McNary, a senator from Oregon and original author of the McNary-Haugen agricultural bill. During the campaign, a series of letters written by Wallace to the Russian mystic Nicholas Roerich fell into the hands of Republicans. In them, Wallace freely discussed his wide-ranging religious views, revealing spiritual interests in Catholicism, Buddhism, Islam, and Christian Science. The Democratic Party leadership viewed the letters as a potential source of embarrassment. The two political parties reached an agreement by which the letters would not be made public by the Republicans, and an extramarital affair of Wilkie's would not be revealed by the Democrats.

Wallace became an active vice president, often considered the first "working vice president." He became a member of the "War Cabinet" and oversaw several boards, including the important Board of Economic Warfare (BEW), which dealt with procurement strategies. Wallace's participation in policy brought him into conflicts with other political appointees and members of the federal bureaucracy, including Secretary of State Cordell Hull and Commerce Secretary Jesse Jones. In response to pressures from other high administration officials, Roosevelt dissolved the BEW, significantly curtailing Wallace's role in war policy. Wallace was never fully accepted into the men's club of the Senate either, and he had little political support within the Democratic Party establishment. He disdained his role as Senate presiding officer and was resented by senators for his attempts to intervene in debates.

Wallace traveled to Latin America as vice president and became a supporter of humanitarian aid to the region. Roosevelt also sent him to the Soviet Union and China toward the end of the war. While in the USSR, he visited collective farms, offering a positive assessment. His stated support for Soviet agricultural policy stirred controversy that followed him back to the United States, but Wallace was undeterred. He wrote a column in the *New York Times* denouncing what he construed as anti-Soviet propaganda and contending that internal fascism was the greatest threat to U.S. democracy.

In spite of Roosevelt's admiration for Wallace's intelligence and idealism, he believed that the vice president's political insensitivities had turned him into a liability, as the nation turned more conservative toward the end of the war. He gave party leaders the discretion to choose an alternative candidate for the 1944 campaign. While Wallace continued to have support among rank-and-file Democrats, the anti-Wallace faction held sway, choosing the relatively unknown but more politically conservative Harry

S. Truman. Still, Wallace remained popular within the left wing of the Democratic Party.

Wallace ran for president in 1948, heading the Progressive Party ticket. The Progressives were considered by some to be too closely aligned with pro-Soviet policies during a period in which conflicts with the USSR were arising. Moreover, members of the U.S. Communist Party were actively involved with organizing the 1948 party platform. Wallace carried a Progressive banner that included support for civil rights legislation and national health insurance, the natural extensions of New Deal–era programs, but the party did poorly, coming in fourth behind Strom Thurman's Dixiecrats.

After 1948, Wallace retired from political life, but over time he showed support for Republican candidates for president, including Dwight Eisenhower and Richard Nixon. In 1960, John Kennedy invited him to attend his inaugural address. Kennedy's New Frontier is sometimes considered to have been inspired by Wallace's book of the same name. Toward the end of his life, Wallace still worked on political and economic issues important to him, including support for humanitarian policies in Latin America. He continued agricultural experimentation at his farm in upstate New York until being diagnosed with Lou Gehrig's disease. He died in Danbury, Connecticut.

Wallace led a rich and complicated life. He had an impact on the business side of agriculture, via his founding of Pioneer Hi-Bred, which continues to be one of the largest seed companies in the world. He also impacted agricultural policy in significant ways, turning the concept of set-asides into accepted public policy (although such programs fell out of favor in the 1970s). He will probably be remembered best as Franklin Roosevelt's agricultural secretary and vice president. His environmental record is mixed. While his work in hybridization laid the groundwork for commercialized genetic modification techniques that are often criticized by environmentalists, his commitment to soil conservation and the protection of small farmers remains an important environmental legacy.

THOMAS SHEVORY

Culver, John C., and John Hyde. *American Dreamer: A Life of Henry Wallace.* New York, 2001.

Lord, Russell. *The Wallaces of Iowa.* Boston, MA, 1948.

Schapsmeier, Edward, and Frederick Schapsmeier. *Henry Wallace of Iowa: The Agrarian Years, 1910–1940.* Ames, IA, 1968.

Schlesinger, Arthur R. "Who Was Henry Wallace? The Story of a Perplexing and Indomitably Naive Public Servant." *Los Angeles Times*, March 12, 2000.

White, E. B. (Elwin Brooks) (July 11, 1899–October 1, 1985). With a long and distinguished career in American letters, White, besides his many honorary degrees, also received several awards, among them a Gold Medal from the American Academy of Arts and Letters in 1960 and the Presidential Medal of Freedom in 1963. White was born in Mount Vernon, New York, the son of Samuel White, a wealthy piano manufacturer, and Jessie (Hart) White. Elwin was the youngest child of a large family. In 1921 he graduated from Cornell University. He had a lengthy association with the *New Yorker* magazine, where he wrote "Talk of the Town," an often wry and bemused column reflecting the urban and cosmopolitan outlook of the magazine. White also wrote poetry, editorials, satires, short stories, children's stories such as the famous "Charlotte's Web" (1952), and the highly successful *Elements of Style* (1959), a revision of a 1918 manual on good writing.

He is notable, as well, for his skill in the familiar essay, a literary form characterized by the use of personal experience and self-revelation, to which he brought a casual charm imbued with grace, wit, and humor. And it is in these essays, many set on his farm in North Brooklin, Maine, that he displays those ideas and attitudes that identify him as a nature writer. These essays are collected in *One Man's Meat* (1944), *The Second Tree from the Corner* (1954), and *The Points of My Compass: Letters from the East, the West, the North and the South* (1962).

White's response to nature can be partially linked to his lifelong interest in Henry David Thoreau. In *The Points of My Compass,* he said that he "should hate to be called a Thoreauvian," but he acknowledges that "the author of *Walden* has served as my conscience through long stretches of trivial days." Certainly White's skepticism about technology and progress suggests a kinship with Thoreau, if not an influence. Also, his desire to live on a farm indicates a predisposition to enjoy natural surroundings, perhaps in contrast to his other life in New York City, and to engage subjects such as blueberries, peas, raccoons, and assorted domestic animals.

Decades before the environmental crisis had been labeled as such and before *ecology* became a household word, White was expressing his conviction that the world is a complex and interrelated community of all life. This fundamental sense of unity finds expression, for example, in *One Man's Meat*, where he "hardly dares to shoot a crow for fear of upsetting the fine adjustment in the world of birds and insects, predator and prey."

White's nature essays are also delicately attuned to the cycle of the seasons. He relishes the close contact with the natural processes in the birth of a lamb; or in a memorable essay, in the death of a pig, which he artfully manages to turn into a moving and significant experience. Like Aldo Leopold in *A Sand Country (Almanac)*, White believes that the land produces much more than commodities. It provides, as well, a cultural and aesthetic harvest, as important as its productive capacity, which humans ignore at their peril. Failure to establish a less exploitative relationship with nature will undermine that which gives meaning and significance to life.

In writing about nature, White is always modest. Instead of trying to manipulate nature and making it submit to selfishness and greed, he advocates the development of joy, sympathy, and love, attitudes that will give the human race a better chance of survival. As do many other contemporary nature writers, he views humans as ephemeral in the long context of time.

White charmed and delighted millions of readers for close to four decades with the style and grace of his essays, many of which, with perceptiveness and foresight, recognized quite early in the twentieth century the dangers of a headlong rush to growth, consumerism, artificiality. In his unabashed appreciation for the natural world, and in his recognition of the essential unity of all living things, he encouraged a potent and growing force dedicated to the preservation and stewardship of the environment.

White married Katherine Angell in 1929. They had one son, John.

WALTER HERRSCHER

Agosta, Lucien L. *E. B. White*. New York, 1995.

"E. B. White" [obit.]. *New York Times*, October 2, 1985.

Howarth, W. E. B. "White at the New Yorker." *Sewanee Review* 93 (1985): 574–583.

Root, Robert L., ed. *Critical Essays on E. B. White*. New York, 1994.

Wilson, Edward Osborne (June 10, 1929–). A naturalist, entomologist, and environmentalist, Wilson was a major creator of and perhaps the leading proponent of the disputed theory of sociobiology. Wilson became deeply concerned by the falloff in insect and animal species and the consequent decline in biodiversity.

Wilson, the son of Edward, an accountant, and Inez (Freeman) Wilson, was born in Birmingham, Alabama. In 1936, though only seven at the time, Wilson found his calling as a naturalist when he spent the summer at Paradise Beach—located on the eastern shore of Florida's Perdido Bay—where the water and its shadowy inhabitants enthralled him. "A child comes to the edge of the deep water," he explained in his autobiography *Naturalist* (1994), "with a mind prepared for wonder." That same summer he largely lost the sight in his right eye in a fishing accident. But his left eye proved to be more acute at close range—where he might study insects—than average. The result, in Wilson's estimation, at any rate, was that he was "destined" to become an entomologist.

That winter, with his parents in the midst of divorce proceedings, Wilson was dispatched to the Gulf Coast Military Academy (GCMA), a private school, four miles east of Gulfport, Mississippi. The routine was strict and the curriculum thorough. Not surprisingly, the school placed an emphasis on hard work, high standards, and military-style discipline—an ethic that, even sixty years later, Wilson found, still stirred "faint and deep" within him.

Because of the itinerant nature of his father's job, (as a government accountant), Wilson led a nomadic life as a youngster. GCMA, for instance, was only one of fourteen schools Wilson attended during an eleven-year span. Two years after leaving the military academy, Wilson, his father, and stepmother moved temporarily, of course, to Washington, DC. Here Wilson's career choice was confirmed and refined by numerous visits to the National Museum, where he was "absorbed" by the unending variety of plants and animals and the National 300. Moreover, Rock Creek Park proved especially valuable to Wilson, as he wandered for hours collecting insect specimens—at first butterflies and then ants. "The course of my life had been set," wrote Wilson.

Wilson graduated from high school in Decatur, Alabama, in 1946. He entered the University of Alabama, whose "generous admission standards and low costs were important preconditions" of upward mobility for Wilson as, he explained, they had been for thousands of others "even less well [financially] secure than himself." A biology major, he "flourished" at Alabama where the "personal attention and encouragement" he received could not have been "surpassed." Wilson received his B.S. in 1949 and M.S. in 1950.

Wilson and a handful of fellow budding naturalists were encouraged to collect insects and amphibians for the university's collection. Since

Alabama's natural environment had been poorly explored, Wilson found "countless" opportunities for discoveries. Indeed, he came across a new kind of blind shrimp, as well as a new species of a "pretty" ant with a dark-brown body and yellow legs. He also assiduously studied the destructive fire ant and was asked by the Alabama Department of Conservation to collect information on the pest and evaluate its impact on the environment. At the age of nineteen, Wilson had his first opportunity as a "professional scientist." With another young biologist, Wilson crisscrossed southwestern Alabama and the western counties of the Florida Panhandle, collecting information. After a thorough study, including surveying fields for crop damage and interviewing farmers, Wilson and his partner submitted a fifty-three-page analysis to the Department of Conservation. Many of its original findings are still in use. One result, for Wilson personally, was a boost in his self-confidence, which, he believed, helped to carry him "through the critical years on intellectual growth and testing."

After graduating from the University of Alabama, Wilson transferred to the University of Tennessee in 1950. But, as he has written, the "academic challenge" there "was not great," and in 1951 he was admitted to Harvard. It was, as he described it, "his destiny," for Harvard had the largest collection of ants in the world. Wilson decided, with the enthusiastic support of William L. Brown, a then young Harvard graduate student, to study the dacentine ants, which abounded in the Deep South. One result of his labors, grubbing in dirt and rotting wood on hands and knees, was that he was very successful in pursuit of the dacentine ants and published two articles from his research. And together with Brown, friend and fellow ant enthusiast, he published a third article in the *Quarterly Review of Biology*, a premier journal.

Wilson and a friend spent the summer in 1952 exploring ants and other insects across North America. "We were naturalist hobos," an apt description. They lived on canned foods and spent their meager funds to keep their frail 1942 Chevrolet running. A few months later Wilson was handed a major opportunity—he was elected a Junior Fellow at Harvard's Society of Fellows. He was chosen because of the promise he showed, and he was anxious to show that his selection was justified.

The society's "final Gift" was to support (financially) his research in the tropics. He began in Cuba where he found two "treasures" of the ant world, one with huge pitchfork jaws and the other the rarest ants in the world. Specimens of both were added to Harvard's Museum of Comparative Biology collection. His trip to Mexico was less rewarding.

More productive was Wilson's trip to the South Pacific. His goal was to collect ant species and assemble notes on all aspects of the ecology and behavior he observed. His sojourn, which began in March 1954, included visits to Fiji, New Caledonia, and the New Hebrides (though he fell ill with a fever that cut short his visit) in January 1955. Later that month he visited Western Australia, where he collected various ant species (including bulldog ants, among the most belligerent species of ants). Even more rewarding was his trip to New Guinea, where he collected several dozen ant species, many new to science. Wilson concluded his journey circling the globe, arriving in New York in September and the following month marrying Renee Kelley, "a scholar by temperament," wrote Wilson, and hence, although not herself a scientist, able to understand Wilson's "dreams" of scientific pursuits in "faraway places."

In 1958, Wilson received tenure in the Department of Biology. By that time the department's members had been engaged in a bitter quarrel. James D. Watson, fresh from his (and Francis Crick's) research unraveling the structure of DNA (and winning a Noble Prize) had joined the department in 1956. Watson soon stirred a departmental dispute since he conceived of biology as a field that had to be transformed into a science directed at molecules and cells and "rewritten," wrote Wilson, "in the language of physics and chemistry." Such an approach, strictly pursued and adhered to, left no place for traditional evolutionary (or Darwinian) biology, the kind practiced by Wilson and a handful of his colleagues. In turn, Watson was joined by a small group of molecular and cellular biologists. There ensued frosty hallway encounters, shunned courtesies, and strained departmental meetings before an accommodation between the two sorts of biologists was reached. Wilson also became more comfortable when, in 1964, he transferred out of the Department of Biology and joined Harvard's Museum for Comparative Zoology.

Between 1965 and 1967, Wilson, with the aid of a very able graduate student, performed creative experiments in biogeography. The goal was to select several small islands in the Florida Keys and, using pesticides, eliminate all the insects and small animals on several islets, leaving surrounding and untouched islands as controls. The physical labor, largely borne by the young graduate student, was arduous, and conditions often dirty, but the experiment was a resounding success. The islets in the experiment were recolonized and an equilibrium reattained. As Wilson and his student explained in an article in the journal *Ecology* (1969), "The colonization curves plus static observation on untreated [by pesticides] islands indicate strongly that a dynamic equilibrium number of species exists for any island."

How ants communicate was another of Wilson's interests. And he devoted to the problem the same level of physical energy and intellectual application he had given to the Florida Keys experiment. Through weeks of study, Wilson, experimenting on his favorite fire ants, discovered that ants leave a chemical trail—or a pheromone—to signal, for instance, the location of food. In all, Wilson estimated that the queen and workers of each colony used ten to twenty kinds of pheromones to regulate behavior and social organization.

More than once in Wilson's career, cooperation with a congenial workaholic resulted in a major work. In the case of ants, what Wilson had not yet achieved was a grand synthesis. But with Bert Holldobler, a brilliant German scientist, "a scientist's scientist" (who brought the European emphasis on ethnology), as his collaborator, Wilson accomplished that synthesis in *Ants*, a 732-page, double-columned tome, published by Harvard University Press in 1990. Strikingly, *Ants*, which was written by specialists for fellow professionals, won the Pulitzer Prize in General Nonfiction, an award given for literary merit.

With one exception, Wilson's career was generally free of controversy. But that exception—Wilson's role in developing and especially in championing sociobiology—generated a fierce acrimonious and at times venomous quarrel. What produced the eruption was Wilson's argument (in *Sociobiology: The New Synthesis* [1975]) that human beings inherited a propensity to certain kinds of behavior—such as conformity, altruism, division of labor between the sexes, bonding between parents and children, suspicion of strangers, dominance order within groups (male dominance overall), and territorial aggression over limiting resources. People have free will, Wilson conceded, but the "channels of their psychological development" are "cut more deeply" by their genes "in certain directions than in others." Wilson concluded by arguing that "heredity interacts with environment to create a gravitational pull toward a fixed mean."

Wilson's chief critics were drawn from the ranks of social scientists who, he pointed out, were attracted to the idea that human behavior is determined by the environment and therefore is almost "infinitely flexible." Wilson was blasted for tending to provide "a genetic justification for the status quo;" and for the "privileges of certain groups" according to class, race, and sex. Indeed, Wilson, on the basis of his hereditarian (or genetic) assumptions, was tarred with the black brush of sexism and racism. A climax, of sorts, to the dispute came in Washington at the 1978 annual meeting of the American Association for the Advancement of Science. Wilson had come to the meeting to defend sociobiology; but before he could deliver his address a young woman dumped water on him, and a few individuals in the hall yelled out "Wilson, you're all wet." There ensued a general condemnation—including Wilson's scientific critics—of the childish act. Although the quarrel over the relationship between genes and culture is unresolved, it remains, in Wilson's opinion, the "central problem in the social sciences."

Though "gun shy" from the sociobiology dispute, Wilson, by his own admission, was "unforgivably late" in becoming an environmental activist. But his article, published in *Harvard Magazine* (January–February 1980), which warned of the loss of genetic and species diversity through the destruction of natural habitat, marked the beginning of his public commitment to environmentalism. (As early as the 1950s and 1960s, Wilson had observed in his travels that a reduction of habitat inevitably led to the decline of animal and plant species.) What decisively alerted Wilson to the dimensions of the problem was a scientists' report estimating the rate of global destruction of rain forests to be a little below 1 percent annually. Galvanized by the report, Wilson joined a loosely organized group of like-minded environmental activists; and he lectured and wrote widely on the problem of habitual liquidation and species disappearance. Moreover, he joined the board of directors of the World Wildlife Fund–United States and became the organization's key external science adviser.

To biologists, the term *biodiversity* means the totality of life forms across all levels of biological organization, from germs and chromosomes within individual species to the broad order of species themselves. Finally, the term reaches to the highest level of living communities and ecosystems (like forests and lakes). Because of his frequently published use of the term, Wilson was often credited, erroneously, with devising the word. But Wilson did invent another and, in the long run perhaps, much more important term: "biophilia."

In his book *Biophilia* (1984), but even earlier in an article in the *New York Times Book Review* (January 14, 1979), Wilson explained that among humankind's "deepest needs" is biophilia—"the rich natural pleasure that comes from being surrounded by living organisms." Included in that definition, wrote Wilson, was "the diversity of plants and animals that live in gardens and woodlands, in zoos, around the home, and the wilderness." (In the United States and Canada, more people visit zoos and aquariums than attend all professional athletic events combined.) "Other creatures," he explained, "satisfy innate emotional needs" and "present unending intellectual challenge." "More complexity," he averred, "exists in a single butterfly than in all the machines on earth." And then he warned that the one truly irreparable damage we can inflict on ourselves is eliminating a large fraction of the earth's species "through careless destruction of the natural environment."

Although Wilson will be remembered as one of the devisers and major defenders of sociobiology, his reputation rests more firmly on his study of ants. If a Noble Prize were offered in entomology, Wilson almost certainly would be a leading candidate. As for his contributions to environmentalism, easily the most significant—nor forgetting his activism—was his conception of biophilia. The idea offers a new and uniquely satisfying reason for environmentalism, as well as complementing Aldo Leopold's environmental ethic spelled out in his *Sand County Almanac.* (1949).

Among Wilson's numerous awards are the Cleveland Award, American Association for the Advancement of Science, 1969; Mercer Award, Ecological Society of America, 1971; Distinguished Service Award, American Institute of Biological Sciences, 1976; National Medal of Science, 1977; the Craford Prize of the Royal Swedish Academy of Sciences, 1990; and the Japanese government's International Prize in Biology, 1993.

RICHARD P. HARMOND

"The Discover Interview. Edward O. Wilson." *Discover,* June 2006.

Eldredge, Niles. *Life in the Balance: Humanity and the Biodiversity Crisis.*
    Princeton, NJ, 1998.

Simmons, John. *The Scientific 100: A Ranking of the Most Influential Scientists, Past
    and Present.* Secaucus, NJ, 1996.

Wilson, Edward O. *Biophilia: The Human Bond to the Other Species.* Cambridge,
    MA, 1984.

———. *Naturalist.* Washington, DC, 1994.

———. *Sociobiology: The New Synthesis.* Cambridge, MA, 1975.

Yard, Robert Sterling (February 1, 1861–May 17, 1945). A writer, editor, and advocate for the cause of national parks, Yard was born in Haverstraw, New York. On completion of his education at the Freehold Institute in New Jersey, he entered Princeton University, receiving his baccalaureate degree in 1883. The next thirty years witnessed a highly varied career in the commercial world of New York City, ranging from an initial position as head of the foreign cables and correspondence department of a shipping firm to successive jobs as a reporter for the *New York Sun* and editor for the city's newspapers and publishing houses. In this latter capacity, he acquired the professional connections and editorial polish that would subsequently be evident in his writings promoting various conservation issues. In 1913, he resigned his post as editor of *Century* and moved to Washington, DC, assuming the post of chief educational secretary at the National Park Service. This marked the beginning of more than three decades of popular education on, and advocacy for, the value of national parks and wilderness areas. His editorial skills were quickly put to use through appointment to both the National Parks Bulletin (a post he held from 1919 until 1936) and the National Park News Service.

One of his first projects was the preparation of an introduction to *The National Parks Portfolio*, a collection of nine pamphlets issued in 1916. Intended as a promotional piece for the major parks then established, its contents cover Yellowstone, Yosemite, Crater Lake, Mount Rainier, Mesa Verde, the Grand Canyon, Sequoia, Glacier, and the Rocky Mountain preserve. Distributed to some 250,000 leading citizens, it quickly became "an invitation to join in rethinking the national park idea." The same year saw the appearance of *Glimpses of Our National Parks*, swiftly followed by *The Top of the Continent* in 1917. This popular volume was subtitled "A Cheerful Journey through Our National Parks" and introduced all the parks contained in the *Portfolio* to a younger audience. In the preface, Yard notes that "it will have served its purpose if those who read it find pleasure in the . . . mountains, the rivers and the valleys of their great land . . . richer in scenery of sublimity than any other." His next work, *The Book of the National Parks* (1919), proved to be the most influential of all, presenting the problems of the new park system along with its physical beauties and making a case for public support for conservation, with special attention paid to Yellowstone. Continuing a theme begun in *The Top of the Continent* for an adult audience, Yard spoke in the preface to both the variety of landscape found within the parks and "what each kind means in terms of world building," thus presenting the idea of national parks as a vast open-air laboratory for the exploration of geologic processes. Following passage of a federal law prohibiting the payment of government employee salaries with private funds, Yard was obliged to quit the Park Service in 1919, only to assume the executive directorship of the newly created National Parks Association. Its aim differed from the Service in its emphasis on working to "defend the National Parks and National Monuments . . . against the assaults of private interests and aggressive commercialism."

The most intensely active period of Yard's work as a publicist for the wild places of America occurred between 1920 and the beginning of World War II. The most important of his early writings were his August 1920 essay in the *Nation*, "The National Parks' Peril"; an August 1922 article, "The People and the National Parks," in *Playground*; and the May 1923 piece for *Scientific Monthly*, "Economic Aspects of Our National Parks." The "peril" referred to was the rash of schemes then under way to make the water resources of Yellowstone available for irrigation of adjacent sections of Idaho, Wyoming, and Montana via a series of dams, a proposal eventually defeated. The second article restates the changed relationship between the majority of the American population and the newly formed system of national parks called into being by Stephen Mather, while the third summarizes the debate over resource access versus preservation, which would mark Yard's later writings. Other articles written at this time introduced their readers to the beauties and unique features of the Grand Canyon, Glacier, and Yellowstone.

In May 1924, a National Conference on Outdoor Recreation was called in Washington by President Calvin Coolidge, at which over one hundred organizations were represented. Its goal was to begin the formulation of national policy in this area. At this meeting, Yard spoke in his capacity as secretary of the National Parks Association, an address subsequently published under the title "The Scenic Resources of the United States" in July 1924. His opening words called for "an immediate survey under the auspices of the government. We should canvass the facts . . . and establish just relationships between recreational and industrial values." It was also at this time that he began to write pieces for popular circulation addressing a variety of ongoing crises facing the national parks across the country. A frequently repeated theme in all his writings was his firm opposition to the idea of opening national parks up to exploitation by mining and forestry interests, on the management model used for the national forest preserves. Beginning in 1925, he served as the secretary of the Joint Committee on the Recreational Survey of Federal Lands (born out of his request and composed of members of both the National Parks Association and the American Forestry Association), a post he kept until 1930. It was during this time that the last of his books, *Our Federal Lands: A Romance of American Development* (1928), was written. The major pieces of conservation legislation passed by Congress in 1929 and opposition to a proposal to convert part of the Arkansas National Forest into a national park on grounds of tourism were discussed in articles in 1929 and 1932. Between 1935 and 1941, Yard served as editor of the *Living Wilderness*, the quarterly journal of the Wilderness Society of Washington, which he had helped to found. The Society's declared purpose was "to preserve for future generations the inherent right to study, enjoy and use the fine examples of primeval America." At the time of his death he was both president and executive secretary of the organization.

His significance for American conservation lies in his clear presentation of the necessity for maintaining unspoiled acres of wild land to a public whose direct experience of such places was severely limited. The volatile economy of the "Roaring Twenties" with its demand for the use of water, timber, mineral, and game resources posed a clear threat to the new and unfamiliar ideas being put forth by the National Park Service. Through Yard's writings and public testimony, the notion of wilderness shifted from a thing to be exploited to a refuge for the refreshment of the human spirit.

ROBERT B. MARKS RIDINGER

Albright, Horace M., with Robert Cahn. *The Birth of the National Park Service: The Founding Years, 1913–33*. Salt Lake City, UT, 1985.

Runte, Alfred. *National Parks, the American Experience*. 2nd ed. Lincoln, NE, 1987.

"Yard, Robert Sterling." *National Cyclopaedia of American Biography*. Vol. 43. 1961.

Zahniser, Howard (February 25, 1906–May 5, 1964). A conservationist, editor, author, book reviewer, civil servant, and political strategist for wilderness conservation, Zahniser was the son of Rev. Archibald Howard MacElrath and Bertha Belle Zahniser. Born into a family of ministers and missionaries, Zahniser applied a missionary's zeal on behalf of the American wilderness during the course of a long and busy career. He summarized his driving vision in a speech to the Second Biennial Wilderness Conference in 1951:

> We are part of the wilderness of the universe. That is our nature. Our noblest, happiest character develops with the influence of wilderness. Away from it we degenerate into the squalor of the slums or the frustrations of the clinical couches. With the wilderness we are at home.

Zahniser secured his place in the history of the American wilderness movement because he combined the skills and knowledge of an experienced civil servant with the skills of a trained writer, and he subordinated all to a love and respect for the wilderness.

Zahniser developed his writing skills at Greenville (Illinois) College, from which he graduated in 1928, and at American University and George Washington University, where he did graduate work. He worked as a reporter, feature writer, and high school English instructor following college, and in 1930 he entered civil service with the U.S. Department of Commerce as an editorial assistant in the division of publications. From 1932 to 1942 Zahniser worked as an editor, writer, broadcaster, and scenario writer for the Bureau of Biological Survey in the Department of Agriculture (which later became the Fish and Wildlife Service of the Interior Department). From 1942 until 1946 he was principal research writer and head of the division of information of the Bureau of Plant Industry of the Department of Agriculture. He also began his involvement with nature groups and conservation issues during this period when his civil service duties were giving him insight into governmental process. He contributed monthly essays to *Nature Magazine* beginning in 1935. The monthly *Nature* article became a book review called "Indoors and Out" in 1938 in which Zahniser surveyed books that had nature or wilderness subjects. In 1940 "Indoors and Out" became "Nature in Print" and continued until Zahniser's final review in December 1959.

Among the many organized conservation and nature groups that he belonged to were the Sierra Club; the Wilderness Society; the Natural Resources Council of America, which he helped to organize in 1946, serving as chairman from 1948 to 1959; the Trustees for Conservation, where he served as Washington representative; the American Nature Association; the National Audubon Society; and the Thoreau Society, serving as president in 1956. Zahniser left government service in 1946 to devote his full time and energy to conservation efforts. He became executive director of the Wilderness Society and editor of its magazine, the *Living Wilderness.*

Zahniser was instrumental in converting the conservation movement from a generally ad hoc coalition of diverse groups that tended to react defensively to perceived threats to U.S. wilderness and parklands to a more politically astute and organized advocate of government policies that mandated specific uses for public domain lands. He believed that the wilderness experience was a vital human experience and that the processes of civilization were gradually eliminating the sources of that experience. He used two assumptions to chart the future course of public policy with regard to wilderness preservation. First, only those places that were deliberately set aside would be preserved in a pristine condition. Second, wilderness areas in private hands had no guarantee that they would not be developed in the future. Therefore, Zahniser reasoned, it was incumbent on the government to preserve what wilderness still existed in the public domain, and it was also incumbent on conservation groups to mount an aggressive campaign to bring about the desired public policy. He issued this call to action during his address to the Second Biennial Wilderness Conference and specified two necessary actions: to designate an adequate system of wilderness areas for preservation and then to allow nothing to alter the wilderness character of the preserves.

Zahniser was involved in two paramount legislative battles that shaped public policy for the wilderness. The first was over the Echo Park Dam project on the Green River, which threatened the wilderness setting of Dinosaur National Monument along the Utah-Colorado border. The issues pitted the value of the wilderness as a public value against another form of public value, electricity to be generated from the Echo Park Dam. The Dinosaur controversy was regarded as a test case for the preservation of noneconomic wilderness values in public policy. Zahniser helped to mount an effort on behalf of wilderness values that was unprecedented for its organization, its awareness of the value of public opinion in the legislative process, and its know-how of the political process. Zahniser is credited with personally persuading 120 congressmen to change their votes during the course of the debate, writing many of the speeches delivered in Congress against the dam project, and in 1956 coordinating the final compromise that protected the pristine condition of Dinosaur National Monument.

After this effort, which consolidated the legislative gains conservationists had made to date, Zahniser helped chart the new aggressive and activist political course of conservation efforts. Legislation was introduced in 1956 to create and define wilderness areas within the National Park System. Zahniser was in large part responsible for the drafting of the proposed law and spent the next eight years in tireless advocacy of the Wilderness Act, as it became known. He spoke at or attended all congressional hearings that pertained to the act from 1957 to 1964. Sadly, Zahniser died of a heart attack in Hyattsville, Maryland just four months before the passage of the Wilderness Act of 1964.

Zahniser's thoughts and opinions on conservation and the wilderness can be found in his essays and book reviews in *Nature Magazine* and in his contributions to the *Living Wilderness*, which he edited. He contributed a chapter, "Parks and Wilderness," to *America's Natural Resources* (1957) and a piece on conservation to the *Encylopaedia Britannica*. Of particular importance is his 1951 address to the Sierra Club's Second Biennial Wilderness Conference, "How Much Wilderness Can We Afford to Lose?"—his call for a national wildlife system (reprinted in *Wildlands in Our Civilization* [1964]). Also of interest is his article "The Need for Wilderness Areas" in *National Parks Magazine* (1955). And reading the legislative record for the hearings and text of the Wilderness Act of 1964 shows how Zahniser's wilderness vision became preserved in public law.

Zahniser married Alice Bernita Hayden in Frederick, Maryland, on March 3, 1936. They had four children: Alison Howard Mathias; Esther Belle (Mrs. D. Edward Knox); Karen Elizabeth (Mrs. John A. Taylor); and Edward De France.

MICHAEL D. NICHOLS

Nash, Roderick. *Wilderness and the American Mind*. New Haven, CT, 1967.

Zahniser, Howard. "How Much Wilderness Can We Afford to Lose?" *Wildlands in Our Civilization*, ed. David Brower. San Francisco, CA, 1964.

Zwinger, Ann Haymond (March 12, 1925–). A natural history writer, Zwinger's intimate portraits of Rocky Mountain meadows, slick-rock river canyons, and Southwest deserts have made her a leading figure in the resurgence of western American nature writing in the last half of the twentieth century. As "a nature writer (which I am, pure and simple)," Zwinger weaves stories about the biological, geological, historical, and cultural worlds in which she hikes, floats, and camps—"these sparse and beset habitats." Many of her books invite readers to travel with her, down the length of the Green River, for example, into the desert depths of Grand Gulch, or through an aspen grove in autumn, and to learn about that place in all its intricate and wonderful detail. To this work, Zwinger brings the careful observation and research of a scientist; the clear, lovely, often wry voice of an essayist; an illustrator's exquisite drawings; and the attentiveness of a person fully in love with the natural world.

It is this combination of knowledge and passion that makes Zwinger's work important to both the environmentalist and literary worlds. A nature writer's challenge, she wrote, is "to describe, to entrap the reader in your enthusiasm, to portray as accurately as possible, to provide information that will alert the reader to the singularity of this environment." Other nature writers may use the natural world as a metaphor for the human condition or as a path to self-understanding. But Zwinger focuses on the natural history of places for their own fascination. By inviting readers to share in this adventure of noticing and seeking to understand, she invites them also to wonder and, ultimately, to care. Although Zwinger does not call herself an environmentalist, there is no doubt about the intent and effect of her work, which is to draw readers into a more intimate, inquiring, admiring relation with the natural world—in hopes that if they truly understand its astonishments, they will be more inclined to protect it.

Although her life and work are deeply rooted in the West, Zwinger was born in Muncie, Indiana, where she grew up near the White River. From her father, a lawyer, she learned the arts of meticulous attention and careful research; from her mother, she learned to love drawing and music and the light on a pond at dusk. Zwinger graduated from Wellesley College with a degree in art history and earned the M.A. from Indiana University. In 1950, she moved east to teach art history at Smith College. There she began studying for the doctorate at Radcliffe. There also she met the man who would be her husband, Herman, an air force pilot who flew amphibious planes for sea rescues. An air force pilot's family is never long in one place, and the Zwingers, with daughters Susan, Jane, and Sara, moved frequently: Florida, Arkansas, Kansas, and finally Colorado.

Today Zwinger's home is an art-filled house in Colorado Springs. But her inspiration is "Constant Friendship," the family cabin beside a pond in ponderosa forest an hour's drive up the east flank of the Rockies. Here is where her family spent weekends and holidays, floating on the pond, fending off beavers, hiking across meadows, learning to love this place of peace and natural beauty. And here is where Zwinger began to make small drawings of the plants around the cabin and notes about the natural history of the aspen openings and meadows that became the subject of her first book, *Beyond the Aspen Grove* (1970).

The story of that book is famous. With characteristic hospitality, Zwinger had welcomed a visitor to Constant Friendship, wandering with her through the forest, identifying the plants, sharing the sketches in her journals. The visitor was, in fact, Marie Rodell, literary agent and executor of Rachel Carson's literary estate. When Rodell suggested Zwinger write a book about Colorado ecology, she thought the idea was "outrageous." But write it she did, and the book was published by Random House. So, Zwinger says, "I came to my current relationship with the natural world purely by chance," although it might be more accurate to say that she came to the publishing world by chance and to the natural world through an attentive, loving relationship with forty acres on the side of a mountain.

In *Beyond the Aspen Grove*, Zwinger told the natural history of the montane ecosystem, weaving family stories with scientific information in an intimate portrait of a place. That book led to collaboration with ecologist Beatrice Willard for a book on alpine tundra ecosystems, *Land above the Trees* (1972). A scientific book for the "interested novice," in Willard's description, it was nominated for a National Book Award. In her next book, *Run, River, Run* (1975), Zwinger found the full expression of the style that has made her a beloved writer and important environmental figure—the linking of art and science, in which "graceful, well-crafted sentences carry scientifically accurate information," as interviewer Paul Rea wrote. *Run,*

River, Run follows the Green River across half a continent to its confluence with the Colorado River, bringing together natural history and cultural history in the course of the journey. This book won the John Burroughs Memorial Association Award.

Her successive books invite the reader to travel with Zwinger on steep, rocky trails or down sliding rivers. As the journeys unwind, Zwinger, like the very best backcountry companion, shows readers the fascinations, the facts, the beauties, the imbricate cultural and natural histories of the place and its denizens: *Wind in the Rock* (1978), in the Utah canyon lands; *A Conscious Stillness* (1982), on Henry David Thoreau's Sudbury and Assabet Rivers; *A Desert Country Near the Sea* (1983), in the seashore deserts of Baja California; *The Mysterious Lands* (1989), in the desert Southwest; the Western States Book Award–winning *Downcanyon* (1995), on the Colorado River as it plows through the Grand Canyon.

Books are, of course, only the bedrock that juts most conspicuously from an author's lifetime of work. A complete list of Zwinger's publications would include edited volumes of natural history writing, the edited letters of John Xantus, and many collaborations in which she illustrated books or provided essays for books of photographs. She has written dozens of articles for journals such as *Audubon* and *Orion*; *Whole Terrain* published an important essay in which Zwinger explained the nature of her art, "A Naturalist's Legacy of Caring" (1999–2000).

Zwinger has been a generous mentor and friend to new nature writers, especially women; thus, her contribution to the flourishing of nature writing goes far beyond her own work, far beyond what can be gratefully acknowledged. In 1991, Zwinger was awarded the Distinguished Achievement Award from the Western Literature Association. Among many other awards, she is the recipient also of the Orion Society's John Hay Award for achievement in writing, conservation, and education.

In 2005, Zwinger suffered a stroke that has made writing difficult. Appropriately, her last book is her credo. In *Shaped by Wind and Water: Reflections of a Naturalist* (2000), Zwinger reflects on the guiding principles of her life as a writer, artist, and naturalist. In the final section, she tells of a dream in which she found herself sitting in a "dazzlingly beautiful mountain world," aware that everyone else had been destroyed in a nuclear explosion. Alone in the world, she was charged with the task of recording "how beautiful the world was, how intricately interwoven, . . . how the oceans rolled in and whispered out, how the rivers gathered." Here are the book's final words: "So much, so much to get down. I took up my pencil and began to write."

In this impulse to share the intricacies and beauties of the natural world with people who do not know it can be found the lasting value of Zwinger's life work. There is a profound moral significance to natural history—the fieldwork, the scientist's close observation, the fact-checking, the careful drawings, the curiosity and constant questioning, the delight in facts, the exhilaration of being *out there* in this amazing world—all these marks of the naturalist's work. Caring grows from relatedness: it is very difficult for anyone to care about what they do not much know. By sharing what she has come to understand and love, by sharing the sources of wonder at the natural world, Zwinger invites readers into an intimate relation with the natural world and, by that work, opens the door to caring.

"I write for people who have no idea what's going on out there." "If I can get people to look," she wrote in *The Nearsighted Naturalist* (1998), "they may become curious about what they see, and if they are curious, they will ask questions, and if they ask questions they will get ten more questions for every answer delivered—and in the process, they will come to be interested, and being interested is just one step from caring, and if they care they will not destroy."

KATHLEEN DEAN MOORE

Kircher, Cassie. "An Interview with Ann Zwinger." *ISLE: Interdisciplinary Studies in Literature and Environment* 1.2 (Fall 1993): 123–132.

Lucas, Susan. "Ann Zwinger." *Dictionary of Literary Biography.* Vol. 275. 2003.

Rea, Paul. "An Interview with Ann Zwinger." *Western American Literature* 24.1 (May 1989): 21–36.

Slovic, Scott. "Ann Haymond Zwinger: A Portrait." *Shaped by Wind and Water: Reflections of a Naturalist,* by Ann Zwinger. Minneapolis, MN, 2000.

——. "Bibliography of Ann Haymond Zwinger's Work." *Shaped by Wind and Water: Reflections of a Naturalist,* by Ann Zwinger. Minneapolis, MN, 2000.

Trimble, Stephen. "Ann Zwinger." *Words from the Land,* ed. Stephen Trimble. Reno, NV, 1995.

1901 John Muir, a cofounder of the Sierra Club who was dubbed "a major voice of the wilderness," publishes *Our National Parks*; a seminal figure in the development of American environmental thought, Muir is recognized especially for the part he played in establishing Yosemite National Park and the expansion of the Sierra Forest Reserve.

1903 Pelican Island Reservation, first bird wildlife refuge; instituted by Theodore Roosevelt.

1906 National Monuments Act; put under public protection Arizona's Petrified Forest, the Grand Canyon, and Mount Olympus.

1907 Inland Water Commission, which studied river systems, waterpower, and reclamation.

1916 Creation of the National Park Service.

1933 Civilian Conservation Corps, which had among its responsibilities the organization and overseeing of a national park system.

1935 Soil Conservation and Domestic Allotment Act; to encourage farmers to allow lands to lie fallow and to plant crops that would return nitrogen to the soil.

Wilderness Society founded by Robert Marshall, Carl Oberholtzer, Sterling Yard, Benton MacKaye, and several others to advocate protection and conservation of public lands and forest resource management.

1949 Publication of Aldo Leopold's *Sand County Almanac*, an ecological study that focuses on wildlife management.

1962 Publication of Rachel Carson's *Silent Spring*, which emphasizes in forceful, readable prose that a good number of wild species were being decimated because of increasing use of pesticides such as DDT.

1968 Wilderness Act; in large part passed due to the efforts of Harold Ickes when he served as secretary of the interior under Franklin Delano Roosevelt.

1970 Formation of the Environmental Protection Agency, which placed an almost total ban on the use of DDT in the United States.

First Earth Day.

Clean Air Act, which limited "smoke stack emissions."

1972 Pesticides Control Act; empowered the EPA to oversee the manufacture and use of hazardous pesticides.

Federal Water Control Act; established standards for potable water.

1973   Endangered Species Act; outlawed activities of federal agencies that threatened endangered species.

1979   Three Mile Island; nuclear power plant accident near Harrisburg, Pennsylvania.

1980   Toxic Superfund Law; imposed fees for violations by chemical and oil companies.

Magnuson-Stevens Act; legislation to protect fisheries and to control overfishing.

1990   Barry Commoner's *Making Peace with the Planet*, a virtual bestseller that covers the origins and significance of ecology and stresses what must be done to avoid deterioration of the environment.

2006   At its Beijing International Center, Daniel Okun honored with the prestigious International Water Association's Grand Award for his outstanding achievements as a water engineer and eminent environmentalist.

2007   Albert A. Gore awarded Nobel Peace Prize for his far-reaching efforts to call the world's attention to the perils of global warming.

✻ SELECTED BIBLIOGRAPHY

Adams, Alexander B. *Eternal Quest: The Story of the Great Naturalists.* New York: Putnam, 1969.

Adler, Kraig, ed. *Contributions to the History of Herpetology.* Vol. 1. Oxford, OH: Society for the Study of Amphibians and Reptiles, 1989.

Albright, Horace, with Robert Cahn. *The Birth of the National Park Service: The Founding Years, 1913–33.* Salt Lake City, UT: Howe Bros., 1985.

Allen, Elsa. *The History of American Ornithology before Audubon.* Philadelphia, PA: American Philosophical Society, 1951.

Allin, Craig W. *The Politics of Wilderness Preservation.* Westport, CT: Greenwood Press, 1982.

Backes, David. *Canoe Country: An Embattled Wilderness.* Minocqua, WI: Northwood Press, 1991.

Birkeland, Peter W. *Soils and Geomorphology.* New York: Oxford Univ. Press, 1984.

Birney, Elmer, and Jerry R. Choate, eds. *Seventy-five Years of Mammalogy, 1919–1994.* Provo, UT: American Society of Mammalogists, 1994.

Bocking, Stephen. *Ecologists and Environmental Politics: A History of Contemporary Ecology.* New Haven, CT: Yale Univ. Press, 1997.

Bonta, Marcia Myers. *Women in the Field: America's Pioneering Women Naturalists.* College Station: Texas A&M Univ. Press, 1991.

Botkin, Daniel B., and Edward A. Keller. *Environmental Science: Earth as a Living Planet.* New York: Wiley, 1995.

Bramwell, Anna. *Ecology in the 20th Century.* New Haven, CT: Yale Univ. Press, 1989.

Bridgman, H. A. *Global Air Pollution: Problems for the 1990s.* New York: Wiley, 1994.

Brooks, Paul. *Speaking for Nature: How Literary Naturalists from Henry David Thoreau to Rachel Carson Have Shaped America.* Boston, MA: Houghton Mifflin, 1980.

Brown, Morrison. *Louis Bromfield and His Books: An Evaluation.* Fair Lawn, NJ: Essential Books, 1957.

Cahalan, James M. *Edward Abbey: A Life.* Tucson: Univ. of Arizona Press, 2001.

Carr, Archie. *The Reptiles.* 1963. Reprint, Alexandria, VA: Time-Life Books, 1980.

Carson, Rachel. *Silent Spring.* Cambridge, MA: Riverside Press, 1962.

Clements, Edith S. *Adventures in Ecology: Half a Million Miles . . . From Mud to Macadam.* New York: Pageant Press, 1960.

Clepper, Henry. *Origins of American Conservation.* New York: Ronald Press, 1966.

Commoner, Barry. *Making Peace with the Planet.* New York: Pantheon Books, 1990.

Coyle, David. *Conservation: An American Story of Conflict and Accomplishment.* New Brunswick, NJ: Rutgers Univ. Press, 1957.

Cronin, John, and Robert F. Kennedy Jr. *The Riverkeepers: Two Activists Fight to Reclaim Our Environment as a Basic Human Right.* New York: Scribner, 1997.

Debus, Allen G., ed. *World Who's Who in Science: A Biographical Dictionary of Notable Scientists From Antiquity to the Present.* Chicago, IL: Marquis, 1968.

Downing, Paul B. *Environmental Economics and Policy.* Boston, MA: Little, Brown, 1984.

Dunbar, Gary S. *The History of Modern Geography: An Annotated Bibliography.* New York: Garland, 1985.

Dunlap, Thomas R. *Saving America's Wildlife.* Princeton, NJ: Princeton Univ. Press, 1988.

Ehrlich, Paul R., David S. Dobkin, and Darryl Wheye. *The Birder's Handbook: A Field Guide to the Natural History of North American Birds: Including all Species that Regularly Breed North of New Mexico.* New York: Simon & Schuster, 1988.

Fahl, Ronald J., ed. *North American Forest and Conservation History: A Bibliography.* Santa Barbara, CA: ABC-Clio Press, 1977.

Farber, Paul L. *Discovering Birds: The Emergence of Ornithology as a Scientific Discipline, 1760–1850.* Baltimore, MD: Johns Hopkins Univ. Press, 1997.

Ferrell, John S. *Fruits of Creation: A Look at Global Sustainability as Seen Through the Eyes of George Washington Carver.* Wynnewood, PA: Christian Society of Green Cross, 1995.

Finer, Herman. *The T.V.A.: Lessons for International Application.* 1944. Reprint, New York: Da Capo Press, 1972.

Fox, Stephen. *The American Conservation Movement: John Muir and His Legacy.* Madison: Univ. of Wisconsin Press, 1985.

Goddard, Donald, ed. *Saving Wildlife: A Century of Conservationism.* New York: Harry N. Abrams, 1995.

Gore, Al. *An Inconvenient Truth: The Planetary Emergency of Global Warming and What We Can Do About It.* Emmaus, PA: Rodale Press, 2006.

Graham, Frank, Jr. *The Audubon Ark: A History of the National Audubon Society.* New York: Knopf, 1990.

Guberlet, Muriel Lewin. *Explorers of the Sea: Famous Oceanographic Expeditions.* New York: Ronald Press, 1964.

Hanley, Wayne. *Natural History in America: From Mark Catesby to Rachel Carson* New York: Quadrangle / New York Times Book Co., 1976.

Hays, Samuel P., and Barbara D. Hays. *Beauty, Health, and Permanence: Environmental Politics in the United States, 1955–1985.* New York: Cambridge Univ. Press, 1987.

Hendee, John, George H. Stankey, Robert C. Lucas, eds. *Wilderness Management.* Washington, DC: U.S. Department of Agriculture, Forest Service, 1978.

Highsmith, Richard M., J. Granville Jensen, and Robert D. Rudd. *Conservation in the United States.* 2nd ed. Chicago, IL: Rand McNally, 1969.

Hynes, H. Patricia. *The Recurring Silent Spring.* New York: Pergamon Press, 1989.

Jones, Holway. *John Muir and the Sierra Club: The Battle for Yosemite.* San Francisco, CA: Sierra Club, 1965.

King, Judson. *The Conservation Fight from Theodore Roosevelt to the Tennessee Valley Authority.* Washington, DC: Public Affairs Press, 1959.

Lacey, Michael J., ed. *Government and Environmental Politics.* Baltimore, MD: Johns Hopkins Univ. Press, 1991.

Lacy, Leslie A. *The Soil Soldiers: The Civilian Conservation Corps in the Great Depression.* Radnor, PA: Chilton Book Co., 1976.

Lutts, Ralph H., ed. *The Wild Animal Story.* Philadelphia, PA: Temple Univ. Press, 1998.

Lynn, Les M. *Environmental Biology and Ecology Laboratory Manual.* 2nd ed. Northport, NY: Kendall Hunt, 1995.

Marsh, George Perkins. *Man and Nature.* 1864. Reprint, Cambridge, MA: Harvard Univ. Press, 1965.

McIntosh, Robert T. *The Background of Ecology: Concept and Theory.* New York: Cambridge Univ. Press, 1985.

Mongillo, John, and Bibi Booth, eds. *Environmental Activists.* Westport, CT: Greenwood Press, 2001.

Morgan, Arthur. *The Making of the TVA.* Buffalo, NY: Prometheus Books, 1974.

Nash, Roderick F. *The Rights of Nature: A History of Environmental Ethics.* Madison: Univ. of Wisconsin Press, 1989.

O'Brien, Mary. *Making Better Environmental Decisions: An Alternative to Risk Assessment.* Cambridge, MA: MIT Press, 2000.

Odum, Eugene P. *Ecology: The Link Between the Natural and the Social Sciences.* 2nd ed. New York: Holt, Rinehart and Winston, 1975.

Odum, Eugene. *Fundamentals of Ecology.* Philadelphia, PA: W. B. Saunders, 1953.

Ogden, Gerald. *The United States Forest Service: A Historical Bibliography, 1876–1972.* Davis, CA: Agricultural History Center, Univ. of California, 1976.

Orr, Oliver H., Jr. *Saving American Birds: T. Gilbert Pearson and the Founding of the Audubon Movement.* Gainesville: Univ. of Florida, 1992.

Outwater, Alice B. *Water: A Natural History.* New York: Basic Books, 1996.

Payne, Daniel C. *Voices in the Wilderness: American Nature Writing and Environmental Politics.* Hanover, NH: Univ. Press of New England, 1996.

Pearson, T. Gilbert. *Adventures in Bird Protection*. New York: D. Appleton-Century Co., 1937.

Perkins, Henry C. *Air Pollution*. New York: McGraw-Hill, 1974.

Pinchot, Gifford. *The Fight for Conservation*. New York: Doubleday, Page, 1910.

Porteous, Andrew. *Dictionary of Environmental Science and Technology*. New York: John Wiley, 1992.

Reilly, William K. *The Use of Land: A Citizen's Policy Guide to Urban Growth*. New York: Crowell, 1973.

Reisner, Marc. *Cadillac Desert: The American West and Its Disappearing Water*. New York: Penguin, 1993.

Rogers, Andrew. *Liberty Hyde Bailey: A Story of American Plant Sciences*. Princeton, NJ: Princeton Univ. Press, 1949.

Rogers, Marion Lane. *Acorn Days: The Environmental Defense Fund and How It Grew*. New York: Environmental Defense Fund, 1990.

Rosenberg, Kenneth A. *Wilderness Preservation: A Reference Handbook*. Santa Barbara, CA: ABC-Clio, 1994.

Simmons, John. *The Scientific 100: A Ranking of the Most Influential Scientists, Past and Present*. Secaucus, NJ: Carol Publishing, 1996.

Singh, Vijay P. *Environmental Hydrology*. Norwell, MA: Kluwer Academic, 1995.

Spellman, Frank R., and Nancy E. Whiting. *Environmental Science and Technology: Concepts and Applications*. Rockville, MD: Government Institutes, 1999.

Sprout, Harold, and Margaret Sprout. *The Context of Environmental Politics: Unfinished Business for America's Third Century*. Lexington: Univ. Press of Kentucky, 1978.

Sterling, Keir, Richard Harmond, George Cevasco, and Lorne Hammond, eds. *Biographical Dictionary of American and Canadian Naturalists and Environmentalists*. Westport, CT: Greenwood Press, 1997.

Stresemann, Ervin. *Ornithology From Aristotle to the Present*. Cambridge, MA: Harvard Univ. Press, 1975.

Tan, Kim H. *Environmental Soil Science*. New York: Marcel Dekker, 1994.

Tower, Edward. *Environmental and Natural Resource Economics*. New York: Eno River Press, 1985.

Trefethen, James B. *Crusade for Wildlife: Highlights in Conservation Progress*. Harrisburg, PA: Stackpole, 1961.

Turco, Richard P. *Earth under Siege: Air Pollution and Global Change*. New York: Oxford Univ. Press, 1995.

Welker, Robert Henry. *Birds and Men: American Birds in Science, Art, Literature, and Conservation, 1800–1900*. Cambridge, MA: Harvard Univ. Press, 1955.

Whitman, Alden. *American Reformers: An H. W. Wilson Biographical Dictionary.* New York: H. W. Wilson, 1985.

Whorton, James. *Before Silent Spring: Pesticides and Public Health in Pre-DDT America.* Princeton, NJ: Princeton Univ. Press, 1974.

Wild, Peter. *Pioneer Conservationists of Western America.* Missoula, MT: Mountain Press, 1978.

Wildavsky, Aaron. *But Is It True?: A Citizen's Guide to Environmental Health and Safety Issues.* Cambridge, MA: Harvard Univ. Press, 1995.

Wirzba, Norman, ed. *The Essential Agrarian Reader.* Lexington: Univ. of Kentucky Press, 2003.

Worster, Donald. *Nature's Economy: The Roots of Ecology.* San Francisco, CA: Sierra Club Books, 1977.

Wright, R. Gerald. *Wildlife Research and Management in the National Parks.* Urbana: Univ. of Illinois Press, 1992.

CONTRIBUTORS

Brian U. Adler
Valdosta State University
Thomas Berry

Shelley Aley
Cottey College
Rachel Carson
Aldo Leopold

Byron Anderson
Northern Illinois University
Clarence Cottam
James Oliver Curwood
Enos Abijah Mills

Karla Armbruster
University of Colorado
Josephine Winslow
Johnson

Rebecca Austin
Florida Gulf Coast University
Stephanie Mills

James Ballowe
Bradley University
Henry Beston
Sherman Paul

Jocelyn Bartkevicius
University of Central Florida
William Vogt

Robert P. Biehl
Boston College
William Dutcher

James E. Bishop
University of Nevada
Reno
Russell Errol Train

Walter J. Bock
Columbia University
Ernst Mayr

Irene Boland
U.S. Protection Agency
Region 2, New York
William A. McDonough

David Boocker
Tennessee Technological University
Anne Morrow Lindbergh
Charles Augustus Lindbergh

Claudine L. Boros
Queensboro College
City University of New York
Jack Miner
John D. Rockefeller Jr.

Michael Branch
University of Nevada
Reno
Robert Underwood Johnson

Michaelene Brown
Chicago, Illinois
George Archibald

Ross Brummer
Queensboro College
City University of New York
Bernard Augustine DeVoto

Adam W. Burnett
Colgate University
Olaus Johan Murie

Paul T. Byrant
Radford, Virginia
Benton MacKaye

George A. Cevasco
St. John's University
Archie Carr
Barry Commoner
Louis J. Halle
David Starr Jordan
Joseph Wood Krutch
Eugene Odum
Daniel A. Okun
John Charles Phillips

Regina Corallo
St. John's University
Pattiann Rogers

Laura Cowan
University of Maine
Sarah Orne Jewett

Laurie Ann Crompton
Glen Oaks, New York
T. Gilbert Pearson

Judith M. Curran
College of Staten Island
City University of New York
Joseph Trimble Rothrock

Thomas J. Curran
St. John's University
Madison Grant (with
Richard P. Harmond)

Kate Darby
Arizona University
Marc Reisner

Gregory J. Dehler
Westminster, Colorado
John Fletcher Lacey
Stewart Udall

Lynn Dickerson
University of Richmond
Louis Bromfield

Steven L. Driever
University of Missouri
Kansas City
Rene Jules Dubos

Janice L. Edens
Macon College
Stanley Adair Cain
Arthur Hawthorne Carhart

Ronna S. Feit
Nassau College
State University of New York
Barry Holstun Lopez

Juliette M. Fernan
Fordham University
Henry Fairfield Osborn Jr.

Jeff Filipiak
St. Francis, Wisconsin
Wendell Erdman Berry

Kelly A. Foth
Dubuque University
Mary Hunter Austin
Sigurd F. Olson

Adrienne Glynn
Rockville Centre
New York
Albert Arnold Gore Jr.

Steven Gray
Rutgers University
William Doyle Ruckelshaus

Gwen Griffin
Minnesota State University
George Shiras III

Mark Grossman
Scottsdale, Arizona
William Temple Hornaday

Richard P. Harmond
St. John's University
Roger Caras
Marjory Stoneman Douglas
Madison Grant (with
  Thomas J. Curran)
Peter Matthiessen
Gaylord Nelson
Franklin Delano Roosevelt
Robert Barnwell Roosevelt
Carl Safina
Edward Osborne Wilson

Michael Hayes
Freeport, New York
Jimmy Carter
Scott Nearing

J. Douglas Helms
National Historian
Natural Resources Conservation
  Services
U.S. Department of Agriculture
Washington, DC
Hugh Hammond Bennett

Andrea W. Herrmann
University of Arkansas
C. Hart Merriam

Walter Herrscher
University of Wisconsin
August William Derleth
E. B. (Elwin Brooks) White

Mark Hersey
University of Kansas
George Washington Carver

Kathryn Hilt
New Jersey Institute of Technology
John B. Burnham
Will H. Dilg

Timothy J. Horan
Massapequa, New York
Ernest Everett Just

Karen Hovde
Northern Illinois University
Charles Sprague Sargent
Ellen Henrietta (Richards) Swallow

Thomas P. Huber
University of Colorado
John Burroughs

William L. Keogan
St. John's University
Paul Mellon

Dave Kuhne
Texas Christian University
William Orville Douglas
Harold LeClaire Ickes

Robert P. Larkin
University of Colorado
Wallace Walter Atwood

Corey Lewis
Humboldt State University
Gary Sherman Snyder

Page West Life
University of North Carolina
William Henry Jackson

Shirley Loui
St. Louis University
David Brower

Lawrence H. Maddock
Pensacola, Florida
J. Frank Dobie

David Mazel
Louisiana State University
Paul Lester Errington

Bernard Eduard Fernow
Robert Cushman Murphy

Cynthia A. Melendy
University of South Florida
Cordelia Johnson Stanwood

Gwynne Middleton
University of Nevada
Gene Stratton-Porter

Bryan L. Moore
Texas Christian University
Edward Abbey
Loren Corey Eiseley
A. Starker Leopold

Kathleen Dean Moore
Oregon State University
Ann Haymond Zwinger

Charles Mortensen
Ball State University
Robert Marshall

Richard Myers
Alaska Pacific University
Gifford Pinchot

Caryn E. Neumann
Miami University of Ohio
E. Lucy Braun

Michael D. Nichols
Texas Christian University
Ansel Adams
Howard Zahniser

Rebecca Onion
University of Texas, Austin
Theodore Roethke

Susie Jin Pak
St. John's University
Theodore Roosevelt

J. Karen Ray
Tennessee Technological University
Emma Bell Miles

John F. Reiger
Ohio University
Chillicothe
George Bird Grinnell

Robert B. Marks Ridinger
Northern Illinois University
William Brewster
Dian Fossey
Louis Agassiz Fuertes
Ira Noel Gabrielson
Emerson Hough
Edward Alexander Preble
Robert Sterling Yard

Suzanne Ross
St. Cloud University
Frank Michler Chapman
Stephen Alfred Forbes

S. Joan Ryan, C.S.J.
St. Joseph College
Edmund S. Muskie

Don Scheese
Gustavus Adolphus College
Ernest Carl Oberholtzer

Ethan Schoolman
University of Michigan
Marcy Cottrell Houle

Arthur Sherman
St. John's University
(Charles) William Beebe
Sally Carrighar

Thomas Shevory
Ithaca College
Roger Tory Peterson
Henry Wallace

Steven V. Simpson
La Crosse University of Wisconsin
  Jay Norwood Darling
  Stephen Tyng Mather

Rodney Smith
University of Dubuque
  Donald Curloss Peattie
  Edwin Way Teale

Patianne DelGrosso Stabile
Yonkers, New York
  Wallace Earle Stegner

Richard Stalter
St. John's University
  Liberty Hyde Bailey
  Victor Ernest Shelford

Stephen J. Stedman
Tennessee Technological University
  Rosalie Edge
  Margaret Morse Nice

Keir Sterling
Command Historian, U.S. Army
Combined Arms Support Command
  Florence Merriam Bailey
  Joseph Grinnell
  *Harriet Mann Miller [Olive Thorne
    Miller]*
  Henry Fairfield Osborn
  Earnest Thompson Seton

Anthony Todman
St. John's University
  William Kane Reilly

Monica Weis, S.S.J.
Nazareth College
  Thomas Merton

Erica Wetter
New York University
  Dorothy Richardson Buell
  Dennis Puleston

Leslie Wolcott
University of Nevada
Reno
  Leslie Marmon Silko

Gioia Woods
Northern Arizona University
  John Steinbeck

Christopher Zeppieri
Sea Cliff, New York
  Laurance S. Rockefeller

Julian Zeppieri
Sea Cliff, New York
  Margaret Rockefeller

Rose Zuzworksky
St. John's University
  John Muir

✺ INDEX OF AREAS OF SPECIALIZATION